D1472806

NOVELS BY JUDITH MICHAEL

Deceptions
Possessions
Private Affairs

JUDITH MICHAEL

Inheritance

LARGE PRINT BOOK CLUB EDITION

POSEIDON PRESS
New York London Toronto Sydney Tokyo

VOLUME 1

This Large Print Edition, prepared especially for Doubleday Book & Music Clubs, Inc., contains the complete, unabridged text of the original Publisher's Edition.

Published by Poseidon Press
A Division of Simon & Schuster, Inc.
Simon & Schuster Building,
Rockefeller Center,
1230 Avenue of the Americas,
New York, NY 10020

POSEIDON PRESS is a registered trademark of
Simon & Schuster, Inc.

**This Large Print Book carries the
seal of approval of N.A.V.H.**

Manufactured in the United States of America

For
Ruth Barnard
with admiration and love

Part I

Part I

CHAPTER 1

LAURA and Paul made the bed together, laughing as they raced to see whose side would be finished first. "I'll never learn," Paul sighed in mock resignation when he lost. "Women were born to make beds; men were born to lie in them."

"They were born to lie *about* them," Laura retorted. "When we're married, you'll be amazed how fast you learn all kinds of things."

"I'm fast at the important ones," he said, "like falling in love with you."

She laughed, loving the way his smile and glance embraced her, the deepening of his voice when he spoke only to her, the memory of his hand on her breast when she had awakened that morning and they had moved into each other's arms, warm and half asleep, closer and closer until he was inside her and they had begun another day joined together, just as they planned to be joined as husband and wife for the rest of their lives.

But then her eyes grew somber. "How can we be so happy? It isn't right to be laughing and doing everything the way we always have, when Owen isn't here. And won't be, ever again. And he won't see us married, and he wanted to so much."

Paul knotted his tie and pulled on his suit jacket, glancing in the mirror as he ran a hand over his unruly black hair. "He knew we were getting married; that was what he cared about." He put his arms around Laura and held her to him. "And you know he hated fancy parties and ceremonies."

"He wouldn't have hated our wedding," Laura said. "Oh, Paul, I can't bear it that he's gone!"

"I know." Paul lay his cheek on her hair, picturing the proud head and piercing eyes of Owen Salinger, his great-uncle and his very good friend. "And you're right, he would have loved our wedding, because he loved you and thought the smartest thing I ever did was agree with him." He held Laura away from him, searching her eyes for what she was feeling. Her slender face, with high cheekbones and wide, generous mouth, was somber in thought, as if frozen in time by a painter who had caught her arresting beauty but could only hint at the changing expressions that made her vivid face come alive with joy or sorrow, warmth or coldness, pleasure or dismissal. And no painter could capture the elusiveness that made everyone, even Paul, wonder if they really knew her or could keep her close, or her biting wit that contrasted so intriguingly with her innocence, making others remember her unpredictability long after they had forgotten the exact chestnut of her hair, glinting red in the sun, or the precise dark blue of her wide, clear eyes.

Paul brushed back the tendrils of hair that curled along her cheeks. "You're so pale, my love. Are you worried about this afternoon? Or is it just your suit? Do you have to wear black? We're not going to a funeral, after all; we're only going to Owen's house to listen to Parkinson read his will."

"It's what I feel like wearing," Laura said.

"A will reading is like a second funeral, isn't it? We keep slamming shut the doors of Owen's life." She slipped out of his arms. "Shouldn't we go?"

"Yes." He locked the door of his apartment, and they walked down the two flights of stairs to the tiny lobby. Boston's August heat rose to meet them in shimmering waves that made trees and gardens ripple like reflections in a pond. Children danced on the grass, dreamlike in the white-hot sun, and sailboats on the Charles were like white birds, dipping and swooping above cool splashing waves.

"I'd forgotten how hot it gets," Paul murmured, pulling off his jacket. "Strange, isn't it, to be thinking about Owen here, in the city, when he'd never spend August anywhere but the Cape?" They reached his car and he turned on the air conditioning as they drove away. "My God, I miss him. Almost three weeks already, but I keep thinking I'll see him for dinner and hear him tell me again what I ought to be doing with my life."

Laura sat close to him and he held her hand as he drove beneath the arching trees along Commonwealth Avenue. "If I didn't have you," he said quietly, "I'd feel as if the center of my world was gone."

"And so would I." She twined her fingers in his, responding to the pressure of his thigh against hers, his shoulder against hers, the strength and desire that flowed between them whenever they touched. It was the same wherever they were, whatever they did: the rest of the world would disappear, leaving them alone with the love and passion that had grown steadily ever since the day, two years before, when he had finally noticed her.

"So would I," she said again. Because even though she had her brother Clay, and Paul's family, who had taken her in four years ago, when she was eighteen, and made her feel like one of them, it was Owen, the head of the family, who had adored her and who had been the adored center of her life, until she met Paul. Then she had clung to both of them. And now, when she still felt young and unsure of herself and hadn't yet begun the things Owen wanted her to do . . . now he was gone and there was only Paul to take care of her.

"Do you think we'll be there long?" she asked Paul. She didn't want to go at all. She didn't want to see everyone gathered in Owen's house where she had lived so happily —and still lived, though she had spent most of her time with Paul since Owen died—and hear the family lawyer read Owen's words when what she longed to hear was Owen's voice. She didn't want to hear Owen's sons Felix and Asa talk about finally being free to do what they wanted with the empire their father had built with love and pride, when their plans were so different from the ones Owen had been sharing with her for the past years, up to the time of his stroke.

"Not long," Paul said, turning up Beacon Hill and finding a parking place near Owen's enormous corner town house. "It's mostly a formality. Felix and Asa get the remaining stock in the company that Owen had held, the girls will get enough to make them happy, and I'll get a token because he loved me even though he knew I preferred a camera to a high-level job in his hotel empire. Half an hour, probably, for Parkinson to read the whole thing." Standing beside the car, he took Laura's hand again. "I'm sorry you have to go through it, but since Parkinson specifically asked for you—"

"It's all right," Laura said, but she was knotting up inside as they climbed the steps to the front door that had been hers for four years, to the rooms where she had lived as Owen's friend, nurse, protégée, and, finally, as close to a granddaughter as anyone could be.

When the butler opened the door she looked automatically across the marble foyer at the branching staircase, almost expecting to see Owen Salinger descending the stairs at his dignified pace—ruddy, healthy, his bushy eyebrows and drooping mustache like flying buttresses as he sent orders, opinions, and declarations to every corner of his house. Her eyes filled with tears. He had been so courtly, commanding, and overwhelming, she couldn't imagine a world without him. Where could she go without missing him?

You'll always miss him. But get today over with and get on with your life. That's what Owen would say. And he'd be right. He was always right.

She looked up at Paul. "Let's get away from here when this is over."

"Good idea," he said, and smiled at her, relieved that her somberness was lifting. It had seemed exaggerated from the beginning, making her appear worried, almost fearful, instead of mournful, as he would have expected. One of her moods, he thought, and reminded himself of how alone she'd been when Owen first paid attention to her and gave her the kind of enveloping love he bestowed on only a chosen few. "Relax," he said as they went in. "I'm here. We're together."

His hand held hers tightly and they went into the library where the Salinger family had already assembled, crowded together on leather couches and armchairs, the younger great-granddaughters perched on ottomans or sitting cross-legged on the Tabriz rugs Owen and Iris had collected in their travels. At the far end of the room, near the mahogany and marble fireplace, Laura saw Clay talking to Allison and Thad, and she smiled at him, thanking him silently for taking time from his job in Philadelphia to be near her for the will reading.

Behind the massive library table Elwin Parkinson, Owen's lawyer, sat with Felix and Asa Salinger, Owen's sons, the heirs to his empire and his fortune. Paul shook hands with them, paused to greet his parents, and then he and Laura went to a far corner, standing before a leaded glass window set in a book-lined wall. He put his arm around her; she was trembling, and he kissed the top of her head lightly as Parkinson began to speak.

"I have before me the last will and testament of Owen Salinger, dated three years ago this month. The non-family members are named first. Heading the list is a bequest of five hundred thousand dollars to Rosa Curren who, in Owen's words, 'kept my house and my family for fifty years and sustained me through the darkest years after my beloved Iris died.'

"There are smaller bequests," Parkinson went on, "to several of the longtime employees and concierges of the Salinger Hotels; various gardeners, barbers, and tailors; the captain of a sailboat in the Caribbean; a salesman at a boot shop in Cambridge; and sundry others I will not take the time to list. There are also sizable bequests to organizations which Owen held dear, foremost among them the Boston Art Museum, the Boston Symphony, and the Isabella Stewart Gardner Museum, but also including the Foxy Theater Troupe of Cambridge, the Wellfleet Oysters, and the Cape Cod Mermaids."

A rustle of laughter whispered through the

room at the reminder of Owen's eccentricities and whimsies when it came to spreading his wealth; the family had long since gotten used to them, sometimes even agreeing with them. Only Felix and Asa were flat-faced; they had never found their father amusing.

Parkinson pulled a separate document from his briefcase and read from it. " 'Of my thirty percent holdings in Salinger Hotels Incorporated, I leave twenty-eight percent, divided equally, to my sons Felix and Asa—' "

"Twenty-eight percent?" Asa sprang to his feet, peering over Parkinson's shoulder. "He owned thirty p-p-percent. We share thirty percent. There was never any question of that." He peered more closely. "What the hell is that you're reading? That's n-n-n-not the will."

Felix sat in silence, staring at his locked hands as Parkinson cleared his throat and said, "This is a codicil Owen added to his will in July."

"Last m-m-m-month?" Asa demanded. "After his stroke?"

Parkinson nodded. "If you will allow me, I should read it in its entirety."

"If we allow you!" Asa repeated grimly. "Read it!"

Once again Parkinson cleared his throat. " 'I, Owen Salinger, in full possession of my faculties, dictate this codicil to the will I made three years ago. Of my thirty percent holdings in Salinger Hotels Incorporated, I leave twenty-eight percent, divided equally, to my sons Felix and Asa Salinger. And to my most beloved Laura Fairchild, who has brought joy and love to the last years of my life, I leave the remaining two percent of my shares in Salinger Hotels Incorporated, plus one hundred percent of the Owen Salinger Corporation, a separate entity, which owns the four hotels with which I began the Salinger chain sixty years ago, in New York, Chicago, Philadelphia and Washington, and also my house and furnishings on Beacon Hill, where she has been living and should continue to live. She will know exactly what to do with her inheritance; she has shared my ideas and helped me make new plans, and I trust her to keep our dream alive and make it flourish.' "

In the brief, heavy silence that enveloped the room, Laura's eyes were closed, warm salt tears flowing down her cheeks. *Dearest Laura, I've left you a little something in my will.* That was all he had said, and she'd thought of money, perhaps enough to buy a small lodge and have something of her own, even when she was married to Paul, where she could put to use everything Owen had taught her about hotels.

Across the room, she saw Clay's look of excitement; his eyes danced and his lips mouthed, "Wow! You pulled it off!" Shocked and angry, she turned away.

Paul had followed her look and was watching Clay with a puzzled frown. In the rest of the room voices had risen to a cacophony while Parkinson banged a brass letter opener against an inkwell, trying to regain control.

"I w-w-won't have it!" Asa fumed. "Enough is enough! We've g-g-given her a home for years—"

"Owen gave her a home," Leni said quietly, but no one paid attention.

"I think it's lovely," Allison exclaimed. "Laura took care of Grandfather; why shouldn't he give her something if that was what he wanted?"

"He didn't know what he wanted." Felix's hard-edged words rode over all the voices in the room. He stood, putting a restraining hand on Parkinson's shoulder to keep him silent, and waited for the family to quiet down and give him their attention. They did; they knew it was he, and not Asa, who was the real head of the Salingers now.

"He didn't know what he wanted," Felix repeated in measured words. "He was a sick old man who was manipulated and terrorized by a greedy, conniving witch and for the entire month after his stroke—"

"Felix!" Paul's deep voice cut across his uncle's raspy one. "What the hell are you talking about?"

"You fucking bastard!" Clay bellowed, riding over Paul's words. "Who the fuck do you—"

"Keep your mouth shut," Felix snapped and went on, never breaking stride. "—entire month after his stroke was a helpless invalid who could neither move nor speak—"

"Felix!" Paul said again.

"He could speak!" Laura said. "He talked to me—we talked—"

"—neither move nor speak intelligibly, and it was obvious to everyone that he had lost his ability to think clearly. And that obvious fact was taken advantage of by this *girl*, who was only one of his whims until she wormed her way into his life, and then, when he was dying, kept the nurses out of his room so she could be alone with him and manipulate him into changing his will—"

"That's enough," Paul said furiously. "God damn it, Felix, you're mad; what the hell has gotten into you? This is a goddam pack of lies—"

"Owen didn't want the nurses!" Laura cried. She had barely heard Paul. "He told me to keep them out!" She shivered with cold; her tears had dried in cold streaks on her cheeks. "He didn't want strangers; he wanted me!"

"He didn't know what he wanted—" Felix began for the third time.

"Shut up!" Paul roared. "Let Elwin finish reading! And by God you'll explain this to me later; you'll apologize to Laura and to the whole family—"

Ignoring Paul, Felix put his head back, looked down his thin nose, and flung his voice at Laura. *"He didn't know anything, did he?* He didn't know that you're a criminal with a record, that you have a criminal for a brother, and that you lied to him—you lied to all of us —for four years while we took you in and gave you everything."

Laura's gasp was like a cloth ripping across the dead silence of the room.

"Four years," Felix said, his words like hammer blows. "And we all know that four years ago, the summer you and your brother appeared at our door, our house was robbed of an irreplaceable collection of jewelry and—"

"We didn't have anything to do with that!" Clay shouted.

Everyone was talking at once, turning to each other in alarm, calling out to Felix to explain what he meant. But Felix spoke directly to Laura. "You don't think we'd believe that! From the evidence I now possess, I have concluded that you came here for one purpose only—to rob us—and then decided to stay when you saw you could wrap you tentacles around my father, *just as you'd done once before with another old man who left you a fortune before he died,* and then!"—he shouted above his family's rising clamor, with a glance at Paul—"then you wrapped yourself around a *young* man of wealth, because professional fortune hunters never miss a chance, do they, Miss Fairchild?"

"I'm not! I loved Owen!" But the words lacked force; she felt crushed beneath too many accusations. "I love Paul. You have no right to lie—"

"Don't you talk to me of *right!* You came to us with lies; you came to entrap, to ensnare; you wormed your way into our household . . . *and you robbed us of my wife's jewels and almost killed my father!"*

"It's a goddam lie!" Clay shouted. "We didn't do that job; we changed our—"

He stopped, his face deathly pale. Laura, her tears gone, almost numb with cold, felt Paul's arm drop from her shoulder, saw Leni's look of disbelief, and saw Allison—dear Allison who had been so good to her—stare at her in shock and growing anger.

"You changed nothing," Felix said with contempt. His eyes had gleamed when Clay blurted his fatal words, but then he masked his triumph and now stood at the table with the look of a remote god. "You're a couple of common criminals, you've never been anything else, and I'm going to see to it that everyone knows it. I'm going to break that codicil in court; I'm going to see to it that you don't get a penny of my father's fortune. You'll leave the way you came, with nothing; you'll leave now,

and you'll never have anything to do with any
of us again!"

Laura put a hand against the windowpane to
steady herself. The glass was warm in the sunlight, but nothing could warm the coldness
within her. She felt a movement beside her
and looked up. Paul had moved away from her;
he was looking at her as if he were meeting her
for the first time.

It was all over. The nightmare she had lived
with for four years had become real.

CHAPTER 2

"IT looks awfully tough," Clay mumbled as he eyed the clustered rooftops of the gray shingled Cape Cod mansions that were their target. "Guardhouse, fence, and I saw a dog . . ." He was trying to sound like a cool professional instead of a seventeen-year-old in unfamiliar territory, but his hand was cold as it clasped Laura's. Hers was cold, too, but she looked calm to him; she always seemed more daring and determined than he, but then she was a year older and had already graduated from high school. Moving closer to her in the back seat of the rented car Ben was driving past the Salingers' summer compound, he said, "I'll bet they have lots of dogs."

"Probably," Ben agreed. He slowed to catch a glimpse of the ocean and the sailboats and motorboats moored at private docks. "But once you get me inside, I won't have any trouble getting away."

"They can follow a boat as well as a car," Clay argued. "Why'd you pick this place, anyway? It's a goddam fortress."

"Cut it out," Laura said, her voice low. "We'll get it over with and then quit. I told Ben this was the last time I'd help him; you can, too. I wouldn't do this one, except I promised. But you know"—her voice wavered as she thought back to the pine forests and stretches of stark sand dunes and wild grass they'd driven past in their circuit of the Cape before coming to Osterville—"it is kinda scary to be this far from home, and everything so . . . different . . ."

Ben caught her last words and grinned at them in the rearview mirror. "I thought I taught you to have more confidence in yourself. Is there any house in the world my clever brother and sister can't break into? You've helped me crack some very tight places."

"In New York," Clay said. "We know New York. It's got alleys and subways and crowds of

people you can disappear in, not a million acres
you have to be a cross-country runner to beat
the dogs across—"

"Five acres," Ben said softly. "The Salingers' summer home. Six houses on five acres
surrounded by a fence with one guardhouse.
That's all we know so far. We'll know more
after you and Laura start working there. Listen, Clay, I'm counting on you. Both of you. I
trust you."

Laura felt the rush of pride Ben's praise always gave her. He was much older than she;
the child of her mother's first marriage. Her
mother had remarried when Ben was almost
nine, and a year later Laura was born, and then
Clay. They'd always adored Ben, trailing after
him around their small rented house in
Queens, trying to peek into his private attic
room, following him outside until he sent
them home. Then, when Laura was fourteen,
her parents were killed in a car accident; and
Ben Gardner, twenty-three years old, handsome, grown-up, with lots of girlfriends, suddenly became Laura's and Clay's guardian.
From then on he was more like a mother and
father than a stepbrother to them: he stayed
home most nights to be with them, he took

them for rides in his car, he helped them with
their schoolwork.

He also taught them to steal.

Of all the jobs Ben ever had, stealing was
the only one that kept him interested. He
didn't make a lot of money at it and kept apologizing for not being professional enough, but
he wouldn't join a gang and never found a way
to become part of the tight-knit group of
fences who controlled prices and outlets in
New York. Still, he stayed with it, and filled in
by working as a waiter. They'd moved to a
tiny, dark apartment way up on West End Avenue, but still they had lots of expenses, and
stealing was what Ben had always done so he
kept on doing it—better than ever, he said,
because now he had assistants.

Clay and Laura were good. Their bodies
were agile, their fingers quick, their minds alert
as they climbed drainpipes or tangled branches
of ancient ivy, slipping silently through narrow
windows into darkened rooms, opening the
windows wider for Ben, afterward climbing
swiftly down and disappearing in the shadows
of the graffiti-coated, anonymous subway.

They learned fast and trained themselves to
remember everything. They could distinguish

between a policeman's footsteps and those of a casual passerby; after one tour of a room they knew indelibly the location of stereo equipment, paintings and objets d'art; they could hear an elevator start up in a lobby twenty floors below; they had a feather touch and were almost invisible when they shoplifted or picked pockets on the subway or among the after-work crowd jostling for cabs on Wall Street.

It was always exciting and dangerous and, best of all, it was something the three of them could share: planning the jobs, carrying them out, reliving them later. So when Laura suddenly found herself wanting to stop, she kept it to herself. She couldn't tell Ben she'd begun to hate what they did; it would be like saying she hated *him*, when he was the only one who loved her and Clay and took care of them.

But then things got harder. She was lonely. It was her senior year in high school and all the other girls had friends to bring home after school, or have sleep over, or stand around in the schoolyard with, giggling about dates and new clothes, Saturday night parties and boys feeling them up, monthly cramps, and their awful parents. But Laura couldn't get close to anyone and so she had no girlfriends or boyfriends; she didn't go to Saturday night parties; and she couldn't have a girlfriend sleep over, because Ben slept in one room and she and Clay in the other, with a pair of drapes that they'd found in a dumpster on Orchard Street hanging between them. She could talk casually to classmates in school corridors about their studies or a show on television, but never about how she felt inside or what she really thought and dreamed about. She was always alone.

But even worse than being lonely, she was afraid. Ever since she and Clay were caught, when she was fifteen, she'd been afraid. Everything about it was still fresh; she'd never forget it: the pounding footsteps chasing them down the street, the gray smell of the police station, the way a policeman pinched her fingertips when he rolled them on the grimy ink pad, the flat face of the policeman who took her picture, growling, "Turn left, turn right, look straight at the camera, you little cunt . . ." and then grabbed her ass and squeezed so hard she cried out.

Ben came down to the station with a lawyer he knew, who got them out on bond, and then nothing happened for almost a year until their case came up. They were found guilty, and put on probation for another year, and released in the custody of Melody Chase. She was just one of Ben's girlfriends, but he'd been sure the social workers in court wouldn't release two kids in the custody of a single guy, and also he didn't want the law to connect him with them, so he brought Melody to court with him and she said she was Laura's and Clay's aunt, and the four of them walked out together. Nobody cared, really; all the court wanted was to pass them on to somebody else.

So they were free. But the police had their pictures and fingerprints, and Laura dreamt about it for weeks: she had a record.

That was one of the reasons she finally told Ben she didn't want to help him anymore. She didn't want to be a thief; she wanted to go to college and make friends. She'd had some parts in school plays, and she thought she might like to be an actress—or anything, really, as long as she could be proud of herself.

They quarreled about it. Ben knew she felt bad about picking pockets; she always mailed wallets back to people after taking out the money because she hated thinking about them losing all the things inside: poems and recipes, scribbled addresses and phone numbers, membership cards, insurance cards, credit cards that were no use to her, and especially pictures of people they probably loved. When she told Ben she didn't want to steal anymore, he thought she was being sentimental, the way she was about wallets. But she'd figure out a way to make him understand that there was more to it, that she was really serious. She had to; she'd promised herself the Salinger job would be the last one she'd do. Ever.

"I know you trust us," said Clay, still clinging to Laura's hand in the back seat of the car, "but we've never done a job in a place like this. What the hell do they want with all this *space* and *light?*"

Ben stopped the car a block from the guardhouse. "You're due there in five minutes. Keep your cool; just remember how we rehearsed it. And don't worry; you'll get hired. Rich people in summer houses are always desperate for help. I'll be right here, waiting for you."

"*He* isn't the one who has to go work for them," Clay muttered as the guard passed them through the gate and they followed his pointing finger to a nearby cottage. "He just sits around while we plan everything and then he waltzes in and lifts what's-her-name's jewels and waltzes out. And we're still here."

"That's not true," Laura said hotly. "Ben won't do anything till we work out an alibi." She turned her back on Clay's scowl, and then kept turning, around and around, as she walked, straining to see as much as she could through the thickly wooded grounds. She caught glimpses of velvety lawns, the windowed bay of a house, splashes of color from flower gardens, a pond with a fountain, a greenhouse roof. The estate of six houses clustered along the ocean was bigger than it had seemed from the road, and much grander. Like a picture postcard, Laura thought: everything beautiful, with no torn-up streets, no graffiti, and no litter. "Anyway," she said to Clay, "we're not hanging around very long after he's done it; just a little while, so nobody thinks we're connected to the robbery."

"We're still *here*," Clay repeated glumly.

They reached the small stone cottage with flowered curtains at the window and slatted furniture on the front porch, and Laura swallowed hard. "Damn it, we've been through this a hundred times. I'm already jumpy, and you're making it worse. Ben knows what he's doing. And he's the one who's really taking chances: he could get hurt, or caught, and what could we do to help him?"

Clay was silent. Laura knew he wasn't really angry; he worshiped Ben. It had been all she could do to keep him in school after he turned sixteen and wanted to drop out and do whatever Ben did. She didn't know what would happen now that she'd graduated. If she could get enough money for college, she wanted to move out; she dreamed of a room of her own, with shelves of books and posters on the wall, and pretty furniture, and her favorite music on the radio. But then what would happen to Clay?

"See you later," Clay said as a tall woman approached them. "She's yours. I'm for the head maintenance guy at the greenhouse." He was gone as the woman reached Laura.

"Laura Fairchild? I'm Leni Salinger; let's sit on the porch and talk, shall we? The cottage belongs to Jonas—the guard, you know—and I don't like to take over his living room unless it's raining. But it's pleasant today, isn't it? June is often a little confused here, not quite spring and not quite summer, but today is perfect. And, of course, we do love the quiet; it all changes in July, when the tourists descend. You said on the telephone you had references from your previous jobs."

"Oh." Lulled by Leni's serene voice, Laura had almost forgotten why she was there. "I have them . . ." She fumbled in her black patent purse. She'd known the purse was wrong for June the minute she saw Leni Salinger's white straw hat; she knew everything else was wrong, too, when she pictured herself beside this tall, angular woman in perfectly pressed slacks and a cotton shirt with ivory buttons, her fingernails long and polished, her face and voice perfectly calm because she had nothing to worry about: she knew that whatever happened to her would always be wonderful.

I could never look like that because I'm never sure of anything.

"Laura?" Leni was studying her. "You mustn't be nervous; I don't bite, you know, I don't even growl, and we do try to make our staff comfortable, but I really must find out something about you, mustn't I, before I bring you into our household."

"I'm sorry; I was thinking how beautiful you are, and how you don't have nothing to worry about. I mean, you don't have *anything* to . . ." Laura's voice trailed away and she bit her lip. How could she be such a baby? She blurted things out and made the same stupid mistakes her grammar teacher always had marked her down for. What would this elegant lady, who never would blurt anything, or talk wrong, think of her? Trying to look confident, she handed Leni the three reference letters Ben had typed out and signed with made-up names, then held her breath as Leni read them.

"Very impressive," Leni said. "To have done so much at eighteen. I'm not familiar with the people who wrote these, and I must say they've been very careless—all of them, how surprising —in not including their telephone numbers. O'Hara, Stone, Phillips; goodness, even with a first initial, how difficult to find the right ones in the directory. Do you recall their telephone numbers?"

"No." Laura paused, just as she and Ben had rehearsed it. "But I can find them. I mean, if you want, I'll call everybody who has those initials until I get the right one and then you can talk to them. I really need this job; I'll do anything . . ."

"Well," Leni said thoughtfully, "it's only a

temporary position, of course . . . and it's hard enough to find anyone, much less someone truly anxious and agreeable . . . I'll have to mull this over a bit." She gazed at Laura. "Tell me about yourself. Where do you live?"

"New York." Ben had warned her it might get personal; she sat very straight and spoke carefully but quickly to get past this part as fast as she could. "My parents are dead, and my brother and I lived with some relatives, but they didn't really want us there, so a year ago we got our own place. I graduated high school last week."

After a moment, Leni said, "And what else? Are you going to college?"

"Oh, I'd love to. If I could get the money . . ."

Leni nodded. "So you need a job. But why not in New York? Why did you come to the Cape?"

Laura hesitated an instant; they hadn't rehearsed this part. "Just to get away, you know. We have a tiny apartment, and it gets awfully hot in the summer and sort of closed in . . . And somebody at school said it was nice here." She looked beyond the porch at the sparkle of the ocean through the trees. "It is. More beautiful than I ever thought."

Leni was watching her closely. "And how did you get here? Do you have a car?"

Laura felt a surge of impatience. Why did she keep asking questions? "A friend drove us," she said briefly.

"And how will you get back?"

"I hope we don't have to." She looked at her hands. "I mean, I was hoping you'd hire us and then we could just . . . stay."

"Stay where?" Leni asked gently.

"Oh, we'd find a place. We bought a newspaper and there are some rooms for rent in Osterville and Centerville . . . If you'd give us a chance I know we could manage everything. You wouldn't have to worry about us; we can take care of ourselves, you know."

"Yes, I think you can," Leni murmured. She looked around. "Yes, Allison, is there something you need?"

"A tennis partner." The young woman who stood at the foot of the porch steps was about Laura's age and looked like a young Leni, as tall and angular, though her long blond hair was straight, while Leni's was short and curled, and she had a touch of arrogance that Leni lacked. "Patricia doesn't feel like playing. Would you like a game?"

"My daughter, Allison," Leni said to Laura. "This is Laura Fairchild, Allison. She's applying for the job of Rosa's assistant."

"Rosa's a sweetie," said Allison. "She's also an absolute tyrant in her kitchen; she'll wear you out in a week. Or maybe she'll take you under her wing and then you'll gain fifty pounds." She turned to her mother. "Can't you just hear her telling Laura she's too thin?"

"Am I?" Laura asked anxiously. She was ashamed of her cotton dress and black patent shoes, bought at a resale shop, and the way her hair hung lankly around her face in the salt air of the Cape, and she knew her face had a city pallor beside these two tanned women, but she hadn't thought about being thin. *I won't get the job if I'm skinny and ugly; they only want pretty people working for them.* Ben and Clay always told her she was pretty, but they were her brothers. Nervously she pushed her hair behind her ears, tried to look taller on the chair's slippery cushion, and kept her legs close together, her feet flat on the porch.

But it wasn't just her looks that bothered her; she was envious of the warmth between

Allison and her mother. She had never known anything like that, even when her mother was alive, and she envied them and liked them at the same time. It's too bad we have to rob them, she thought.

Another one of Ben's warnings came back to her. *It's better not to know the mark at all. But if it's unavoidable, don't get close; keep your distance.* Laura felt a pang of regret. It might be nice to be close to Leni and Allison.

"There's nothing wrong with your figure; you mustn't worry," Leni said. "Well, perhaps a few pounds, a little rounding out . . . young girls do seem gaunt these days. They want to be willowy or sway like a reed or some such thing—it always seems to involve some damp and probably unhealthy plant. Yes, I do believe you could use a few pounds . . . Perhaps you don't eat properly. Do you have a hot breakfast every day?"

Laura and Allison looked at each other and burst out laughing. "Oh, well," Leni sighed. "I suppose you do hear that a great deal." But she wasn't really thinking of her words; she was hearing Allison's laughter and watching it banish the supercilious amusement that usually curved her daughter's perfect lips without allowing laughter to escape. Leni often worried about Allison's cool, amused silence; and at that moment, as her daughter and this strange girl continued to smile together, and even though she was sure those reference letters were faked, she decided to hire Laura Fairchild as a kitchen helper for the Salingers' summer stay on Cape Cod.

Clay worked in the greenhouses and flower gardens shared by the whole family while Laura was at Rosa's side in the kitchen of Felix and Leni's house. It was the biggest in the compound, and Ben had instructed her to explore and sketch it for him. But by the end of their second week at the Cape she still had not done it, nor had she looked for Leni's jewels so Ben could go straight to them when he broke in. She knew what they looked like because Leni was frequently photographed wearing them at dinner parties and balls—she even took them to the Cape for the big parties in July and August—but Laura had to find out where she kept them.

"What are you waiting for?" Clay demanded, looking up from his own drawing of the layout of the compound. They were sitting in the tiny two-room apartment Ben had rented for them over a garage in downtown Centerville before he went back to New York, and Clay had been trying to figure out the exact distance from the guardhouse to Leni's bedroom window. "How are we going to get out of here if you don't do your part?"

"I'm *trying,*" Laura said. "But Rosa expects me to be with her all the time."

"Rosa's a dictator," Clay said.

"Rosa's a sweetie." Laura remembered Allison saying that and wondered why she hadn't seen her once since she started working in her parents' house.

In fact she saw hardly anyone but Rosa and the house staff from the time she and Clay rode up in the mornings on the bicycles Ben had bought them to the time they rode away in the late afternoon. Leni was the only one of the Salingers to come to the kitchen; she came every afternoon, to plan the next day's menus with Rosa. They sat in the sun that stretched the length of the great room, from the panes of the wide breakfast bay that faced the rose garden, swimming pool and tennis courts, all the way to the brick fireplace at the other end.

On the long maple table recipes were fanned out, and books of menus from past summers, and with them the two women, like generals planning a campaign, put together the schedule for the next day: usually a luncheon for a small group and then a dinner party for fifteen or more. But none of the other family members came to the kitchen, and after two weeks Laura was not even sure who was at the compound and who was away.

"In Maine," Rosa said when Laura finally worked up the courage to ask where Allison was. "You'll find this family is very big on travel. Somebody's always somewhere and just when you think you know where everybody is, somebody comes back and somebody else goes."

"They just leave their houses empty?" Laura asked casually. In her white kitchen uniform, her hair in a neat ponytail, she felt almost like a cook, almost Rosa's equal, and that made it easier to ask questions about the family. Still, as she stacked breakfast dishes in the double dishwasher, she was careful not to sound too curious.

"Some of them are empty," Rosa replied. "Some with the staff, some stuffed to the ceiling with houseguests. You'll find this family is very big on houseguests, probably because they're in the hotel business and they think something's wrong if all the bedrooms aren't full."

She chuckled and Laura smiled with her. It was easy to be comfortable with Rosa. At sixty-seven, with unflagging energy, she was short and round with small hands that were always moving, nimbly flicking pastry from marble board to pie plate, or cutting vegetables and stirring soup almost at the same time, or knitting a vest for her nephew while she waited for bread to rise or a roast to be done. She had promised to make Laura a sweater when the vest was finished. And no matter what she was doing, she talked steadily and shrewdly about the Salingers and the other families from New York and Boston who, generations before, had come to the towns of Osterville, Centerville, and Hyannis Port on Nantucket Sound, on the south coast of Cape Cod, to build the sprawling summer estates now being used by their children and grandchildren.

"Mr. Owen built this one," Rosa said as she and Laura took salad ingredients from the wall of refrigerators and spread them on the long maple work table. It was the first time Laura realized that Rosa casually called all the Salingers, except Owen, by their first names. "In 1920 he brought Mrs. Owen here—Iris, her name was, she was a lovely lady—and a year later Felix was born. That's when I came; there were only the three of them, and I cooked and cleaned and took care of the baby, and Asa, too, when he was born a year after Felix, and had time to get married myself and not too long later be a widow, and some time after that, I nursed Mrs. Owen when she got sick and died, and all that in the space of ten years. Which I suppose is why I never married again; I was so busy being a mother to Felix and Asa, and Mr. Owen, too, at least for those first few years when he was mourning, I just never had time."

"But who are all the others?" Laura asked. "I don't even know all their names."

Rosa reeled them off in a rhythm that matched her busy hands, chopping and slicing vegetables for the salads she was making for lunch. Owen Salinger, founder of the Salinger hotel chain, had two sons, Felix and Asa; Felix had one daughter, Allison; Asa had a daughter, Patricia, by his first marriage. So Owen had only granddaughters. "Not one grandson he can count on to keep his empire going," Rosa said. "No nephews, either. This family is very big on women, and not one of them shows the slightest twinge of interest in running hotels. Mr. Owen's great-nephew could do it—that's Paul Janssen, the son of Leni's sister, Barbara, and her husband, Thomas—but he's something of a playboy, Paul is, and even if he does settle down, which I may not live long enough to see, it's photography that makes his eyes light up, not hotels. Who'll take over the company after Felix and Asa retire I can't imagine."

As Laura asked questions, Rosa described them all, with their foibles and eccentricities and triumphs. "Allison broke her finger on the slide when she was seven and never went near a swing set again, even though Felix offered her a hundred dollars because he wanted his daughter to have courage and said he'd buy it if he had to." She told Laura about the house Felix built for his father. "It's attached to this one; the door is at the end of the long gallery. After Mr. Owen gave this house to Felix and Leni, Leni wanted him to live with them in the summers—he has a mansion all to himself in Boston—but he said he liked being on his own and planned to build a small house for himself. Well, they argued and argued, and finally Mr. Owen said all right if he could draw the plans himself and also have a door he could lock. So everything worked out. When a man is seventy-eight, he should have people nearby, but he has a right to privacy, too."

She told Laura which houses belonged to the other family members, and where they lived the rest of the year—mostly New York, California, and Boston. And she told her who was in grammar school, high school, and college, who was working and where, and who spent most of the year in Europe.

Gradually Laura put together a picture of the whole family, even though she hadn't yet met most of them. Owen was in Canada, visiting friends; Asa and his family would not arrive from Boston for another week; Leni's sister, Barbara Janssen, her husband, Thomas, and their son, Paul, were returning from Europe in two weeks; others had arrived at the Cape but were always sailing or taking flying lessons or shopping, and when they came to Felix and Leni's for dinner Laura had either left for the day or was working in the kitchen while the maids served.

"You could serve," Rosa said, studying her. "You're not bad looking, you're quick and neat, you have a nice smile which you don't use often enough and if someone asked you to do something, you'd remember it. What a memory you have! I told Leni you'd memorized everything in the kitchen in one day; never have I seen such a memory, I told her."

Laura flushed and turned away, striking her elbow against the table. "Shit," she muttered, nursing it.

"But you're not ready," Rosa went on. "You need to be smoothed out. A real lady doesn't use vulgarity, my young miss. A real lady doesn't have a temper, either, and I've seen signs of one in you. And you have a lot to learn. You'll find this family is very big on form, and you don't know which side to serve or take a plate from, or how to bring somebody a clean knife, or when to refill a water glass. It's a wonder to me those people wrote those fabulous letters about you, unless of course they just liked your smile."

Laura flushed again and concentrated on

slicing red peppers. "I didn't serve; I worked in kitchens."

"My eye," Rosa said pleasantly. "You never worked in a kitchen, my little Laura, not a decent one, anyway, unless it was to wash dishes and scrub the floor." She watched Laura's face. "You needn't worry, I'm not about to tell anyone, or ask questions, either. I've been there myself, you know, a long time ago: poor and hungry and willing to do any job people would give me. I'm sure you worked hard for those people; I'm sure they liked you and that's why they wrote those letters. You'll find I'm very big on instincts, and my instinct says I trust you."

Laura's hand slipped and the blade slashed her finger. "Damn it!" she cried, slamming the knife on the counter. Tears filled her eyes. She wanted to curl up inside the circle of Rosa's plump arms; she wanted to tell her how wonderful it was to be in her warm kitchen with her warm voice and her trust. But she had to hold it all back, just as she had to keep her distance from Leni and Allison. She couldn't return Rosa's trust, she couldn't let herself like anyone in this family, she couldn't let down her guard.

She was there to rob them. And she couldn't ever let herself forget it.

The hallway was silent and cool and her feet slid silently on the hardwood floor as she opened doors for a quick survey, then closed them to go on to the next room. She had already sketched the first floor: Owen's house, at one end, was a blank, since she'd never been inside, but she had drawn the kitchen at the other end, and the full width of the house stretching between them, with a long porch in front and the wide glassed-in gallery along the back, opening onto the living room, den and dining room.

Now, for the first time, she was on the second floor. *Guest rooms across the back of the house, each with its own bath; Allison's suite along the whole east side—bigger than our apartment in New York—then Felix's office, bedroom, dressing room and bath, then Leni's sitting room, dressing room and bath, and her bedroom on the west side.*

That was the one she wanted. Silently she opened the bedroom door and slipped inside, taking in with a swift glance the seafoam and ivory colors, ivory shag rugs on gleaming hardwood floors, the bed in the next room draped in seafoam silk and ivory lace. The rooms were cool and serene, like Leni. Laura thought of what it would be like to come to a mother in rooms like these, and curl up and talk about the things she worried about.

Well, I never will, that's all. And it doesn't matter; I've outgrown that.

She had to hurry. She surveyed the spacious rooms with a more calculating eye. Sitting room desk, coffee table and armoire—all of them with drawers. In the bedroom and adjoining dressing room, four bureaus and a dressing table, nightstands flanking the bed, a wall of closets. Swiftly and silently, Laura opened them all, her slender fingers slipping among silk and cotton and lace without disturbing one perfect fold; she looked beneath the furniture without moving it; she tilted pictures from the walls without changing one angle.

Nothing, nothing . . . where would she keep them . . . there's no safe . . . Then she came to the last closet, and found it locked. *Finally . . .* She knelt before it. She could get it open; she'd done it so many times. She reached in her pocket for the small set of steel picks Ben had bought her for her birthday, and it was at that moment that the sitting room door opened.

"What the hell—!" Allison's voice exclaimed. She stood in the doorway, her eyes changing as she recognized Laura. "A burglar!" she cried in mock alarm. "How terrifying! But I know you! Rosa's new assistant . . . yes?"

Laura nodded. She had leaped to her feet but she was dizzy and her legs were weak, and she leaned against the closet. Her throat was dry, her heart was pounding; she thrust her clenched fists deep inside the pockets of her uniform to hide the picks in her shaking hands. Rosa had said Allison wasn't due back from Maine until tomorrow, and everyone else was spending the day on Felix's yacht. *It was supposed to be empty up here all afternoon.*

"But what are you doing in my mother's room . . . Laura, isn't it? Have we started cooking dinner up here? Or were you looking for my great-grandmother's sterling that she brought over from Austria? It isn't here; Rosa could have told you it's in the dining room commode."

Laura shook her head. "I wasn't looking—"
She cleared her dry throat. "I wasn't looking
for sterling." She took a step forward. "I ought
to be downstairs . . ."

"Indeed you should. But first let's have a
talk." Allison strode across the room, grasped
Laura's arm, and forced her to walk beside her
out of the room, down the full length of the
hall, and into another suite at the opposite corner from Leni's. "This is mine. Perfectly private. Sit down." Laura stood indecisively. "I
said, sit *down*."

Laura sat down. Her white cotton uniform
seemed plain and harsh in the delicate white
wicker chair with its chintz cushion. The room
was bright and airy, in gold and white with
lamps and throw pillows of sea green and in-
digo blue. It seemed that all the colors of the
Cape were there, shimmering in the sunlight
that streamed across the ocean and the beach
and the smooth lawns of the estate for the sole
purpose of brightening Allison Salinger's
rooms.

Finally Laura's eyes rested on the stack of
suitcases in the corner of the room. "I came
back early," Allison said. "I was exceedingly
bored." She had watched Laura survey the sit-

ting room and the bedroom, visible through its open door, and now she gave her a keen look. "Maybe this isn't the first time you've been here." Laura, frozen in her chair, said nothing. "Have you already been here?"

Laura shook her head.

"My God, have I petrified you into silence? What are you afraid of? It isn't a crime to look at people's rooms; I poke around to see how my friends fix up theirs; why shouldn't you do the same? I won't turn you in, if that's what you're worried about. I don't care what you do; you work for Rosa, not me. It would be different if you'd been going through Mother's closets; if the alarm had gone off there'd be hell to pay."

Laura's heart began to pound again, the blood hammering in her ears. *I should have thought . . . I should have known . . . What's happened to me that I don't do things right in this house?* "Alarm?" she asked, making it sound as casual as she could.

"A siren that wakes the dead. It's because of Mother's jewelry, you know, all the incredible stuff my great-grandmother brought from Austria with the sterling. My father keeps telling Mother to keep it in the safe in Boston, but she says what good is jewelry if you can't wear it. If something is really important to you, you ought to do whatever you want with it, right? She loves all those things because they came from her grandmother to her mother and then to her and someday they'll be mine, so if she wants to wear them anywhere in the world, why shouldn't she? What do you do besides explore bedrooms?"

Laura flushed deeply. For the first time she was angry. Allison was playing with her like a cat trying to trip up a mouse. "I work," she said shortly and began to stand up.

"Not yet," Allison snapped. Her voice made it clear that she knew exactly where the power lay between the two of them. "I said I wanted to talk. You work for Rosa. What do you like best? Do you like to cook?"

Her tone had become warm and curious, catching Laura off guard. "I guess so. I haven't done it very long."

"You haven't? Mother said you'd done it forever. Lots of good references, she said."

"Oh, sure," Laura said swiftly. "I've worked in kitchens for years. I thought you meant cooking here, for your family."

"Well," Allison said when she stopped, "do you like cooking for my family?"

"Yes."

"What else do you like?"

"Oh, reading and listening to music. And I'm getting to like the beaches around here."

"And boys?"

"No."

"Oh, come on. How old are you?"

"Eighteen."

"Same as me. And no boys? Not even one little date? Everybody dates, for heaven's sake."

"Why do you care?" Laura burst out. "I'm just a cook—not even that, really; I'm just Rosa's assistant. What do you care whether I date or not?"

"I don't know," Allison said frankly. She contemplated Laura. "There's something about you—something about your eyes—like you're thinking of two things at once and I don't have all your attention. It's like a game, getting to know what you're thinking, getting you to . . . *see me*. Do you know what I mean?"

"No," said Laura flatly.

"I'll bet you do. You're not from around here, are you, like most of the summer help?"

"I've lived in New York."

"You still live in New York?"

"Yes."

"So what do you do in New York?"

Laura tossed her head. "I go out with five university guys. A couple of them are just friends but the other ones I see a lot, and on weekends I pick one or the other of them and we go to their apartment and screw. Sometimes I'm with two of them at once. Is there anything else you want to know?"

Allison tried to stare her down but Laura stared back. *Prying bitch. Who says everybody dates? What do you know about it?* "Do you have a good time?" Allison asked curiously. Her voice had changed again—not quite believing Laura, but not quite sure.

Confused, Laura was silent.

"I don't," Allison said. "I've been with three, no four, guys, one at a time, I'm not gutsy enough for two at once, and I don't much like it. I tell myself I should because everybody else does—or at least they say they do —but, I don't know, all the boys seem so damn young. If you have college guys, you're lucky.

They're probably better. The ones I know can't *talk*. All they want to do is get in your pants, and as soon as they get a finger in they think they've got it made and they start to babble and slobber and it's all so stupid. I mean, I have a brain, and feelings, but every boy I know treats me like some kind of doll they can play with but don't have to pay much attention to. I think they ought to carry a cantaloupe with a hole in it and whenever they get the urge just stick their cock in and jack off, and then they'd never have to make conversation at all."

Laura broke into nervous giggles and Allison giggled, too, and then they were laughing as they had when they met. "They're probably scared to talk," Laura said. "They can feel like big men when they screw, but they sound pretty silly when you want them to talk about something serious, and I guess they know that."

"That's it; you've got it." Allison sighed. "You know that bit about the cantaloupe? I've been thinking that for a long time but I never said it to anybody before. I haven't got anybody to talk to, that's the problem. I mean, everybody from Boston and around here thinks

I'm so fucking grown-up and cool, and they all know each other, and with people like that, if you show them you're worried or not happy about something, in an hour everybody knows it and . . . oh, what the hell. It's just that I feel alone a lot of the time. Do you know what I mean?"

"I know what it's like not to have anybody to talk to."

"Well, we're talking. Do you have a good time in bed with your college guys?"

"Sure." *She's not a friend; I can't confide in her; I'll never see her again after a few more weeks.* "I always have a good time. You just have to know what you're doing." She hesitated. She hadn't the slightest notion of what it felt like to be in bed with a man. All she had had were quick couplings in the back seats of cars that had made her feel, for a few minutes, like she was special to the boy she was with, and then, afterward, more lonely than ever. "You have to care about him," she said, letting her fantasies fly. "And keep the lights on so you can see each other, 'cause it's more sexy that way and you feel like you're with somebody you know. And do it slow and easy so you have time to feel good. And make him know

what you want. Don't let nobody take you"—
she cleared her throat—"don't let *anybody*
take you without your being ready. You just tell
them: *God damn it, I'm a real person! Listen to
what I want!* That's all there is to it. I've got to
get back; Rosa said three o'clock sharp—"

"Sit down; it's only quarter to." Allison was
frowning again. "I tell myself that, that I
shouldn't do anything I don't want to, but
they're all over me and it's just easier to go
along and get it over and then get out of there.
I don't want to be *raped*, after all . . ."

"You're raped every time you do it and don't
want to," Laura said in a clear voice. And as
she said it she realized she was right; it was the
first time she'd known it. *I'll never do it again,
never, unless I really, truly want to and really
care about somebody. And then he'll have to
care about me, too.*

"You're smart," Allison said. "God, that is a
smart thing to say. Do you want to come up
here a lot, and talk? It's a pretty room, isn't it?
I used to hate it because it's so different from
my rooms in Boston—they're all velvet and
satin, sort of like a warm bed—but now I like
this, too. It's different, but it's just as comforting, and God knows I need that."

"You've got your mother's room, and your mother," Laura blurted.

"Well, of course, but . . . Well, you know Mother. She's wonderful and I love her, but she's perfect. And how do I go to somebody who's perfect and say, 'Listen, I fucked up'?"

"If she's perfect she'll understand," Laura said, and they burst out laughing.

"Right," Allison agreed. "She's not quite perfect. But close."

Their smiles held and Laura felt warmth flow through her. Maybe they could be friends after all; only a little bit, because she had to be careful, but closer than any friendship she'd had until now. After all, here she was, sitting in a girl's room for the first time ever, talking about private things the way girls were supposed to. Even if she'd lied a lot, she'd told some truths, too, and having to lie didn't change anything: it was still the kind of afternoon she'd always dreamed of. Why shouldn't it go on? Why shouldn't she have a real friend, just for these few weeks?

Allison was studying Laura's face. "I really would like to talk to you again and get to know you. I like you. Did I get it right about what you were doing in Mother's room? Or were you doing something else?"

The spell was broken. Laura's warmth was gone; she was tense and calculating. *This is how it always has to be.* She lowered her eyes and made her voice a little higher than usual, sounding young, very earnest, very innocent. "No, you were right; I just wanted to see what it was like. Rosa mentioned that everyone was gone—she doesn't know I came up here so *please* don't blame her—and I thought I'd just take a little peek because I've never ever been in a house like this—it's like a fairy-tale castle, isn't it?—and I thought just once I could see how it felt to walk around in it and even pretend I lived here or might live somewhere like it, someday . . ."

She raised her eyes and looked at Allison with a little quiver on her lips. "I didn't mean any harm."

Allison's frown was deep and angry. "You're very complicated, aren't you? And maybe a good actress, too. I think I *will* get to know you better."

Laura jumped up. "I'm sure it's after three. I have to go—" She was at the door, pulling it open, almost running into the hall and toward the stairs.

Allison was close behind. "I'm interested in you. And I intend to get to know you *very* well. In fact," she added, leaning forward a little as Laura stood on the top stair, frozen, "I'm going to find out everything about you."

CHAPTER 3

CLAY slipped the manila envelope into the mailbox at the Centerville post office, then pushed off on his bicycle to catch up with Laura. "That gives Ben the layout of the grounds and houses," he said as they rode toward Osterville. "I wrote him everything you told me about the alarm on the closet, and I said we'd find out what kind of a security system they've got. Oh, and what's-his-name, the guard's, schedule—"

"Jonas," said Laura. "And Billy and Al on the night shifts."

"Right. You know them all. All that shit that doesn't matter. But then you find an alarm and you don't even have the smarts to ask Allison or Rosa what kind of system it is and how it hooks up to Leni's closet!"

"Mrs. Salinger to you," Laura snapped. "And I wish you'd leave me alone. I couldn't ask, right then. When I have a chance, I'll find out. I've never let Ben down and I won't this time."

She sped ahead, rounded a corner and turned down a private drive she knew Clay had not discovered, to come out on the beach. It was early and no one was about; it was as if she had a private ocean, all to herself. She walked her bicycle in the soft sand, listening to the gulls and the wash of the waves, tasting the salt air on her tongue. Two weeks earlier, she would have preferred Main Street in Centerville, or even downtown Osterville, crowded with gift shops, fudge shops, bayberry candle shops, restaurants, and boutiques, because even though they were small they were more like New York than were the silent stretches of beach. And in some ways she still felt peculiar on the beach, alone in all that space and stillness.

She felt even more peculiar about the forests of pine, beech, oak, sassafras and fifty-foot holly trees that shared this part of the Cape with drifting sand and clumps of wild grass bending in the wind. The idea of forests terrified her. How would she find her way out without street signs, and familiar sidewalks beneath her feet, shadowed by buildings crammed together so that wherever you looked there was a place to get shelter from the rain or to hide if somebody had felt you pick his pocket?

There were no hiding places on the beach, either, but this morning Laura found its quiet and emptiness comforting. For the first time she felt its serenity, and she was annoyed when she saw someone up ahead and realized she didn't have the ocean to herself after all. It was an old man, she saw as she drew closer, very tall and thin, with a white, drooping mustache and white hair that reached his shoulders. As she approached, she was struck by the contrast of his heavy eyebrows and wide, sensual mouth in a face so thin it was almost gaunt.

"Have you ever noticed the way this shell swirls?" he asked conversationally as she passed within a few feet of him. They might have been old friends sharing an early morning stroll. "It's peculiar to this part of the country, you know; I've never found another like it."

Laura stopped and took the shell he was

holding out to her. Pink and white and rose, it curled in on itself like a whirlpool reflecting the sunset. She traced its whorls with her fingertip: silken smooth except for a tiny raised ridge in the center of each curve. "I've never seen one like it either," she said, not telling him that she had never seen any shell at all.

"Like people," the old man said. "Like fingerprints. Each has its own character. No, keep it," he added as she handed it back. "I like to give them away to people who appreciate them. Just as I like to share the morning solitude with someone who appreciates it." He bent closer to peer at her. "But I've intruded on your solitude, haven't I? You thought you had all this to yourself and then I pop up and obstruct the view."

Instinctively Laura looked at the wide expanse of empty beach all around them and a small smile curved the corners of her mouth. The old man saw it and smiled broadly. "You think there might be room for both of us? Of course we can go our separate ways, but we might also share our pleasure." His speech had an old-fashioned cadence that reminded Laura of books she had read, and his smile was warm and private, drawing her toward him.

But she held back. He had known she didn't want anyone else on the beach, and no thief can afford to hang around a mind reader. She put her hands on the handlebars, ready to walk off. "I don't own it. It's somebody's private beach; we shouldn't even be here."

"But now that we are, we can enjoy it," he said gravely, and she looked up, and met his eyes, slate gray, serious, intent on her own. "Are there a great many things that you do own and wish to protect from intruders?"

"No," Laura said sharply—why did people have to pry?—and she turned again to leave. "I don't own anything," she said over her shoulder.

"Yourself," he responded quietly. "And I hope you're the only one who does." Laura frowned. "Aren't you valuable enough to own?" the old man asked.

She looked back at him. "I never thought about it."

"I think about it," he said. "About myself, that is. How much I value myself, how much pride I take in myself." He studied her gravely as she stood some distance away, like a wary bird poised to fly. "Perhaps you don't take enough pride in yourself. I'm sure you care about yourself, but perhaps not enough, or for the wrong reasons. You might give some thought to that. Having faith in yourself."

Laura nodded, fascinated but also afraid, because once again the old man had seen inside her. How could he know about the things she'd been wanting for over a year, almost more than anything else?

He was still studying her: about eighteen, he thought, and still gangly; not yet a woman. Long, well-formed legs, though, with good muscles, probably from riding her bicycle. Her hair was tied back with a ribbon, and she wore a cotton shift and sandals. She should wear silk, the old man thought suddenly, and then wondered why he would think that about a rather ordinary, pretty girl with poor posture and an uncomfortable wariness in her stance. Perhaps it was her eyes: dark blue, almost too big for her slender, delicate face, showing in their depths a strong will that did not yet know its own strength or direction.

"Of course," he went on, "usually it takes a long time to have faith in ourselves. I've had seventy-eight years to work at it. But I think you'll do it; one of these days you'll truly believe you are the most valuable possession you have." He smiled at her again. "And you'll protect yourself from intruders."

Laura stared at him. Without realizing it, she had moved closer and now stood beside him. "I have thought about it," she confided. "I'm going to change my whole life. I have to figure out how to do it, but someday I'm going to change everything; I won't even look the way I look now—"

"I like the way you look," the old man said gently.

She shook her head. It was nice of him to say it and it was nice to hear, but he was old; what did he know? "I'm not beautiful or glamorous; I don't know how to dress right or even walk the right way."

"One foot in front of the other," he suggested.

"You wouldn't joke about it if you knew how serious it is," she said angrily. "Rich people have a way of walking that's different: they come into a room as if they own everything and can just reach out and take whatever they want. They're not unhappy and they're not afraid they'll do something wrong; they just do what they want."

"You mean they have confidence."

"I guess," Laura said doubtfully, thinking that was a poor word to describe the way rich people made the world their own.

"But their confidence rests on their money," he said. "What about inside themselves? Don't you think rich people ever worry about love and friendship and health, and doing things well, and being whatever they most want to be, deep inside?"

Laura shook her head again. "Not like the rest of us."

"And how many people have you known like that?"

"I haven't—a few."

There was a silence. So young, the old man thought, contemplating her small frown. And yet she is close to being a woman. "Tell me what you like about the beach," he said.

"The way it goes on forever." She turned to take in the shining sand, pale and sparkling in the sunlight, darker where the waves slid up and then retreated. "There's so much space, like a huge house, and I can go from room to room and it's all mine."

His eyes brightened. "I've called it my castle ever since I was a small boy. Even when I was unhappy, if my father had scolded me or I was

worried about something, when I came out
here I was king of everything I could see. And
I was always very selective about which friends
I'd bring with me."

"I wouldn't bring anybody," Laura said decisively.

"No one? Not even your closest friend?"

"I don't have no—I don't have very many
friends. I don't need them." He was watching
her and she shrugged. "They're all right for
people who need them, but if you're strong
you don't." She looked at him as if daring him
to contradict her. "You just need yourself.
That's what you said a few minutes ago. You
should believe in yourself."

"That wasn't exactly what I meant," he responded quietly. "Poor child, isn't there anyone you want to share your happiness with?"

"Don't feel sorry for me!" Laura said furiously. "I don't want anybody to feel sorry for
me! I don't give a shit—" She bit her lip. "I
don't care about sharing, and I wouldn't bring
anybody here; it would be my secret."

Casually, as if she had said nothing unusual,
the old man gave a bow. "May I visit you in
your house? I'd like very much to sit down."
He pointed to a hillock of sand covered with

tufts of wild grass. "Lately I've begun to tire easily, and I would appreciate the use of your sofa."

Laura felt a sudden rush of warmth; he was trying to make her feel better. For the first time she laughed. "Please do. I'm sorry I can't serve tea."

He laughed with her but inwardly he was stunned at the change in her face. She wasn't ordinary, he thought. She could be a beautiful woman, with a smile that would break men's hearts. She lay her bicycle on the sand and they sat down, contemplating the ocean's long gray swells and furling white caps that broke along the shore in rhythmic whispers. "I've never told my family about my castle on the beach," he mused. "They think I'm often tyrannical and occasionally wise, mainly because I've reached an advanced age, and I don't want them to think I fantasize empty rooms around every sand dune. And I certainly can't tell them that what I like best is the silence. In my family everyone has a vocal opinion on everything. The silence here is wonderful. I never get enough of it."

"It makes me feel odd, though," Laura said. "As if it's going to swallow me up."

"Ah." He nodded. "That's what an empty beach does. Swallows you up. A lot of people find the silence too much and they bring those terrible radios . . . they have a name . . ."

"Ghetto blasters."

"Blasters," he echoed. "I gather they're called that because they blast ghettos."

She laughed. "They blast everybody's ears. They make little people feel big because you can't ignore them. And it's even better if you hate the noise, because then they've really made you notice them and they feel important. More real."

He looked at her sharply. "You're very perceptive."

She shrugged. "You have to be on top of what's happening around you or you don't make it."

A child of the streets, he thought. No wonder the beach makes her feel odd. "Where do you live?" he asked.

"In Centerville."

"And when the summer ends?"

She hesitated. "New York."

"New York is your home?"

She nodded and in the silence she drew a circle in the sand with her finger, and another circle inside that. Could she talk about herself? She never had, except with Cal, and now he was dead and his bookstore was closed. But why not? she thought. The old man was a stranger; she loved his smile and the way he paid attention to her; and she was longing to talk to someone. "I've always lived there; I never went nowhere—anywhere—until we came here. For the summer. I like the crowds, and the buildings, all piled against each other, and everything has a beginning and an ending so you always know where you are, and you can find your way where you're going." She paused. "It seems awfully far away."

"And do you feel lost when you're here?" the old man asked.

"I never feel lost," she said strongly. "Just not always sure how I'll get where I want to go. But I'll get there, and I won't let nobody— anybody—stop me."

The old man stared into the distance, smiling faintly. "I said that, too, when I was young. And I was lucky; nobody stopped me." They looked at the waves. "What else do you like about New York?"

"The noise," Laura replied promptly. "It never stops, you know, even if you close all the windows. Even then the noise comes in, and it's nice because you're always part of it."

"You mean the noise there swallows you up as much as the silence here," he said, watching the changing expressions on her face.

It had never occurred to her. She narrowed her eyes as she thought about the city and the beach in a new way, and then she laughed. "I like that. I love new ideas. I had a friend once, named Cal—you remind me of him—and he did that: told me new ways of looking at things. He owned a bookstore in the East Village, in New York—used books—and he'd let me sit near his desk in the back and read dusty old books full of wonderful new ideas. I loved him a lot."

He noted the wistfulness in her voice. "I once spent a lot of time in used bookstores," he said reflectively. "Then I got too busy earning a living. Lately I've rediscovered them. Old books and new ideas. That's nicely put. Are you in school in New York? Where do you live?"

"I'm starting at the university in the fall," Laura lied swiftly. "And living in the dormitory."

He gazed at her. *He knows I've lied. It's not*

definite; I can't go unless Ben helps me. And even if I do go, I'll still live with him and Clay; I can't afford a dormitory. He knows I'm lying and now he won't like me anymore.

"I went to a university for two years," the old man said. "Then I left and started my own company. I made a great deal of money but I always disliked it when people asked me about college, because I didn't have a success to talk about. Perhaps when you graduate and have a success to talk about you won't mind questions."

"Thank you," Laura said in a low voice. Reluctantly, she stood up. "I'll be late for work if I don't go."

He nodded and stood with her. "If you come this way tomorrow, we can talk some more. I'll be right here, swallowed up in my thoughts."

"If I can," Laura said, though she knew she wouldn't. Ben wouldn't like her talking about herself so much and she knew it really wasn't smart. *But it isn't fair that I can't make friends with Allison or this nice old man, or anybody else around here who's nice.* She picked up her bicycle. "Good-bye," she said, and wondered if it sounded like she meant it for good.

He held out his hand. "I hope you come back."

Awkwardly, Laura touched his hand, not shaking it but brushing his palm with hers. Then, as she put her hands on her handlebars, he kissed her forehead. "I hope I haven't made you late."

He was smiling at her in that personal way and Laura became angry. Why did he have to be so nice? "Good-bye," she said loudly and pushed off, struggling to keep the bicycle straight in the shifting sand. She wished she were smoother about getting along with people. It was like collecting shells: something she'd never had a chance to practice. To make up for her abruptness, she turned to wave good-bye. He was watching her, holding up his hand. It was a farewell wave but it was also like a benediction.

All day, working in the kitchen, she carried the memory of the old man's private smile and the way he had raised his hand, palm toward her, as she walked away. She wished she could see him again but she couldn't; one of these days she and Clay and Ben would do the job and then they'd be back in the city, together again. Her two brothers, her family.

"Laura, stop dreaming," Rosa said. "I'm asking you to work tonight. Is it yes or no?"

"Yes," Laura said.

"We might be here late."

She shrugged. It was better to work in Rosa's bright, warm kitchen than sit in a tiny room over a garage and watch Clay make endless schedules of guards and watchdogs to impress Ben.

"A real lady doesn't shrug her shoulders, my young miss."

Laura started to shrug, then she caught herself and put her head back, standing straight. She'd never heard that ladies didn't shrug. But Rosa would know. Rosa knew all about ladies.

"—home from Europe," Rosa was saying. "And Mr. Owen is back from Canada, and Allison from Maine. The whole family will be together for the first time this summer. Twenty-four, at last count."

"Who's home from Europe?" Laura said, thinking that all the houses would be full now and maybe Ben had lost his best chance. She should have told him about the empty houses. But she hadn't told him or Clay most of the things Rosa told her about the Salingers. After she'd told them about the jewels in the closet and the alarm, she'd felt so awful she stopped telling them things. It wasn't important, anyway; they didn't have to know Rosa's little stories about— "What?" she asked. "I'm sorry, Rosa; I didn't hear you."

"I said for the third time, my dreaming miss, that Paul and his parents are back from Europe. You really ought to show a little more interest in this family, Laura. You'll never be a success at any job unless you're interested in everything about it."

"You're right," Laura murmured and went on rolling pastry and wondering what it would be like to be part of a family of twenty-four people. It isn't size that counts, she told herself. It's being loved and cared for and having a place to go when you're afraid of being alone.

But still, that evening, listening to the rising tide of conversation as the Salingers came into the dining room from the ocean-facing front porch where they'd had drinks, she wished again she belonged to so many people. From the many voices she made out Leni's and Felix's—"he sounds like a fingernail on a blackboard," Clay had said after meeting him—and she heard Allison's cool laugh. Finally, when the cold soup had been served, and Rosa sent her to the pantry for extra platters for the roasted game hens, she couldn't resist stopping on the way to inch open the swinging door and take a quick look into the dining room.

Her stomach contracted. The old man from the beach was sitting at the head of the table, his head bent courteously as he listened to Felix, on his left. She felt faint with fear. *Owen Salinger.* Who else could it be? The head of the family at the head of the table. *Mr. Owen is back from Canada.* Rosa had said that this morning. And Laura Fairchild, her tongue running like water from an open faucet, had talked to him about herself as if he were a friend, not part of a family they were planning to rob. Frantically thinking back, she didn't think she'd given anything away, but that wasn't the point. Ben's first rule had been that no one in the Salinger family could know anything about them, and not only had she violated that rule, she'd picked the head of the family to do it with, the one all the others would listen to if he had suspicions about her. *Stupid. Unprofessional.* What was it about these people that caused her to let down her guard? What would Ben say when he found out?

"Laura?" Rosa called. "The platters?"

Rapidly, Laura's gaze swept the table and she filed each face in her memory. Her swift glance stopped when she found herself looking directly into the eyes of a young man seated next to Allison. His eyes were almost black beneath straight brows; his face was thin with a long, narrow nose above a wide mouth and quick smile, and he brushed his thick dark hair back from his forehead with an impatient hand. He was young and handsome, with the piercing gaze of Leni and the barely disguised arrogance of Allison, and he was looking at Laura with amusement and a faint curiosity that infuriated her. Backing away, she let the door swing shut, grabbed three platters from the shelf, and marched into the kitchen.

"What's got into you?" Rosa asked.

"Nothing." Laura concentrated on arranging the platters on the counter. "I had trouble finding the platters."

"My eye," Rosa said amiably. "You put them away two days ago after we used them for lunch. All these moods you've got . . . But it's not my business; you'll find I'm very big on letting people work out their own demons. But you'll have to forget yours for a while; we have work to do." She looked up sharply. "Mr. Owen! Do you need something? Is something wrong?"

"Look on the happy side, Rosa," Owen Salinger said with a grin, more lighthearted than Laura remembered him. "Maybe I came to tell you everything is perfect."

"Well, I should hope—" She saw Owen looking at Laura. "This is my assistant. Laura Fairchild, Mr. Owen Salinger."

Owen held out his hand. "Welcome, Miss Fairchild." Meeting his eyes, Laura saw that he was inviting her to play a game, and she felt the same rush of gratitude she had felt earlier when he'd tried to put her at her ease. "Have you met our family?" he asked as she put her hand in his. "Or has our strict Rosa kept you too busy? Perhaps she'll spare you one of these days so you can be introduced to everyone."

Laura flushed deeply. He had seen her spying on them and was making fun of her. She worked her hand free of his. "I'd rather stay with Rosa."

"Laura!" Rosa frowned in disapproval. She couldn't understand what Owen was thinking of—when had he ever introduced temporary help to the family?—but no one in her kitchen was going to be rude to Mr. Owen Salinger if she had anything to say about it. "You owe Mr. Salinger an apology for your rude behavior. You should be grateful."

"I'm sorry," Laura said to Owen. "But I've seen your family." She heard her voice waver.

"But you haven't been properly introduced. Rosa, can you spare Laura for a few hours one of these days?"

He and Rosa discussed days and times while Laura silently repeated Owen's words. *Properly introduced.* Maybe he hadn't been making fun of her; maybe he knew she'd felt like an outsider when she peered at his family and he wanted to make her feel better about herself.

"Next week?" Owen was asking her courteously.

I'll do it for Ben, she thought. To learn more about the family. "Thank you," she said. "I'd like to meet everyone. Properly."

"Very good." He turned to go. "Oh, by the way," he said casually to Rosa, "I'm reorganizing my library and I could use some help. Do you know anyone who wants to work eight to ten hours a week, shelving and cataloguing? Someone who loves old books and new ideas." Laura looked sharply at him. What was he up to? "Hard work, good pay," he went on, smiling at Laura.

Rosa pursed her lips. "There's always people looking for work. But . . . books? I'll have to give it some thought."

"I'd like to do it," Laura said in a rush. "I'd like to try, anyway. I know about books."

Owen's smile broadened. "A good idea. A very good idea. We'll start tomorrow, shall we? Two to four every afternoon."

"Mr. Owen . . ." Rosa began. She was distinctly uncomfortable. "Are you sure—? I mean to say, Laura learns fast and remembers everything you tell her, and she's nimble as a cat, but she sometimes—I don't mean to criticize her; I'm fond of her—but she is very big into saying she's done a thing when I'm not at all sure she's really . . . done it."

"I do know books," Laura said quickly. "I've been in bookstores a lot—in one bookstore, anyway—and sometimes I helped catalogue. I really do know books!"

"I believe you," Owen said, smiling again at the fierce determination that reminded him of his own when he was about her age and starting to make his own way. He had seen it on the beach that morning; together with her wariness it was what had most attracted him. But this evening, she had touched his heart, as well, when he looked up from his talk with Felix and saw her looking at the family. He had had only a glimpse of her slender face and enormous, longing eyes as the pantry door swung shut, but it was enough: as wild as she seemed, she was hungrier for love than anyone he had ever known and it was that vulnerability that sent him looking for her.

Someone new, he thought. We don't see new people often enough. The same faces at parties, the same circle of friends, whether we're in Boston or the Cape or New York. Even the same conversations. I can use something new to think about, someone to help. And why not help someone who reminds me of myself, so long ago?

"We'll try it," he said firmly to Rosa. "I'm sure you can spare Laura from two to four every afternoon; if she has to stay later at night, I'll pay her overtime." He gave neither Rosa nor Laura time to respond. "We'll start tomorrow. And," he added to Laura, "I'm uncomfortable with uniforms. Can you bring something casual to wear in my dusty library?"

Laura avoided Rosa's eyes. Rosa loved uniforms and had told her to wear hers whenever she was on the Salinger grounds. "Yes," she said. And the next day, promptly at two, when she knocked on the door leading from Felix and Leni's long gallery to Owen's house, she wore blue jeans and a pink cotton shirt, scuffed loafers, and a pink ribbon tying her hair in a ponytail.

"Ah," said Owen, admiring the color in her cheeks and the depth of her deep blue eyes, less wary, more eager than the day before. "Come in, look around, then we'll begin work."

It was a man's house, with oak floors, Persian rugs, and oversize couches and chairs upholstered in dark suede. On the walls were oil paintings of the Cape and its wildlife in different seasons; the lamps were pewter, the windows bare. Beyond the living room was the library, its walls lined floor to ceiling with books, precarious towers of books stacked on the floor, books on reading stands, books strewn on long tables, window seats, and the arms of chairs. "It needs order," Owen said thoughtfully.

Laura gazed at the chaos. "I thought you said *re*-organize."

"I did. What you see is my first organization. You and I will accomplish the second. Perhaps it will be more successful."

Laura looked at him and they laughed together. "I guess it can't be any worse," she said, and rolled up her sleeves.

Every day they worked side by side, alphabetizing, cataloguing, labeling shelves, wading through the new piles they made as they sorted old ones. And they talked. Owen told Laura about his parents and grandparents, the first four hotels he bought—still his favorites though his company owned over fifty in America and Europe—and about Iris, the woman he had loved since he was fifteen, his wife and the mother of his children, whom he still longed for every day, though it had been almost forty years since she died.

And Laura talked, too, carefully choosing the memories she would share. She told Owen the same story she had told Leni: how she and Clay had lived with relatives after their parents were killed in an automobile accident, and recently moved out because they didn't like it there. She told him, truthfully, what she remembered about her mother and father, a few anecdotes about her brother Clay—*but nothing about Ben; don't slip and say anything about Ben*—and the classes she had liked best in high school. For the first time she talked about her dreams of being an actress. "I've had three parts in school plays and everybody says I'm really good. And I love being on the stage, all that makebelieve . . ." She talked about studying acting in college, if she ever found a way to go. "I mean," she fumbled when she remembered she'd lied about college the day they met, "I was going to start this fall, but I don't know, it may not work out . . ."

"There's nothing wrong with pretending," Owen said gently.

"I wasn't pretending!" she said hotly. "I thought I'd go! I will go!"

"I'm sure you will," he said, still gentle.

She bit her lip. "I'm sorry. I don't know exactly what I'll do about college. I'll figure something out."

"Well," he said offhandedly, leafing through a leather-bound book, "I could loan you the money for tuition. And board and room, too, if you need it." He heard Laura's sharp breath and nodded slowly. "I could certainly do that. A loan, of course, though I wouldn't expect you to pay it back until you had graduated and were earning your living, acting or perhaps something else. However, there would be one condition." He looked up and met her quick frown. "I'd expect you to write to me, and visit me, too. I wouldn't want to lose track of you."

Laura's face was radiant, her mind racing. "It's so wonderful . . ." *I never have to steal again. I can go to college and learn to be somebody. And I have a friend.* She put out her hand, then drew it back. She wanted to touch Owen, she wanted to kiss him, but she thought he might be angry. All he'd done was offer to loan her money. He probably loaned money to lots of people, and he wouldn't want them to start slobbering over him. She kept her hand in her lap. "*You're* wonderful. Thank you, thank you so much . . . I'll make you proud of me, I'll work so hard . . ." She turned her head away to hide the tears that stung her eyes. "I'll write to you every day," she said briskly and picked up a book, staring at it blindly until her tears dried.

"Once a week will be sufficient," Owen said with a calm smile, and they went back to work.

From that day, Laura found it easier to talk about her life in New York, her favorite books, the hours she had spent in Cal Hendy's bookshop. She was still careful, she still had to stop herself sometimes in mid-sentence, but by the end of their first week together the best time of her day was with Owen. It was a time when she could almost relax and forget everything outside his quiet rooms.

The only thing she couldn't forget, as hard as she tried, was Clay's admiring voice when she had told him about her part-time job. "God, you're clever, Laura. Who else could have wormed her way into the family and made the old guy trust you in less than two months?"

Owen met her in the kitchen just after lunch and took her to meet the family. They went from house to house along paths lined with old-fashioned gas lamps and rhododendron bushes, and Laura was reminded of books she had read about an earlier century, when people made calls in the afternoon, leaving calling cards if no one was home. But for Owen, everyone was home. And though they were puzzled, and Laura was almost mute from shyness, everyone was kind. Only Felix and Asa made clear how peculiar they found the situation, even allowing for their father's famous whims, and Asa's wife, Carol, didn't know whether to echo her husband's chilly greeting or Leni's pleasant one.

As they were leaving Asa's house, Allison arrived with her cousin Patricia. "Oh, we've met," Allison said casually when Owen began his introduction. Laura held her breath, but Allison breezed on. "When mother hired you, remember? I was so glad she did. When Rosa does the hiring she always finds elderly ladies with thin lips who play bridge and only cook lamb chops and Jell-O. She did hire a terrific college girl last summer who mixed up oregano and marijuana. Fortunately Rosa discovered it before we ate the lasagna. Grandpa said we would have been known as the Stoned Salingers, which annoyed my father, but his sense of humor is rather dim."

"Allison," Owen said, "that is no way to talk of your father."

"You talk about him that way." Allison's voice deepened and she drew her brows together like Owen. " 'Felix, you'd live longer and make the rest of us much happier if you learned to laugh occasionally.' "

Owen smiled, but Laura thought there was a

sharpness in the way Allison talked about everyone, from elderly ladies to her own father.

"I assume," Allison was saying to her, "you can distinguish between oregano and marijuana and you excel at something besides lamb chops and Jell-O."

"I don't excel at anything yet," said Laura, *but I can make it in a tough neighborhood better than you ever could.* Standing beside Owen, staring at the porcelain beauty of Allison and her silent cousin, she felt a surge of anger. Why was it that people who had lots of money also had perfect figures and beautiful faces and respectability, too? Why weren't those things parceled out so everybody could at least have something? "But I will. I'm going to college and be an actress, or maybe"—she cast about, trying to sound as self-assured as the Salingers —"I'll own something, a business or a bookshop, or maybe a restaurant, and hire people to work for me."

"Why not a hotel or two?" Allison asked with amusement.

"I might," said Laura. She raised her chin. "I'd like that."

"Would you? From what I can see, it's hard work."

So is being sent to Cape Cod to help my brother rob your house. "I don't mind work. There are so many things I want and there's no other way . . ." Her voice trailed off. How would someone like Allison ever understand what that meant? All she and Laura had in common was that they were both eighteen.

"I think you'll do and be whatever you want," said Owen. "But one thing you may not do: when you open your first hotel you may not steal Rosa from us to run your kitchen."

Laura smiled, grateful for his intervention when she was feeling inferior, and in a few minutes they left for the Janssens' house down the road.

"Come back another time," Allison said, keeping pace with them. "We can talk and get to know each other. I'll teach you to play tennis, if you like. When could you do it? Rosa gave you time off today; she'll do it again."

Laura was silent, ignoring Owen's curious glance.

Allison's eyes gleamed. "I'll invite you for dinner; you won't have an excuse."

"I work for Rosa at night."

"Which nights?"

"As often as she needs me."

"I'll invite you on your day off."

"I like to spend time with my brother."

"All day?"

"Allison," Owen said as they reached the Janssens' front porch, "why do you press someone who seems reluctant to accept?"

There was a pause. "You really are, aren't you?" Allison said to Laura. "Reluctant to be with me. Most people think it's a big deal to socialize with the Salingers. And here's Grandpa wanting us to be friends and you absolutely refuse. Because you don't like me, right?"

I'm afraid of liking you. I'm afraid of talking to you. "I'm just so busy," she started to say, but she stopped. It would be socially right to say that, but not personally right, because Allison would know it wasn't true. Laura Fairchild had never thought about the difference between socially and personally right. I'm learning, she thought. I could live the way they do. And what's wrong with learning? As long as I have to be here for Ben, I might as well get something out of it. And if Owen really wants us to be friends . . .

"Maybe I could get away for dinner some

time," she said to Allison. "And I'd like very much to learn tennis."

"Then it's set," Allison said with satisfaction. "I'll tell Rosa and we'll do it in a couple of days. Tennis in the afternoon and then a swim."

"I don't swim," Laura said, ashamed that there were so many basic skills she had never learned.

"Well, you'll learn that, too. We have all summer. What fun; I love being a teacher. Maybe we could tackle some other things, too. Have you thought about a haircut?"

"Allison," said Owen.

"I'll let you know which day," Allison said hastily to Laura. "Wear tennis shoes and bring a swimsuit—do you have a swimsuit?"

Laura shook her head.

"I'll loan you one; I have dozens. Talk to you soon." Without waiting for a reply, she ran back to join Patricia.

Laura looked at the ground and then raised her head and met Owen's eyes. "I feel like I'm her newest project."

He looked at her thoughtfully. "You're very wise. Allison needs projects; she needs to feel needed. You could make her very happy." He paused. "And I think she could help you be happy."

"I am," Laura said swiftly. "I am happy." And then Thomas Janssen opened the door and Laura was led into another large house with bright, spacious rooms facing the ocean, a volleyball court and horseshoe strip on the beach, and a long oval swimming pool like a bright blue gem in the center of the smooth lawn. The rooms were furnished in pale blue wicker with blue and white cushions and straw-colored raffia rugs strewn at angles on bleached wood floors. Barbara Janssen was arranging roses, and she turned as Laura and Owen came in with Thomas.

"How nice of Owen to bring you to us, Laura; I hardly know the people in my own kitchen, much less my sister's. Rosa is a dear, isn't she? A trifle opinionated, but very clever. Would you like iced tea? Do come and sit for a while. I'm hoping Paul will get back soon; he took Emily shopping and they've been gone some time. Do you take lemon?"

Laura started. "No. Thank you." She took the glass and sat next to Owen, sinking back into Barbara's steadily flowing words that sounded so like Leni's. The two sisters looked alike, as well: tall, blond and angular, with long necks and imperious heads, their voices like murmuring rivers in a cool forest. "I was always hoping for blue roses to match my furniture," Barbara was saying to Owen. "But a blue rose would be quite unnatural, and one shouldn't try to circumvent nature unless one is incredibly arrogant or incredibly clever. I've never been either, so I don't try." Laura listened, now and then looking up to find Owen watching her, or Thomas, his quizzical eyes moving from Owen to her and then back again. He was small and dark, with a short black beard and rimless glasses, and he almost never spoke. Laura tried to imagine him and Barbara in bed together, or even happily married, when they were so different, but she couldn't.

Barbara stopped talking. The silence was as palpable as if a cloud had covered the sun. It was broken when Thomas said quietly, "Come in, Paul, we were hoping you'd be here."

Paul Janssen stood in the doorway, a camera slung over one shoulder. His eyebrows went up when he saw Laura, then he smiled broadly and went to her, holding out his hand. "I see my uncle had the good sense to bring you out from behind that kitchen door. I hope you feel more friendly toward us now."

Laura took the hand he offered, shivering slightly as his long, thin fingers enclosed hers. His distant amusement at the dinner table was gone; his smile was warm and open and his body curved above hers as she sat in the deep wicker chair, looking up at him. Suddenly she felt heavy, and hot inside, as if she were melting and everything was going to run out, all over the floor. She tightened her muscles, trying to hold herself in; then, her face burning, she let out her breath in a sigh as Paul shook her hand, like a business associate or a casual friend. He kissed his mother on her cheek and sat on the arm of his father's chair. "Have you met everyone else?" he asked Laura.

She nodded. There was a small silence. Then Owen began talking about their other visits.

"And did Allison take you in hand?" Paul asked.

Laura nodded again. She felt like a fool, clumsy and tongue-tied, not clever. That was Barbara Janssen's favorite word, and it was probably her son's, too. Paul would expect cleverness. He probably couldn't wait to get out of there and find someone clever. And beautiful.

Owen stood up. "I promised to return Laura to Rosa in good time." He turned to Barbara. "I had a thought on the way over here. Would you talk to Leni about that caretaker's cottage in the south corner? It's been empty for some time, and I thought we might offer it to Laura and her brother. They're living over a garage in Centerville, and I'm sure they'd be much more comfortable here. And of course that way they can work longer hours if we need them." He put his hand on Laura's shoulder, giving a brief smile to her stunned look. "Of course she may prefer living apart from us, or she may want to pay rent instead of having free lodging, but we might ask Leni if she has other plans for it, don't you think?"

"A lovely idea," said Barbara serenely. "Leni and I have talked about doing something with that cottage. We could let Rosa's assistant have it every summer, whoever she is. I see no reason why Laura and her brother—Clay, isn't it? —I've seen him in the orchard and he has a wonderful way with the orchids in the green-house, have you noticed?—yes, it would be far more comfortable for the two of them if they lived here. Laura, I'm so pleased we met; do consider the cottage. I know how much young people treasure their independence, but you might enjoy it here as much as we do."

She walked with them to the door as Thomas nodded a farewell. Laura heard him say to Paul, "What about Emily?"

"I'm driving her to New York," Paul answered and then the door closed and Laura heard no more. *Emily. New York. I'll bet she's beautiful and rich and very clever.* But it was a fleeting thought as she and Owen walked back across the compound; she was still dazed by Owen's offer.

"Did you mean it?" she asked when they reached the kitchen door.

"I never make an offer I don't mean," he replied. "I told you, I like your spirit. When a family lives behind high fences it needs new people, my dear, and it pleases me to make sure we find them. Call it an old man's whim; a strong desire to shake up my family at frequent intervals. And I think you could use some shaking up, too. You might even let Allison talk to you about cutting your hair."

Laura felt herself grow hot again. "You don't like it."

"Not especially," he said frankly. "I could be wrong—I'm getting old, after all—but I once was considered an expert on women's beauty, and when Allison mentioned it, I knew I still had my eye. But don't worry about it; you don't have to do anything you don't want to do. Take what you want from us; we'll have a good summer and perhaps the beginning of a real friendship. Can we agree on that?"

This time Laura didn't hesitate; she flung her arms around his shoulders and kissed his cheek, soft and lined beneath her firm lips. "Thank you for making me feel like a nice person." He held her, and then she ran into the kitchen. "I'm sorry, Rosa, everyone talked and the time passed—"

"That is the story of this family," Rosa said. "Lots of talk, not enough time. By the way, your brother was here; he asked if you'd stop by the greenhouse as soon as you can. Better do it now, before we start stuffing the ducks."

Clay had never done that before. Something was wrong. Laura dashed across the flagstone path to the other end of the estate and found Clay in one of the greenhouses. They could see the head gardener through the doorway. "Listen to this," Clay said as Laura came close to him. "Ben called at noon: he says he can't wait any longer. We've got to set up our alibi; he's set the job for Sunday. A week after that we can wave good-bye to this place and take ourselves off. And we'll be through with the Salingers for good."

CHAPTER 4

BEN picked them up a few blocks from the Salinger compound, and they drove to Falmouth for dinner, blending into the crowds of tourists along the waterfront as they made their way to a table at the edge of the dock outside the Clam Shack. Ben turned the chairs to face the fishing boats in the harbor, their backs to the restaurant. "I like to watch the people," Laura protested. "No one knows us here; nobody even cares who we are."

"We can't be sure of that." Ben sat down and waited until she did the same. "How many times have I told you never to take anything for granted? Maybe next week, after we've pulled this off and the police are looking around, someone will remember the three of us. These are small towns; people who work in them know each other."

"Then why are we here?" Clay demanded. "I told you we should stay on the beach or somewhere private."

"I wanted to buy you a dinner." Sitting between them, Ben put his arms around their shoulders. "It's been almost two months that I haven't been able to take care of you. You're here and I'm in New York and there's nothing I can do for you." He sat back as a waiter approached. "I've missed you. Too damned quiet around the apartment."

Laura swallowed hard against the love and guilt that welled up inside her, and she looked away while Ben ordered for the three of them. He'd been missing her, but the truth was, she'd hardly missed him at all, after her first week with the Salingers. She'd been too busy envying the way they lived and thinking about college and how to make a life for herself even farther from Ben than she was that summer.

She heard him ordering the dishes she and Clay liked best, and she loved him with a kind of helplessness that made her want to cry. He was so good to them and she'd always been able to count on him; how could she turn her back on him and walk away?

"I've worked out the rest of the plan," Clay said to Ben as soon as the waiter left. His voice was low but Laura heard his excitement; he'd done what Ben wanted and now Ben would be proud of him. "It's simple and it's neat. The kind you like."

Ben looked at Laura. "Do you like it?"

"It's Clay's plan," Laura said evasively. "I couldn't do much; Rosa's very strict."

"But a sweetie," Clay said pointedly. "You spend an awful lot of time with her."

"I work for her," Laura retorted. "And I don't have the run of the place the way you do."

"You have the run of Owen's little pad," Clay said blandly.

"Owen?" Ben asked. "Owen Salinger?"

"I've done some work for him. That's all. Why are we talking about things that aren't important?"

Ben gave her a long look. The waiter returned with oversize paper cups filled with steaming clam chowder; overhead, a gull swooped past; at the tables behind them people laughed and chattered, isolating them in a small island of silence.

"All right," Ben said at last. "We'll talk about that later. Let's hear your plan, Clay. Laura did find out about the jewels, and you've been the best partner I could want; I have you to thank for these." He took two keys from his pocket and put them on the table.

"You got them made," Clay said, flushing with pleasure. "I wasn't sure I did the wax impressions right; I was in a hurry. Leni was on the yacht but I didn't know for how long, and it took me a while to find the keys in her dresser drawer." He picked up one of them. "I think this turns off the alarm and the other one unlocks the closet."

Ben glanced at Laura, but she was gazing at the fishing boats, her chin in her hand. He sighed. "Let's go through it," he said to Clay.

They bent over a small diagram, and Laura turned to look at their blond heads, so close they were almost touching. They looked so much alike and yet they were so different: Ben handsome and sophisticated at twenty-six, the cleverest man she knew; Clay, nine years younger, still unsure of himself, almost as handsome but without Ben's smoothness.

From their mother both of them got blond hair, a rounded chin, and heavy-lidded blue eyes, but Ben inherited from Judd Gardner, his father, a devil-may-care look, while Clay inherited from Alan Fairchild the cautious look of someone worried about all the obstacles life could throw in his way. Laura admired Ben; she felt protective toward Clay; she loved them both and knew she wasn't like either of them.

"We'll be on Felix's yacht," Clay was saying. "There's a big deal with some politicians he wants to impress, so he and Leni are giving a dinner on the boat on Sunday night. The whole family will be there, and a few of us volunteered to help out."

"So you're safe," Ben said. "Nobody can accuse you of robbing a house if you're on a boat in the middle of Nantucket Sound."

Clay nodded. "But before we go out, I'll fix the alarm. I did what you told me and bought a timer, and I found the alarm system in the basement, and I'll hook up the timer the way you said, so it goes off at one in the morning. You break in at midnight when the party is going strong; you've got my diagram of where you climb the fence, and the path to the house, and then the drainpipe to the second-floor hall window. Leni's room is to the right, at the end of the hall. You jimmy the window open, turn off the alarm with that key, and break the lock on the closet door, or use the key and break it afterwards to make it look like an outside job, whatever's fastest. Take the jewels and anything else you find, open all the other closets and dresser drawers so it'll look like you had to search around, and use a rope to rappel down the outside of the house."

Ben was smiling. "And leave the rope behind."

"Right. And tire tracks too, if you can, on the road outside the fence. Then, at one o'clock, the alarm goes off, the guard calls the police and they find all the evidence of a break-in, while Laura and I are with the hired help on the yacht."

"What about the timer on the alarm?"

"I'll get to it as soon as we come in. I figure the guard will call the police first, and then the yacht, and we'll get back in about an hour, while the police are still checking the house and the grounds. They won't have any reason to check the alarm; as far as they know, it worked fine. I can have the timer off in less than a minute."

"Without anyone seeing you?"

"Everybody'll be busy with the police, and nobody uses the back stairs until Rosa comes in to start breakfast around six."

Ben nodded again. "I like it. Good job, Clay."

Clay beamed. "I thought you'd like it. It's foolproof."

"No plan is foolproof! I've told you that. The minute you think it is, you've begun to make it fail."

"Sorry," Clay mumbled.

"But it's good," Ben said. "Damned good. I'm proud of you. Laura? Don't you think Clay deserves some praise?"

"Sure." Laura drew on the table with the moisture that had beaded on her glass of iced tea. "Clay's very creative. He worked hard and he wanted you to be pleased."

"But," Ben said flatly. "What's the rest of it, Laura?"

"I don't want to do it," she said in a rush. "Please, Ben, can't we change our plans and not do it?"

"Not do it?" Clay echoed incredulously. "After we went to all the trouble of getting jobs with them, and I worked out this neat plan? *Not do it?*"

Ben was watching Laura closely. "Pretty sudden change of heart."

She shook her head. "I've thought about it a lot."

"It's Owen," Clay said abruptly. "Ever since you started mooning around after him you've been different about all of them. Like you're choosing them over us. Like you like them better than us."

Vehemently, Laura shook her head. "I'm not choosing them. I'm not choosing nobody —anybody."

"Not your brothers?" Ben said softly. "You're not choosing your brothers?"

"I didn't mean . . . oh, damn it, Ben, you know what I mean. I don't want a contest; I just want to skip this one job. We've done so many and we can do another one—somewhere —I'll keep my promise; it's just that I don't . . ."

"Want to rob the Salingers," Ben finished when her voice trailed off. "Why not?"

"Because they trust us and they've been nice to us, and—"

"That's a stupid reason," Clay cut in, but Laura rushed on.

"—and we *know* them. It's not like other times when we'd break into a place and never meet anyone or even know their names . . . I mean, if I saw pictures on a desk or dresser, I'd wonder what they were like and how they'd feel when they came home and found their things missing, but I never *knew* them, and I do know Allison and Leni and Owen . . ."

"So we know them," said Clay. "So what? What have they ever done for us? We work our asses off to earn a few lousy bucks a week, and we're always working overtime—"

"You wanted overtime," Laura flung at him, "so you could check the guards' schedules."

Clay shrugged. Ben looked at her through narrowed eyes. "They can afford to lose a few jewels; their insurance will pay for them anyway. So maybe the real problem is you're afraid they'll suspect something after you leave and not like you anymore. Right? But you'll be gone, so what's the difference? Anyway, why should you care whether they like you or not? You're better off if they don't; they're a rotten bunch of crooks. They take care of themselves and fuck everybody else and wouldn't let anybody who's not a royal Salinger have even a little piece of what they've got—"

"That's a lie!" Laura cried, striking the table with her fist. "They're not like that! They're just the opposite—they've been good to me, and Clay, too—they're going to let us live in one of their cottages, and Owen is loaning me money for college and—"

"*What?*" Clay shouted. "Live *where?*"

"Wait a minute." Ben's face was frozen. "Keep your voice down, Clay. Felix Salinger offered to let you live in the compound and send you to college?"

"Not really," Laura conceded. "Owen thought of the cottage, and everybody goes along with him, and he was the one who talked about college—"

"Felix won't agree," Ben said.

"Why not?" Laura asked hotly. "I mean, he's not as friendly as the others—well, Asa isn't either, I guess—but if the others want to help us, why wouldn't Felix go along? Is there some reason he wouldn't?" She stared at him. "You know something about him that you're not telling!"

Ben looked at his hands as they gripped his mug of beer; the knuckles were white. "Amaz-

ing," he murmured. "The Salingers, of all people."

"Why not the Salingers?" Laura demanded.

"It's a wonderful chance for you," he said
slowly, as if she had not spoken. "I couldn't
have swung college for you, at least not this
year. And you'd have a place to live for the
whole summer, and save your money . . ." He
stared at his hands, then shook his head heav-
ily. "I can't do it, Laura; I can't give up this
job. Maybe someday I'll tell you why, but right
now you'll just have to trust me. You could stay
with them after I do it, but I think they'd find
you out. Damn it, Laura, I'm the one who
cares about you, not them, and I'm asking you
to help me. I've been thinking about this job a
long time, and I can't throw away the chance
now that I'm so close."

"How long? How long have you been thinking about it?"

"Longer than you can imagine. Years. Why
can't you just go along and not ask questions?
I'd do the same for you. If you told me you had
to do something and I had it in my power to
help you, I'd do it, no questions asked."

"I have to like myself," Laura said coldly. "I
want to go to college and be respectable, and

not sit with my back to a restaurant because I'm afraid somebody will notice me."

Ben winced. Clay scowled at Laura. "You never mentioned living with them or getting money for college."

"You were too excited about robbing them. I wanted to see what Ben said."

"You wanted to pull this out from under me." Clay's voice rose. "My whole plan. You wanted to talk Ben into killing it, and you didn't even tell me."

"What would you have said if I did tell you?"

"What Ben said. We have to do it."

"So what difference does it make that I didn't tell you?"

"I had a right to know what you were going to do! We're in this together!"

"You're in it alone! I told you, I don't want to do it!"

"Stop squabbling," Ben ordered, "and keep your voices down. Laura, I'll do everything I can to help you, *but I've got to do this, first.* Can't you understand? It's like getting something off my chest. Once I've done it, I can concentrate on other things, like getting you to college."

Slowly, Laura shook her head. "I don't want you to keep stealing to give me money for college. That's what you'd do, isn't it? You've always stolen and you like the excitement, so you wouldn't even try something else."

"What, for instance?"

"Like a better job, for instance! Aren't you ever going to think about that? Or about what happens to Clay?"

"What about me?" Clay demanded.

"He thinks you're wonderful," she said to Ben. "But what's so wonderful about a guy who spends his whole life being a waiter part of the time and breaking into places the other part? And feeling scared every time there's a policeman around? Why don't you quit all that and get a better job? You'd probably have to work harder; so big deal! Don't you give a shit —don't you care what happens to us? You think we like the way we live?"

"I like it fine!" said Clay hoarsely. Everything was happening too fast; the conversation was getting out of hand. "It's fine; why don't you just shut up!"

"I can't get a better job," Ben said to Laura. "I never went to college; I haven't any skills—"

"How do you know? You're the smartest person I ever met; how do you know what you could do if you tried? You could be an executive! Or something like that. But you won't even try! Well, the hell with it. I don't care what you do; I'm talking about me, and *I don't want to steal anymore!* It's not exciting or fun like it used to be . . . and I'd go to jail if I got caught again—it would be a second offense—and I won't take the chance. I don't want to live on your stealing, either; that's almost as bad as doing it myself. And I don't want to rob the Salingers! I'm asking you, Ben, please, *please,* don't rob them. I like them; they make me feel nice, and I want to stay with them as long as I can."

She saw the hurt and anger in Ben's eyes and she felt she was being torn apart. "Don't be unhappy, Ben, please, I love you and you've been wonderful to us, but I've got a chance to change things, to change *me,* and maybe I'll never have it again! Owen asked me to write to him and visit him when I'm in college—he's my friend!—and I don't want to risk losing him, losing all of them . . . *I don't want them hurt!*"

They were silent, looking away from each

other, and the talk and laughter behind them
seemed louder and happier than before. The
waiter brought coffee and Ben drank his black,
hot and steaming. Laura, who had decided she
should drink it because Allison did, poured in
cream and sugar and then sipped it, telling herself it tasted good. Clay, watching Ben, drank
his black, making faces as it scalded his tongue.

"I'll think about it," Ben said at last.

"No, Ben, tell us now," Laura pleaded. "Say
you won't do it. Say you'll think up another
job, and we'll come to New York and help you
do it—we can come on a weekend and then
come back—"

"I didn't say I was staying!" Clay exclaimed.

"I want you to stay with me. That way you'll
finish high school and maybe think about college instead of—" She bit back her words.

"Instead of being like me," Ben said flatly.

"I want to be like Ben!" Clay stormed.
"There's nothing wrong with that. You wanted
it, too, once. And if you'd shut up about Owen
and his rich bitch family, we could get going
on my plan and then get out of here and go
back to New York where we belong!"

Laura bit her lip. "I don't want to go back to
New York; I want to move into the cottage.

Ben, we'll visit you, we'll still be a family, and I'm sorry if you'll be lonely but I want this so much . . ." She took his hand. "Ben, *please.*"

He shoved back his chair, pulling his hand away. "I told you I'd think about it. That's the best I can do. It's more than I want to do." He stood and took out his wallet. "I'll drive you to Centerville, then I'm going back to New York. I'll call in a few days." His lips were tight. "Listen to me, Laura. I'm still your guardian; when I decide, you'll do what you're told."

"Damn right," Clay muttered. He and Laura walked to the car while Ben paid the waiter. "Ben wanted a reunion and a nice time, and you ruined it."

"You don't care about Ben. You just don't want to give up your plan."

"What's wrong with that? What good's a plan you can't *do?*"

Ben joined them and they drove to Centerville in silence. All around them were cars filled with people on vacation; the sidewalks were kaleidoscopes of people all looking happy. Laura watched them and wanted to cry.

She kept wanting to cry all week, waiting for Ben to call, but she couldn't cry in front of Rosa, and she refused to cry in front of Clay, so she held it in. It was easier because they were so busy; Felix and Leni had houseguests, which meant fifteen or more people at every meal, and Rosa had already begun preparations for the Sunday night dinner dance on the yacht. As the weekend approached, she grew more frenzied, her fingers a blur as they flew from mixers to mandolins, whisks to rolling pins, terrines to casseroles. Laura was mostly on her own, preparing breakfast and lunch for the large groups that seemed to materialize in the dining room or on the porch for another meal before she had even finished cleaning up from the last one. As she cooked, Rosa would appear beside her now and then with a sharp criticism or brief suggestion or, best of all, a touch on the arm and word of praise that made Laura feel she loved Rosa and all the world.

But then she would see Rosa putting covered dishes in the two wall freezers, for the party on the yacht, and she would remember she could lose it all in a few days. She began to avoid everyone, talking to Rosa only about food, never anything personal; telling Allison she couldn't take tennis or swimming lessons; telling Owen she couldn't work in his library that week: there was too much to do in the kitchen.

Then, on Friday, two days before the party, Ben called. "I talked to Clay yesterday; he says you're not very friendly to him."

"I'm busy and tired," Laura said shortly. "And he keeps telling me I'm crazy to pass up a golden opportunity, and he won't listen to anything I say. I guess I don't feel very friendly."

"Well, I've been thinking about what you said." Ben let out a long breath. "We'll call it off, Laura."

"Ben—!"

"I still have to deal with Clay, but I can handle him. I guess what I can't handle is the chance that you'd hate me."

"Oh, Ben, I love you—thank you—I love you. Are you coming here soon? We'll have another dinner, we'll have a good time, better than last week, I promise. When can you come? I can get off early; we could even spend a day together. We haven't done that in so long . . ."

"How about Saturday? I have to be in Boston that night; I could come to the Cape in the morning and we'd have all day. Don't you have Saturday off anyway?"

"Oh. Yes, usually, but . . ." She debated thinking up a lie to tell Rosa, then decided she couldn't. "Not this week. There's so much still to do for the party on the boat Sunday, and the Janssens are having a hundred people for dinner Saturday night; they're putting a tent on the lawn. Any other Saturday . . ."

"We'll find a time." Laura heard the smile in his voice and thought how nice it was when Ben was happy and loving. "I'll call soon," he said cheerfully. "Maybe that busy family will let you go next Saturday."

After they hung up, Laura repeated his words to herself, wondering how much disappointment and anger he might have been hiding. She didn't have to wonder about Clay: his frustration and fury burst out and then he stopped talking to her completely. And late that night he went out and didn't come home.

Laura found him Saturday morning in the orchid greenhouse. "We still live together," she said angrily. "We have to get along. Clay, I was worried about you!" *And I hated being alone; the garage underneath me creaked and our apartment creaked and I thought of how I'd never once been alone all night and I was scared to death.* "Where did you spend the night?" she asked.

"With a couple of guys passing through. They let me sleep in their car."

"Which guys? Who?"

"I didn't ask. We fooled around for a while and had dinner at that place in Bass River."

"Which place?"

This time he looked sheepish. "I don't remember. I think I had a little too much to drink."

Laura gazed at him. "How much money did you lose?"

"Lose?"

" 'Fooling around.' When Ben says that, it means poker."

"Shit, Laura, I don't do everything Ben—"

"How much did you lose?"

He shrugged. "Not too much."

"How much?"

"A bill."

"You lost a hundred dollars?"

"You want me to lie?"

He needed taking care of. She knew that. She admired Ben, but she wanted to protect Clay. "Well, it's done; we won't think about it.

We can't get it back. But from now on things are going to be different around here; we're going to have a real home and a chance to be somebody, and I won't have you ruining it by getting drunk and gambling and sleeping in cars—"

"You can't make me stay!" Clay shouted. "I'm going back to New York!"

"You're going to live with me!" Laura tried to sound stern and grown up but she was beginning to feel frightened. She needed Clay. Because as wonderful as the Salingers were, she didn't want to be all alone in the midst of their big family; she wanted somebody of her own to cling to. Then she saw the confusion in Clay's face. "How come you're still here? Ben isn't going to do the robbery, so why haven't you taken off for New York?"

"I'm going to," Clay mumbled. "Soon as I get around to it."

"When? What are you waiting for?"

He shrugged. "There's a lot of work to do for the party."

"And you love the Salingers so much you want to do it all." When Clay was silent, she turned away. "Well, then, don't tell me. I don't care. You can leave any time; it doesn't matter to me."

"I didn't want to run out on you," he said quickly.

Laura turned, her face bright. "Really? Oh, Clay, thank you. I was hoping you'd want to stay with me." She watched his face redden. "What is it?"

"Well, there was something else."

"What else was there?"

He mumbled something.

"What?"

"Allison asked me to do the table flowers; she's got these complicated ideas . . ."

"*Allison?*" In an instant Laura recalled a host of small incidents: Clay talking about Allison's favorite orchids, Clay mentioning that Leni and Allison had been in the greenhouse, Clay saying that Allison liked the cutting garden . . . She started to say something about Allison being a year older than Clay and looking for older men, but she held her tongue as Clay's face grew even redder. She felt like putting her arms around him and telling him everything would be fine. "Well, that's fine," she said, and added casually, "How long do you think you'll stay here?"

Clay gave her a grateful look. "I thought I might stay for the summer, but if you move into that cottage I don't know what I'll do."

"Move in with me," Laura said quickly. "There are two bedrooms."

"You think I'll change my mind and stay with you for good."

"Maybe." She grinned at him, feeling good again. Clay couldn't resist a real home once she'd made one, and then she'd be able to take care of him. And she wouldn't be alone.

"If I stay for the summer, you won't tell Allison what I said?"

"What do you think I am? Of course not. It's our secret."

It was the first nice secret she could remember between the two of them. Nothing would come of it because Allison was going to college in the fall and Clay still had a year of high school, but it kept him at the Cape and it made them friends. And when she saw him that afternoon in the garden with Allison, she thought he was even handsomer than she'd realized.

He and Allison were cutting flowers for the Janssens' party that night, and Laura caught glimpses of them while she worked in the kitchen with Rosa. Rosa was grumbling as she sifted flour into a huge bowl. "Why I always end up cooking for the Janssens when they're having a catered dinner is more than I can understand. There's the yacht party tomorrow night, which I have slaved over for two weeks; there's regular meals for all the houseguests—I might as well be cooking in a hotel—and I predict there will be a great demand for a substantial brunch on Monday, when everybody recovers from being on the yacht all night—"

"You love it," Laura said, "having Barbara Janssen ask for your special cake instead of trusting her own cook or the caterers."

Rosa chuckled. "You're getting cheeky, my young miss. A month ago you wouldn't have talked to fierce Rosa that way."

"You weren't ever fierce. I was just scared."

"And now you're not. For which we have Mr. Owen to thank."

"And you. I have you to thank, too."

They worked all day, talking quietly or not at all but comfortable with each other as they followed the timetable Rosa had made that morning. *I'm part of Rosa's kitchen, and that means I'm part of the household. I belong here.*

She belonged with all of them, she thought

that night at the Janssens'. She was helping Rosa in a corner away from the caterer's staff, and through the open door she could see Clay and Allison, in a huge white tent across the lawn, arranging centerpieces on round tables draped in creamy linen. Clay wore dark pants and a white shirt and tie, Allison a long silk dress that was like a pastel flower garden, and the two of them talked companionably as they moved among the tables placing white lilies and ruby red ginger flowers in crystal bowls. The setting sun turned the sky to copper and pink, the air was cool and still, and everything seemed so perfect that Laura had to give someone a kiss, and Rosa was the closest, so she did. "My oh my," said Rosa, beaming. "We seem to be very big on affection tonight."

"Yes," Laura said simply, and when Owen stopped in briefly to say hello before everyone gathered for drinks, he saw a new look on her face. Calmer, he thought; no longer that skittish child on the beach. And something else; she looked more open, as if she finally believed she didn't have to hide her feelings after all.

He wondered who had done it for her: Allison through her offer of friendship, Rosa through her mothering—and perhaps I had something to do with it, he thought as he joined the party, by making her feel needed and letting her know I need her, too. He let his thoughts drift as the members of his family moved from one group of guests to another, meeting the political and entertainment celebrities Felix always brought to the Cape to enliven his summer. Ambitious, aggressive Felix, Owen reflected. He takes after me.

But in fact he knew Felix did not take after him at all. For the past few years, as he grew older and more detached from his family, he gradually had admitted to himself that his eldest son was pompous and humorless, a rigid man who thought he could impose his idea of order on the world around him. I wasn't like that, Owen thought; Iris would have let me know if I ever was as insufferable as Felix. Everyone would have let me know. And I still have many friends, so I must be a fairly pleasant fellow. I don't suppose Felix will ever be pleasant. What a shame; he's got such a lovely wife, too.

Once the thought would have made him smile at the tricks life played on people, but tonight he felt only sadness for Leni and regret that neither of his two sons was as attractive or likeable as his great-nephew Paul, who was standing nearby, looking politely bored as a senator expounded something at great length.

I don't feel well, Owen thought; that's probably why everything seems sad. I feel tired. In fact I feel rotten; I wonder if I'm coming down with something. Why the devil am I spending a whole evening with a bunch of people I don't care anything about? He made his way to Leni and said quietly, "My dear, do you think Barbara would mind if I leave as soon as we've had coffee?"

A look of worry shadowed her calm eyes. "Aren't you feeling well?"

"Just tired," he said. "And, I confess, a trifle sick of celebrities."

She smiled faintly. "Felix does collect them, doesn't he?"

"Well," Owen sighed, "I suppose he could have worse hobbies; it's expensive but not dangerous. And he worries too much about running the hotels; he does need something to help him relax."

"Wouldn't it be nice," Leni murmured, "if he came to his wife for that."

Owen turned his shrewd eyes on her. "Have you suggested it?"

"When was the last time Felix listened to something you suggested?"

"When he was five. But if you told him you're unhappy?"

"I'm not unhappy, dear Owen. Don't worry about me."

"You are unhappy. I can always tell."

"If I am, I'll take care of it. You have yourself to take care of. Shall I walk home with you? Or I can ask Clay; he's helping in the pantry and I'm sure they can spare him. I don't think you should be alone."

He shook his head. "If I can't make it across the compound I shouldn't be out without a wheelchair."

They smiled at each other, and when the guests had finished coffee and crepes and the waiters were serving cognac, Owen quietly left his chair and made his way from the tent. Through the open doorway of the house he caught a glimpse of Laura in the kitchen, and Rosa nearby, and the staff in the pantry, and then he walked slowly home.

There was no moon but he knew the way from memory and the feel of the flagstones beneath his feet. To the right here, to the left there, just past Leni's rose garden to the door of his house. He slipped inside, breathless and a little dizzy—probably ate too much, he thought; damn stupid thing to do when I already felt sick—and he was reaching for his armchair when he heard a door softly close somewhere in the main house.

One of the staff, he thought, and then remembered there was no one there; they were off for the evening or working at the party. The wind, then. But there was no wind; the night was still. Odd, he thought; Felix or Leni must have come back, too. Better see if everything's all right.

His door was ajar and he slipped through it into the gallery, where he stood motionless, listening. Nothing. Imagination, he told himself. A tired old man with not enough to think about. But then he heard the whisper of careful, stealthy footsteps in the upper hall. They came from the direction of Leni's room. A moment later Owen heard them on the stairway directly in front of him.

"Ho, there!" he called and flicked on the light switch. As he closed his eyes against the chandelier's sudden blaze, he heard a curse and a rush of footsteps, and felt rather than saw the dark form that flung itself upon him. "Damn!"

he cried. "Get off me—!" But it came out as a strangled croak; he was face down on the floor, struggling to push himself up beneath the weight on his back. Then a terrible pain burned through his chest, like stabbing flames. *I'm going to die,* he thought and, in the midst of a dizzying terror, fell headlong into darkness.

CHAPTER 5

"HOW could you?" Laura cried. The telephone was wet with her tears and it kept slipping in her hand as she sat hunched over in the cramped booth, wiping her nose with a wadded tissue. Through the glass door she saw lunchtime customers filling the restaurant and she turned her back on them, leaning her elbow on the small shelf beneath the telephone. "You promised you wouldn't! You told me—you told Clay—*you said you wouldn't do it!*"

"I didn't do anything! Laura, goddam it, if you'd listen for a fucking minute—"

"I listened once and you lied to me!"

"I didn't lie! I told you I wouldn't rob them—"

"And I believed you! I trusted you! And you went ahead and did it anyway! It didn't matter what I wanted, you didn't *care* what I wanted, all you cared about was your damned robbery, and Owen had a heart attack and he's in the hospital, and everybody's crazy with worry—"

"Shut up and listen! I didn't rob the fucking Salingers. I've been in New York since I was with you at the Cape; I was with a friend last night—"

"It wasn't last night; it was three nights ago."

"I was with a friend three nights ago, too. Why didn't you call when it happened?"

"I did; I've been calling you for three days! You haven't been there—where have you been?—never mind, I know where. You've been selling the jewels you stole . . . after you promised—!"

"I kept my promise! Look, damn it, I don't work that way; I wouldn't jump a guy just because he turned on the light—"

"How do you know he turned on the light?"

There was a pause. "You told me."

"I did not. I just said he had a heart attack and he's in the hospital. I never said anything about a light."

"Well, so I figured it out. There wouldn't be any other reason to jump him, would there? But that's not my style, and you know it. I stay away from people and get out, clean; I don't get into wrestling matches that make a mess of—"

"That's what you did. You made a terrible mess of everything and the police are everywhere and I'm scared to death. It feels like everything I've got in the whole world is falling apart."

"You've got me. I'm not falling apart."

"I haven't got you! I don't trust you; I'll never trust you again!"

"I didn't do it! Damn it, I told you—"

"All right, then, if you didn't, who did? How come somebody just happened to rob the house the same way you and Clay planned it, practically on the same night you planned it?"

"I don't know who did it. Have you asked Clay?"

The blood rushed to Laura's head. "He was with me all night! Anyway, he doesn't do jobs alone and he doesn't lie! Don't you ever, ever say anything against Clay again—how could you—"

"All right, all right, I'm sorry. All I meant was you should talk to him."

"You were accusing him! Throwing blame on a . . . *kid* . . . because you don't have any excuses!"

"I don't need excuses! Listen, I've taken care of you for three years; you can't believe I'd—"

"You won't take care of me anymore! I won't let you!"

"You haven't got any choice; I'm your guardian and you'll do what I tell you. And I'm telling you to come back to New York. That's an order, Laura! You're coming back to me, where you belong!"

"I'm never coming back to you!" Laura felt once again that she was being torn in half. She hunched lower, holding herself tight to keep her voice from shaking. "I'm staying here. I'm going to make up to them—somehow—for what you did."

"I didn't do a goddam—!"

"And Clay's staying with me. I'm not letting him go back to a thief . . . and a . . . liar . . ." Tears choked her and she wiped her nose on the back of her hand. "We're not coming back to you, and that's all."

"I'm coming up to get you. I'll be there this afternoon. I expect you to be packed and ready."

"I'll be at work. I have a job. *And a family,*" she added cuttingly.

"What the hell is that supposed to mean?"

"I have the Salingers."

"You're crazy. You really think you 'have' the Salingers? You're out of your mind. The Salingers don't give a shit about you or Clay; you aren't their kind of people. You *work* for them, for Christ's sake, and if you think they care about servants, or play fair with them, you're more stupid than I thought."

"Then I'm stupid, and you wouldn't want a stupid person in your family, would you, Ben? So you don't care whether I stay here or not."

There was a small pause, the space of a heartbeat. "I do care. I'm sorry I said that. I know you're not stupid; you're wonderful and I miss you. You're my family, Laura."

"Not anymore," she said defiantly.

"God damn son of a bitch!" Laura heard his fist strike the table. She knew where he was; she could picture him sitting in the kitchen, on a chair she had painted red to make the room more cheerful, making marks with his thumbnail in the linoleum that covered the table. "One last time," he said. "I didn't do it and I expect you to come back. We'll forget we said all these—"

"You're lying. You told me you'd be in Boston on Saturday; you wanted to spend the day with us. And I told you we'd be working at the Janssens' party, so you knew the house would be empty." She shook her head. "I never should have told you. If I hadn't, you wouldn't have robbed them. I'm going, Ben; I told Rosa I'd only be gone half an hour for lunch."

"You stay right there and listen! I'll be at the Cape this afternoon, and if you and Clay aren't packed you'll leave everything behind, because I'm taking you out of there! We'll go to Europe. You'd like that, wouldn't you, Laura? We've talked about doing it for a long time and I've already got tickets—"

"*You've got the tickets?* You knew you were going to rob them—you were all ready to get out of the country—you only pretended to be thinking it over!"

"I bought them when I thought I'd do the job; I just didn't get around to returning them. Listen to me, Laura: we've got all these tickets and reservations; everything's settled. We'll take a month, before school starts, and travel all over. . . . Are you listening?" She was silent. "You're coming home with me!" Ben roared. "I've had enough of your—"

Laura slammed down the telephone, cutting off his furious voice. Her hand was shaking. Ben always had been able to dominate her, and now she felt herself wanting to call him back to beg his forgiveness so he would be loving toward her again. Instead, she ran from the booth, snatching a handful of paper napkins from an empty table and ignoring the curious looks from the lunchtime crowd as she wiped the tears from her face.

Clay was waiting in a small park nearby. "Ben's going away," she said.

He sprang to his feet. "Where's he going? Why did he do the robbery? After he promised . . ."

"He didn't say." Laura wheeled her bicycle onto the path. "He even tried to deny he did it."

Clay waited for more. "And?"

"He expected us to go back to New York with him."

"Well, we are, aren't we? Everything's changed. Where's he going?"

"Europe. He says."

"And we're meeting him? When? Where?" He waited. "Laura, when are we going to Europe?"

"We're staying here." She got on her bicycle. "I haven't figured it out yet, but that's what we're doing."

Clay let out a yell and caught up with her on his bicycle, and they argued all the way to the Salingers'. At the shed where they kept their bikes, Laura put her hand on his arm. "It's just the two of us now; we'll take care of each other and we'll be just fine."

Clay ignored her hand. "Where *exactly* is Ben going?"

She shrugged. "All he said was Europe."

"I'm going with him."

"No you're not." She thought of telling him Ben had tried to blame him for the theft, but she couldn't. Let him think some good things about the stepbrother he'd idolized for so long. "You're going to stay with me and finish high school and learn something useful. After that you can go anywhere you please. Clay, I need you," she said, her assurance crumbling. "I can't count on anybody else; please stay and help me. Just for . . . for a year, that's all, one year, till I get used to being on my own, and then if you really want to go away I won't say anything. I'll even help you."

Clay studied his shoes, his blond eyebrows drawn together. "What did you mean about staying here? You mean on the Cape?"

"With the Salingers. I hope, anyway. We still work for them, we're earning money, and most of them like us. And if we work hard enough we can make up a little bit for what Ben did."

"It's not our fault he robbed them."

"Yes it is. You figured out the way to do it and I found out where the jewels were and about the alarm, and I told him we'd all be somewhere else that night. It's because of us that Owen may die. Clay, we *owe* them something."

Still staring at his shoes, Clay said, "What happens in September, when they go back to Boston?"

"I don't know. Maybe we can keep working for them."

"In *Boston?*"

"Maybe."

"We don't know the first thing about Boston."

"We could learn. There are plenty of high schools there, and colleges."

Clay gave her a long look. "You really like them."

"Well, you like Allison," she said defensively.

"Yeh, but I'm not changing my whole life because of it. Anyway, she thinks I'm just a gardener." He hoisted their bicycles and hung them on hooks in the shed. "If you really want me to, I guess I'll stick around for a while. It might not be so great living with Ben without you around. And maybe I'll do school for another year. I won't promise I'll finish, but I guess I could try. Shit, I thought I was through with that crap, those fucking little desks and being ordered around by people who don't know shit about real life . . . I'll just try, that's all. I'll probably flunk."

"You won't. You're too smart." Laura put her arms around him and kissed him. "I love you, and I'm so glad you're staying. Everything's going to be fine." She kissed him again. "I have to go; I'm awfully late. I'll see you after work."

But late that afternoon Owen began asking for Laura, and Leni sent her to the hospital in one of the family limousines. Laura had not seen him since his heart attack, and as she tiptoed into his room behind the nurse, she expected to see a dying man. Instead, he looked no different from before, except that he was lying flat in the narrow bed and his eyes were closed.

"Mr. Salinger," the nurse said softly, "Laura is here."

His eyes opened. "Ah. My dear." He motioned slightly to the nurse. "You can go."

"I'll be right outside," she said and kept the door open when she left.

Owen winked at Laura and gave a small grin. "She's an ogre. Now you can kiss me."

She bent down and kissed his forehead. It was cool, almost cold. "Does anything hurt?"

"My pride. Old man jumped by a burglar. No respect for age. Rotten coward."

"He wouldn't have done it if he'd known— I mean, I can't believe anyone would hurt you if . . . if he knew you were a lot older than he is."

Owen squinted slightly as he studied her. "Maybe he's eighty. Thought I was a youngster."

Laura gave a small laugh. She was knotted

up inside, angry at Ben but defending him, loving Owen but angry at his calling Ben a coward. *But Ben was a coward—I shouldn't defend him—and it's wonderful that Owen is making jokes because that means he's going to get well; he won't die because of us.* "You're going to get well," she said.

"I expect to. Sit down; I can't see you this way."

She pulled a chair close to him and leaned over, her elbow on the bed, her chin on her hand. "The nurse said I could only stay a few minutes."

He shook his head. "I want you to stay." He opened his palm and waited until Laura put her hand in his. "I have plans."

He had no strength to grip her hand, but Laura felt the warmth of his palm against hers and she twined her strong fingers through his. "What kind of plans?"

"For you. I want you to come to Boston and live at my house and help me. Would you mind?"

A wave of excitement surged through Laura, and then just as quickly began to fade. *The Salingers don't give a shit about you or Clay;*

you aren't their kind of people. "I'm not a nurse. I don't know anything about—"

Owen was shaking his head. "Not a nurse, a companion. A job. Talk to me, read to me, help with my library. It's even bigger than here. And messier." He squinted again, watching her. "And you could go to college."

Her breath came out in a long sigh.

"I thought you'd like that," Owen fretted.

"I do. It's everything I want. I'd love it. But . . . I have Clay with me."

"Clay." He paused, his breathing quick and shallow. "Leni likes Clay; she'll find something for him. But you're what I want. Tough and hurting. Like I was once." A small chuckle came through his lips. "Like I still am sometimes. You'll do it?"

"Yes. Oh, yes. Thank you, I can't tell you . . . thank you."

His breathing slowed, barely stirring his mustache. He smiled at Laura, too weak for the grin he had given earlier. "Read to me now." He tilted his head slightly toward the windowsill, where Laura saw, amid a small jungle of flowers and green plants, his favorite collection of short stories. She brought it to the bedside. "What would you like?"

"Something funny. With a happy ending."

She leaned over him and kissed him, holding her lips against his bristly cheek for a long moment. "I'll take care of you and you'll get well and strong. I promise. I love you."

Slowly, Owen raised his hand and rested it on her head. "Dear Laura. Lay here thinking —can't die yet; too many things to do. And Laura will help me." His eyes closed and his hand slipped back to the bed. "Read. I might sleep. You don't mind?"

Laura smiled, blinking back hot tears. "I don't mind."

"You'll be here, though. When I wake up."

"I'll always be here, as long as you want me." She bent her head and a tear splashed on the book in her lap. Carefully she wiped it away with her fingertip. "Thank you for caring about me," she whispered. And then she leafed through the book, looking for a happy ending.

Part II

CHAPTER 6

AT eight in the morning the other courts were empty and the only sound in the huge, high-ceilinged room was the hollow bounce of the tennis ball in the long, steady volleys Laura and Allison played before one or the other scored a point. "Damn!" Allison exclaimed as her shot landed outside the baseline. "What was I thinking of when I taught you to play this game?"

"You were thinking you'd improve me," said Laura. "And you did."

They played in concentrated silence, well matched, both of them hard, fast players; but it was Allison who finally scored the winning point by making a cross-court drop shot beyond Laura's reach. "Haven't lost it all," she said breathlessly, touching Laura's arm affectionately as they changed sides. "But I will if I don't watch it. I can't believe you never played until three years ago; are you sure that wasn't a put-on?"

"You know it wasn't; I never held a racket until you taught me. It's because I love it. Don't you always learn faster when you love something?"

"Probably. But you're a natural athlete, you know. I never saw anyone move the way you do, like a cat."

A shadow seemed to touch Laura's face, then it was gone. "I learned it all from you," she said smoothly. "One more game?"

Allison nodded and served, and from above, in the glass-walled restaurant overlooking the courts, Paul Janssen watched the fast play, admiring his cousin Allison but drawn again and again to watch Laura Fairchild, whom he hadn't seen in almost a year. That had been the summer before, when he'd come home for a week after traveling through the West with friends. It had been obvious then that she'd become a part of his family, but he had given her no more than passing attention. He remembered noticing that she was growing up: no longer the brusque, uncomfortable girl he'd met at the Cape, or the elusive one who kept to herself when she arrived in Boston, spending her time with Owen, or at Rosa's side in the kitchen, or at the university. But she was still rough-edged then; pretty, but self-conscious and withdrawn, with none of the beauty and confidence Paul Janssen required before he was attracted to a woman.

He was twenty-eight years old, and experts had told him he had a brilliant eye and a future as a great photographer if he concentrated on it. But he'd never stayed in any one place long enough to concentrate on anything or anyone. "You're young," his mother said. "You'll settle down when you're ready." "You'll regret these years," his great-uncle Owen said. "They could be your most creative ones, and you're frittering them away." But his aunt Leni told him not to hurry: "It's better to go slowly and make no mistakes." His father said only, "You'll find your own way," frustrating Paul, who occasionally still looked to him for advice. And his uncle Felix snorted contemptuously, "He's spoiled"; and Paul, though he had no fondness for his cold, rigid uncle, in this case had to admit that Felix was probably right: he was spoiled by wealth. Earning money wasn't urgent, and so it was easier to drift, dabbling in photography and other agreeable pastimes and avoiding commitments, whether to a job or a woman or even to a particular country, as he wandered from one playground for the wealthy to another.

The trouble with that, and the reason he had come back to Boston, was that he was finding it harder to get absorbed in anything: after a while, casinos and clubs and chic restaurants all began to look alike. He was bored; he needed to figure out what to do next. Now, watching Laura, he felt his interest stir. He wondered at the change that had occurred in her, giving her poise and grace and a distinctive quality for which beautiful was too weak a word. Striking, he thought, and not easy to categorize. His artist's eye studied her slender face: her broad forehead and enormous long-lashed eyes, her high cheekbones with delicate shadows beneath, and her wide, expressive mouth, free of makeup, lips parted in the excitement of the game. Her thick chestnut hair was no longer tied back, though she had restrained it, for tennis, with a band around her forehead; still, the loose waves fell below her shoulders, and damp tendrils escaped the band, framing her flushed face, making it seem smaller and somehow vulnerable.

Yet there was toughness in the determined lift of her head, her powerful serve, and the muscles of her strong, lithe body uncoiling with explosive energy as she sprang across the court. Tough but delicate, Paul thought. Sultry but innocent—or, rather, untested; there was experience in that lovely face, though it was impossible to tell what kind without knowing her. His family told him she was cool but loving, private but grateful for affection, hot-tempered but quick to laugh. And watching her race across the court to scoop up and return a low-bouncing ball, he saw she was graceful but fiercely bent on winning. Of all the beautiful women waiting to hear from him in Europe and America, none, at the moment, intrigued him with so many contradictions.

He watched as Allison gained the advantage. Laura was pressing to tie the score when she returned a serve into the net. "Fuck it," she said, then swiftly looked on all sides to see if anyone was close enough to hear. Paul, reading her lips, laughed aloud. A gamine, he thought, and also very much a woman. He opened a nearby door and stepped out onto a balcony just above the court.

"Paul!" Allison called as the movement caught her eye. "When did you get here? Doesn't Laura play wonderfully? Would you like a game?"

He shook his head, trying to catch Laura's eye, but she had turned away and was putting a towel over her shoulders.

"Then come to a party," Allison said. "Tonight. Laura, do you mind if I invite Paul to your party?"

Laura said something Paul could not hear.

"Well, I know it's my party," Allison said, "but you're giving it." She looked up at Paul. "Laura's throwing a gala in honor of my engagement to the most eminent Thad Wolcott the Third. I didn't know you'd be in town, so I didn't invite you. But you will come, won't you?"

Paul looked at Laura until, as if forced by his steady gaze, she raised her eyes and met his. They looked at each other across the space between them. "Yes," Paul said to Laura. "I'd like very much to be there."

The guests arrived at seven, taking the small mahogany-paneled elevator to Laura's fourth-floor apartment in Owen's Beacon Hill town house. The windows were open to the soft June night, and the sounds of the party reached the quiet orderliness of Mount Vernon Street as old and new acquaintances mingled in small shifting clusters like jeweled fragments in a turning kaleidoscope. Piano music came from the stereo; Rosa's nephew Albert tended bar; her other nephew, Ferdy, took silver trays of hors d'oeuvres from the dumbwaiter on which Rosa sent them up from the kitchen, and carried them around to the guests. "The place looks terrific," Thad Wolcott said to Laura, his arm carelessly around her shoulder as he surveyed the living room. "You've transformed it."

"With Allison's help," Laura said, but her eyes were bright with pleasure in what she had done. For months she had worked on the three-room apartment to make it as softly glowing as a garden at sunrise. Oil and water-color paintings by Nantucket artists hung on the walls; antique fire irons, restored with hours of rubbing, stood by the fireplace; and silk shantung drapes framed the high windows. Once she had longed for a room of her own; now she had three, more beautiful than any she had ever dreamed of, and she had made them truly hers.

"I made a few suggestions," Allison said. "The rest Laura did by herself. Who'd ever guess my father and his brother grew up here? It was as dark as a bat's cave, with the walls covered with cork so they'd never run out of bulletin board. I love it now; don't you think she has an artist's eye?"

"She has something special," said Thad appraisingly. "She's kept you friendly for three years, and you usually get bored with people long before that."

As Allison's color rose, Laura said coolly, "Maybe we like each other. And Allison is much more than friendly; she's generous. You didn't admire my dress, Thad."

He stepped back and gazed at her. "By Carolina Herrera, from Martha at Trump Tower, worn, to great applause, by Miss Allison Salinger at last year's Thanksgiving Ball."

"Thad never forgets a dress," Allison commented dryly.

"And Laura Fairchild looks fabulous in midnight blue satin." He kissed Laura's hand. "It's your color; you should wear nothing else. Though"—he was still holding her hand—"as I recall, you also look terrific in red. And emerald. And of course white. And—"

"He never misses a chance to hold a lady's hand, either," Allison said.

Laura pulled away, trying to think of a simple, sophisticated quip. As hard as she worked at it, she still wasn't as quick as Allison and her friends, who always seemed to have a sharp comment on the tips of their tongues. "Is everyone here?" she asked, looking around the room. "I should tell Rosa what time we'll want dinner." *Why isn't he here? He said he'd be here. He said he'd like very much to be here.*

"Everyone but Paul," Allison said. "But he's frequently late; he's known for it. And Rosa knows nobody expects dinner before nine. I'm going to take Thad away and introduce him to your college friends; do you mind?"

"No, of course not," Laura said automatically, wondering why someone would be late so often he would be known for it. "I should be circulating, too; I'm not acting like a hostess."

It was the first time she had ever been a

hostess. It was the first time she'd worn midnight blue satin, the first time she'd decorated an apartment, the first time she was waiting for a man who had looked at her with admiring eyes.

For a long time everything had been new, beginning with the moment three years before when she entered Owen's Beacon Hill house, walking beside his wheelchair as the chauffeur pushed it into the foyer. Owen held up a restraining hand and the chauffeur stopped halfway to the elevator that was tucked into the wall beside the branching stairway. "I thought I might never see this place again," Owen murmured, almost to himself. He looked up at Laura and a joyous smile lit his face. "But here I am, and I've brought you with me."

He reached his hand toward her and she held it in hers. "How I love this house," he mused. "There was a time when I thought I hated it, when I even planned to sell it." He shook his head, his gaze moving past the marble statue in the center of the foyer to the French drum tables with huge arrangements of gladioli and roses. "So much laughter here, so long ago . . . And now I can share it. Have you noticed how we appreciate all the more what we have when we can give its pleasures to someone new? There's a selfishness in appreciating what we almost lost; there's a different kind of happiness in sharing it. I hope you are very happy here, Laura, and I bid you welcome."

"I will be," Laura said. "Happy, I mean." She bit her lip. Why couldn't she speak elegantly, as he did? "Thank you," she burst out. He might think she was clumsy, but at least he'd know she was grateful.

Owen smiled and folded his hands in his lap. "Let Rosa take you around; she'll help you figure out the maze Iris and I created. Make yourself at home while I take a nap; then come to my room when I ring for you. My dear," he added as the chauffeur turned the wheelchair, "I am so very pleased to have you here." And then the elevator doors opened and closed behind him.

Rosa appeared in a doorway on the other side of the foyer. "Come on, my young miss, we'll have a fast tour and then you can unpack. I'll take care of Clay when he gets here, after he finishes at Felix and Leni's." Rosa had never asked how it happened that Laura Fairchild, a summer kitchen assistant who had appeared from nowhere to apply for a job in mid-June was, in mid-September, moving into the Beacon Hill house as Owen Salinger's companion, and bringing her brother with her. Owen always did as he pleased, and his family had long since stopped telling him he was arbitrary, whimsical, foolish, or, far worse, vulnerable to clever people who could take advantage of him. Rosa knew they all thought it, but, because they were smart, they kept their mouths shut.

And so did she. But it was easy for Rosa; she had no stake in Owen's fortune. Besides, she was fond of Laura. "Don't put your hands all over the furniture," she said as they walked through the main salon on the second floor. "Fingerprints, you know."

"I never leave fingerprints," Laura said hotly. "I was trained better than that."

"My, my," Rosa said mildly, wondering why the girl suddenly looked frightened. "I wasn't criticizing the way you were raised—I'm not big on criticizing people—but how would you know that too much polish ruins fine woods and so we try to keep fingerprints off the furniture?"

"Sorry," Laura muttered.

"No harm done. I should remember how people like to touch something they're seeing for the first time. Go ahead; I won't say a word."

Laura forced herself to smile, afraid to say anything. *Be careful; be careful. Even now, even in Boston, be careful.* She found herself holding her breath and walking on tiptoe as they passed through rooms leading to more rooms; down long hallways lined with portraits of staid men and satin-gowned women; past nooks, closets, cupboards, unexpected stairways, and window seats. And then she began to relax beneath the spell of enfolding luxury, and soon she was reaching out and touching the silkiness of polished woods, the nap of gleaming velvets, the tightly-woven wool of the French tapestries on the walls.

Something stirred within her and came awake: a longing for luxury and beauty she had kept locked away because the chance of having them was so remote. Her fingertips felt alive; she seemed to merge with everything she touched, as far away as she could be from the linoleum-covered kitchen table where Ben would sit, making marks with his thumbnail, while she cooked dinner and told him about her day at school.

"Mr. Owen bought the house as a wedding present the month he and Mrs. Iris were married," Rosa was saying. "All twenty-two rooms of it. They'd always dreamed of living on Beacon Hill and having a family and giving big parties in a ballroom. And that's what they did. Here it is, the ballroom, closed up now; it has been since she died."

The ballroom, surrounded by dormer windows, took up the top floor. Below, on the fourth floor, was the apartment Felix and Asa had shared, as well as two extra rooms and baths for friends. Owen and Iris had a suite on the third floor with a guest suite across the hall; on the second floor a spacious salon stretched the width of the house, with the dining room and library behind it; and on the ground floor were the kitchen and pantry, Rosa's apartment, a receiving room, and the entrance foyer and an elevator leading to the upper floors. In the basement were a laundry room, a pantry lined with Rosa's jams and preserves, and a paneled room with a billiard table, fireplace, leather furniture, and a full bar.

"Mr. Owen always said those were the ten

happiest years of his life, when he lived here with Mrs. Iris. He was building his company in those years, going like a house afire, buying hotels and building new ones right and left— there must have been two a year, sometimes three. The company got so big they finally took up half the top floor of the Boston Salinger. You haven't seen it yet; it's on Arlington Street, just off the Public Gardens. And he and Mrs. Iris were at all the parties, their pictures in the paper, their closets full of new clothes. . . . Then they started giving dinners, one a week, very intimate, just twelve people. Nobody else was doing it and pretty soon everybody was hinting for invitations. They had style, Mr. Owen and Mrs. Iris, and if I could have bottled and sold it I could have gotten rich. But style isn't something you can buy; either you have it or you don't."

I'll have it, Laura vowed silently. Whatever it is, whatever it looks like, I'll figure out how to get it. And people will admire me and love me and beg to be invited to my parties.

"But then Mrs. Iris died," Rosa said as they took the elevator from the basement billiard room to the fourth floor. "Mr. Owen shut the door on their suite and never went in it again.

He talked about selling the house but he couldn't bring himself to do it; he said the thought of someone else living in the rooms Mrs. Iris had made drove him crazy. So he stayed. He moved into the guest suite, and a couple of years later the housekeeper and I made the old master suite into guest rooms, even though there aren't any guests in this house and haven't been since Mrs. Iris died. Until you, that is."

"I'm not a guest, I work here," Laura said.

"Well, yes, that's true. It's just that we never had a companion in this house before."

But now you do. I'm here, I'm part of this. I don't have to climb out a window and leave it all behind. I belong.

On the fourth floor Rosa opened the door to the three rooms where Felix and Asa had grown up. "This is yours."

Laura looked at her uncomprehendingly. "What is?"

"The apartment. Not beautiful, by a long shot, but Mr. Owen said it's to be yours."

The walls were covered in dark cork, the furniture was scarred walnut, everything was brown. "Felix and Asa did the decorating, if you can call it that," Rosa said. "It's the only part of the house Mrs. Iris didn't touch. It was theirs, it was private, and we didn't go in until they'd both moved away." She gazed at it. "My oh my, it is definitely a dark and dreary place."

"Change it," Owen said to Laura the next day after Rosa told him it was a grim place for a young girl. "Tear it apart, paint it, furnish it, and have the bills sent to me. Felix and Asa aren't interested in it anymore and I approve of progress. Make it yours."

"I think I should wait, if you don't mind," Laura replied. She was sitting beside his bed, a book in her lap, thinking about the word *dark*. Felix and Asa's dark apartment was harsh; Owen's dark rooms were a sumptuous haven of paisley velvets, Oriental rugs, heavy silk drapes in green and gold, and gleaming brass floor lamps. "It isn't as beautiful as yours," she went on, "but just having three whole rooms to myself is so wonderful—I have to get used to being alone, without Clay and Ben—" Her nails dug into her palms. "One of—one of Clay's friends, you know; all his friends would come over and it would be so crowded and noisy"— *just change the subject*— "and I want to learn about Boston; it's so different from New York, so old and beautiful . . ." She took a deep breath. "I'll decorate the rooms later, if that's all right with you."

"They're yours to do with as you please, Laura," Owen said gently. "They're your home." Watching the play of alarm and confusion on her face, he longed to banish her fears, but he would not pry into what was bothering her. She would tell him when she was ready, or not at all. But as so many times before, he was amazed at how strongly he wanted to help her, to make her happy. Something about her brings that out in me, he thought, and he wondered how many other men would feel the same and go out of their way to bring back her smile.

He closed his eyes as she picked up the book and returned to her reading. He loved the sound of her voice, low and vibrant, slipping occasionally into a roughness that hinted at a harsh background, but then becoming smooth again, with a slight lilt, almost as if she were learning English as a new language. When she read aloud, whether from his favorite books on Cape Cod, or collections of short stories or poetry, her voice found a rhythm that sounded to Owen almost as if she were singing, and he dozed and woke and dozed again to that musical cadence that made him regret that he was past the age of courtship.

Laura knew none of this, though she knew he liked the sound of her voice and rang for her frequently. He had at his bedside an array of buttons with which he could call one of the around-the-clock nurses who had taken over a guest room across the hall, or Rosa or any of the maids, or the housekeeping couple in the carriage house. But it was Laura he called most often, and even after she began classes at Boston University, she sat beside his bed when she was not at school, reading to him, talking, even doing her homework when he fell asleep.

Owen had arranged for her to start college. He had instructed his secretary at the Salinger executive offices to call a few key people at the university, and since none of them had to be reminded of his generosity as a benefactor, Laura was accepted as a special student within a week.

From the first she loved it. Everyone else seemed to take college for granted, but to Laura it was always a dream. The robbery at the Cape faded away; so did the police who were still working on it. And so did Ben. She was in a new life. Now and then she reminded herself how fragile it was—it all depended on Owen and she walked a thin line of possible discovery with him and his family—but then another month would go by, filled with the excitement of new ideas, new friends who accepted her without question, even a small part in the freshman class play, and she would forget there was any danger at all.

And with each month she knew she was becoming less like the Laura she had been. She explored the little side streets and enclosed neighborhoods of Boston, not because she was looking for homes to rob or escape routes or crowded shopping malls for picking pockets, but because she wanted to learn about her new home. She loved the narrow cobblestone streets of Beacon Hill, each like an old English town frozen in time, with gas lamps burning day and night, solid rows of narrow, five-story houses of worn, mellowed brick with high, narrow windows, most of them fronted with wrought-iron balconies just deep enough to hold window boxes of geraniums, and tiny front yards with even tinier flower gardens. It was all snug and private and privileged, and often Laura found herself breaking into a small skipping step as she walked along Mount Vernon Street from Owen's huge corner house, because everything was settled and secure—and hers.

In New York, even though many buildings had been preserved from earlier times, everything seemed to be rushing toward tomorrow and the day after, but Boston always seemed to make room for yesterday, its history and memories, its small-town feel. Laura stood on street corners, craning her neck to see glass and steel skyscrapers towering above small brick buildings with white steeples, or stone churches so old the walls had taken on the color of the earth. In small byways, tiny houses crowded the narrow streets, and she could almost hear the clip-clop of horses and the crunch of wooden wagon wheels as they negotiated the tight corners. Time-worn cemeteries and brass plaques were everywhere, marking the nation's oldest church, its first bookshop, Paul Revere's house—and at every plaque Laura stopped and tried to imagine the city as it had been.

She had never understood what history meant until she seemed to walk within it in Boston. And when she did, she discovered another meaning for family: a private history, the story of where each of us came from, just as Boston was the story of the nation's birth and growth.

Ben's smile came to her, and his serious frown as he helped her and Clay with their homework or planned their next break-in. *Ben is my history, part of what I am now. And I've lost him. But maybe someday . . .* She tucked the thought away. Someday, maybe, she would have a history she didn't have to hide.

Each week she discovered a different part of Boston, a different kind of city. She spent hours in its museums and wandered through the Fens and sat in the Public Gardens. She would glance at the Boston Salinger, which faced the Gardens, with Felix's office at the corner of the top floor, and then look back to the lush landscape where she sat, watching the ducks, squinting at the statue of George Washington, and wondering who had planned the perfect symmetry of the flower beds. She window-shopped along Boylston and Newbury streets, and once, by herself, bought a ticket for the symphony and discovered the soaring joy of a full orchestra. And wherever she went, she eavesdropped, listening to the broad Boston *a* and clipped syllables and watching the people as they talked: they had a careful way of holding their mouths that kept the corners almost motionless while the lips softly opened and closed, making murmured pronouncements.

"Prim," Owen said, laughter rolling from him as Laura mimicked the speech at dinner. "Perfect."

"You're not like that," she said.

"No, I escaped. Felix does it for the family. He thinks he should sound like Beacon Hill. I'd rather look like it: old, a little prudish, proud of my heritage, protective of my privacy."

"But that's what Boston is like," Laura said.

"Much of it, not all; it's a modern city with race riots and crime and poverty and the rest. A lot like New York."

Laura shook her head. "New York is like somebody running, dashing across the streets, always in a hurry. Boston is . . . Boston is like people walking and crossing at the corners and waiting for the lights to change."

Owen laughed again. "You've figured us out." But he noted that once more she had avoided telling him about her life in New York.

Most of the time in those first months in

Boston no one asked any questions, and Laura was content to listen, making friends at school, reading to Owen or letting him reminisce about his life with Iris, and listening to Clay, who, for once, was not complaining. He lived in one of the rooms on the fourth floor, across the hall from Laura's apartment, and after school and on weekends he worked at Felix and Leni's sprawling home in the leafy North Shore suburb of Beverly. He and Laura had dinner together twice a week; on the other nights, when she ate with Owen in his rooms, Clay ate in the kitchen with Rosa or out with friends Laura did not know. But she didn't try to find out who they were: he was happy, he was busy, he was away from Ben. And that left her free to make her own life.

She was always learning something new, and everything she learned she remembered. Some of the family had ideas about how she should look and behave, and she stored in her memory all their suggestions. She also was discovering in herself a flair for doing things in a way that was uniquely hers.

It began with gentle lessons from Leni on buying clothes, and more peremptory ones from Allison when she came home from college for Thanksgiving. "Winter colors," declared Leni, appraising Laura's skin and hair as they stood before a three-way mirror at Jana's on Newton Street. So Jana brought out dresses in midnight blue, wine, rose, hunter green, white, ivory, and black, and Laura tried them on.

"Makeup would help," observed Jana.

"Yes," Leni agreed. "But that is for Laura to decide. I think she will, when she has proper clothes."

Laura contemplated herself in the mirror. Even beneath the rose-colored lights in the small, jewel-like salon, she was pale, with faint freckles from the summer sun at the Cape. Her hair was a mass of long, loose chestnut curls with stray curls on her forehead; her eyes were a darkly anxious blue. "I wouldn't know what to buy or how to put it on," she said.

"You need a few lessons," Jana told her. "My services are available; I have taught the most photographed ladies on the eastern seaboard. It is very simple, believe me. You would have no difficulty; you have excellent bones. It is like an artist, working with the finest canvas; even the most basic materials make such a difference you would not believe—"

"Yes," Leni repeated. "Laura will decide."

Jana fell into practiced silence, handing Laura the dresses to try on. Their vivid colors brought a glow to her pale skin. Soon, without realizing it, she was standing straighter, her head higher, and the worry was fading from her eyes. She saw hints of the kind of sophistication that seemed so natural in Allison: straight shoulders, the confidence of a level gaze, the smooth line from neck to back, with no slouch. That could be learned. It was much easier to learn it in an expensive dress. With Leni's approval, she bought two, all she could afford until next month's paycheck from Owen.

Then Allison cleaned out her closets and gave eight dresses and skirts to Laura, who added her own touches to them: in the flea markets around Salem and Marblehead, she bought Afghan belts, an ivory choker and stickpin, a fringed stole, sodalite beads which she twined with a strand of faux pearls, and a lace collar and cuffs from France.

Allison took her to buy sports clothes. "You're tall enough for long lines and bulky tops. No frills and curlicues—you can't ever be cute; you're definitely the elegant type—so stick with long sweaters, long skirts and jackets, wide belts, high boots. Then if you'd remember to stand straight you'd look like a dancer." Laura concentrated on standing straight. And in the next weeks, on her own, she added long fringed scarves that made her look almost like a gypsy, her delicate face like a cameo above the vivid folds at her long throat.

"Wear hats," said Barbara Janssen. "It's such a shame women have forgotten how much they do for one. They frame the face with refinement and distinction, and who doesn't benefit from that?" Tilting her head, she gazed at Laura. "Wide brims, small crowns. You have a wonderful head if you'd only hold it high." Laura concentrated on holding it high, and added feathers and silk bands, scraps of lace and antique buttons, and, in summer, fresh flowers to the hats Barbara gave her from her closets, saying she had new ones and didn't know what to do with last year's.

"Why is everyone doing so much for me?" Laura asked Rosa.

"Well, they like you," Rosa said. "But I think mainly it's because you take care of Mr. Owen. They love him and they visit often enough, but they're very big on their own busy lives, and this way they know he's not counting the minutes until they come again." She glanced at Laura's downcast face. "Of course they do like you. I'm convinced that's the main reason."

"Thank you," Laura said and kissed her.

On their first Christmas together, she and Owen exchanged gifts. They sat on the sofa in his study, flames softly burning in the fireplace, their breakfast on trays on the coffee table before them, and she gave him a scrimshaw letter opener, not rare, but of singular beauty. "For when you go back to work," she said, and he grinned with pleasure because he was strong again and because Laura had chosen his gift with love and care.

"And for you," he said, handing her a leather briefcase. "For college. I thought of jewelry, but perhaps this is more useful right now."

"It's perfect," said Laura. She ran her palm over the soft suede and smelled the pungent odor of fresh leather when she opened the case to see the compartments inside. She rested her head on Owen's shoulder. "But I don't need a gift; just being here is like getting a gift every day. I don't need any others."

"You need dozens. Hundreds. Everyone does; don't ever believe we don't need expressions of love and admiration. I mean," he added when Laura looked puzzled, "all of us need to be told how wonderful we are, and how much we're loved and needed, but it's just as important for us to know that someone was thinking of us at a time when we were apart. If I suddenly wandered off to climb the Himalayas, wouldn't it please you if I brought you a gift when I returned so you would know I thought of you even in the midst of overwhelming new experiences? Isn't that another way of telling you I love you, to think of you and bring you something that allows you to share at least part of my exciting adventures?"

A smile curved Laura's lips. "You could take me with you, and then I could share all of them."

Owen burst into laughter. "By God, so I could. So I shall. Would you like to go to the Himalayas?"

"I'd love to go to the Himalayas."

"Then we shall, someday. But I also intend to buy you gifts, because there aren't enough ways to tell you how happy you make me or to thank you for making this house a happy place again."

Rosa knocked at the door and came to take away the trays. "Laura, this is for you," she said, handing her an envelope. "It came yesterday but it got buried in all the Christmas cards. Is there anything else you need, Mr. Owen?"

"Coffee and brandy," he growled.

"You know perfectly well—" Rosa began amiably.

"Then find me a doctor who says it's all right."

"You keep following orders and one of these days your own doctor will say it's all right." Rosa picked up the trays and as she straightened up, she glanced at Laura. "Good heavens, child, what is it? What's wrong?"

Owen, too, had seen Laura's stricken look. "She's probably shocked by the idea of brandy for breakfast. We don't need anything else, Rosa. What time are you leaving for Felix and Leni's?"

"As soon as I clean up. We're forty for dinner, so I'd like Laura, too, if I can have her."

"Later," Owen said. "I'll send her over

about two." When Rosa left, he asked gently, "Would you like to talk about it?"

Laura shook her head. "I was just . . . surprised . . . for a minute. I'm fine now. Would you mind if—"

"Of course not. Go off by yourself and read your letter."

"Just a few minutes . . ." Her words trailing away, Laura left the room so she could read Ben's letter by herself.

Dear Laura,

I haven't written in all this time because I was afraid you'd still be angry and not want to hear from me. I didn't like leaving the way I did but after what happened I had to get out, as far and as fast as I could. I miss you. I think of you a lot and remember what it was like when we were all together. I wonder what you're doing and how you and Clay are getting along with the Salingers and whether they've ever suspected you of anything. I wish you'd write to me at this address; I'm working as a busboy and a bellhop in a hotel. Not great jobs, but they give me time to think and to decide what I'll do next. I keep remembering what you said about being an executive. Maybe I'll get back to the States one of these days and see you. Write to me, Laura. I feel awfully far away and I miss you and I've got to know what's happened since the Salingers were robbed.

" 'Since the Salingers were robbed,' " Clay scoffed when Laura read him the letter. "Why doesn't he say since he robbed the Salingers? He makes it sound as if it just sort of happened. All by itself."

"He sounds lonely," Laura said.

"I guess." Clay stretched out his legs and stared at his feet. "But we can't help that, can we? He did it, we didn't. I mean, I'm sorry for him, but things are really good here and what are we supposed to do?"

"I think we should write to him."

"Not me!" he said vehemently. "And I don't think you should either. Aren't you having a good time here? I mean, why risk it? I'd rather not even know where he is."

"In London, at a hotel called Blake's. And I think he really wants to hear from us."

"Damn it, it's too dangerous! I'm sorry, Laura, but—"

"You think Ben is dangerous? Or it's dangerous for us to write to him?"

"I don't know. Maybe both. Anyway, he only wants us to write because he's afraid we might give him away."

"That's ridiculous; he knows we wouldn't."

Clay shrugged. "I just think we've got something pretty good going here; why should we risk it?"

Laura gazed at the letter in her hand. As long as Clay liked it with her, he wouldn't leave. As long as he thought Ben was dangerous, he wouldn't go to him. "Will you go to college?" she asked.

"Oh, shit." Clay made a face. "Listen, I'm a lousy student and I know it. I'll learn on the job; I'm good at that."

"What job?"

"I don't know yet. Maybe in a Salinger hotel. Felix was saying there might be a chance."

"Felix?"

"He probably only said it because Leni told him to. But I didn't ask; he brought it up and I said I might be interested."

"What about high school?"

He shrugged. "Shit, I've gone this far; I might as well finish and wear that cute little cardboard hat and get that cute little rolled-up diploma and then tell 'em all to fuck off. By then I'll be smart enough to do anything I feel like, right?"

Laura smiled. She felt good about Clay and even about Ben. She hadn't forgiven him, but he missed her, and whether she liked it or not she missed him, too—she couldn't help it— and now that she'd decided to write to him she felt better. It wouldn't hurt to keep in touch with him and maybe she could even find a way to get Leni's jewelry back—if he hadn't sold it all. "Are you helping with Christmas dinner?" she asked Clay. Ben wouldn't have a family dinner, she thought; it would be the first Christmas he didn't.

"Allison and I are hanging holly and greens all the hell over the house."

"Is that all you two do? Handle plants?"

"Very funny. I'd rather handle her, but she's hung up on"—he put his nose in the air— "mature cocksuckers."

"Clay! She never said anything like that!"

He shrugged. "You should know; you're always yacking, the two of you. I'm just the baby brother, right? What do I know? I'm not big enough for mature screwing or any other fucking thing."

Laura bit back a question about how much screwing he'd done. He would be eighteen in a couple of months and she'd be nineteen; they were old enough to have their own affairs and they were entitled to privacy. "Find someone your own age," she said lightly. "It's a lot simpler and probably a lot more fun." She kissed him on the top of his head. "I'll send Ben your love and tell him you miss him."

"Bullshit." Suddenly his truculence vanished; his voice was young and almost wistful. "You can tell him I'm fine and I don't even remember what it was like to live with him."

"I don't think I'll say that," she said quietly, and that night, on the walnut desk that had been Felix's, she wrote to him.

Dear Ben,

I miss you, too, and I want us to write and be friends again, but please don't come here or call us. No one knows about you and it has to stay that way. You've got to understand that. Everything is wonderful here, we're happy, and we don't want to leave. We don't want to be forced to leave. I'm doing so many new things. . . .

It was three months before Ben replied: a very short letter about London and a new job he had in a different hotel. He sent his love to both of them, as if they were just good friends. After that, he and Laura wrote every few months and sent cards on their birthdays. Laura would have liked more, but she wasn't sure what. She was still angry at Ben, but the robbery seemed so distant that her anger had lost much of its force. And she missed him and wanted back the strong brother she remembered, but she didn't know how they could do that. So she went along with the sporadic correspondence he had started. At least she knew she hadn't cut all her ties with him.

Clay refused to read any of Ben's letters, though Laura always offered them to him, but he listened when she told him about Ben's new job in London, and another one after that, and then about his moving to Monte Carlo, where he worked in two hotels in eight months, and finally about his moving again, this time to Amsterdam, where he had a job at yet another hotel, on the security staff.

"What a good place for a thief," Clay said.

Laura did not reply. By then it was Christmas again; she was in her second year of college and she didn't get as emotional about Ben as she had. In fact, it was hard to remember what it had been like to depend on him and be part of his life. It was Owen she depended on now.

They had breakfast on Christmas morning, sitting in his study as they had a year ago. This time Owen's present to Laura was an envelope, and inside it she found a blank check.

"To redecorate your apartment," Owen said. "Stop living in Felix and Asa's shadow. Make those rooms your own. I can't imagine why you've waited so long."

"I thought I should make sure you liked having me here. What if you'd sent me away?"

He smiled in that quiet, intimate way she had loved from the first time she saw him. "You didn't really worry about that."

She returned his smile, shaking her head, but it wasn't true. The worries were always there, even when she thought she'd forgotten them for a while. Even at this late date the police could find something about Ben and tell Owen, or the Salingers might learn from the New York police that she had a record as a thief, or Clay might let something slip and give them away. She felt safer with the passage of time, but the worries were never really gone, only held down beneath the surface of her new life; and in the early dawn hours when a garbage truck rumbled by or a car door slammed, she would awaken with a start and lie curled up in bed, fighting off her fears.

But she kept them to herself, and after another year she found she could turn over when she woke at night and go back to sleep. It had been three years. The police had a thousand new crimes to solve; no jewelry was worth fretting over for such a long time. Besides, Owen was fully recovered, playing golf in the summer and tennis in the winter, and spending a few hours a week in the Salinger executive offices, semi-retired but still insistent on knowing what was going on in his hotels. And Laura was no longer the girl she had been. If anyone came looking for her, it would be evident immediately that she had become someone else, that the girl who had been a thief was gone.

Clay was different, too, handsomer than ever and beginning to achieve a smoothness like Ben's. He had graduated from high school and was working in Philadelphia; surprisingly, Felix had kept his word and had found him a job as assistant desk clerk at the Philadelphia

Salinger. He visited Boston on weekends to see friends he'd made in high school, and when he came to Laura's engagement party for Allison he brought a pretty blond girl whom he introduced as Bunny Kirk. "Bunny waitresses at Fotheringill's," he told Laura. "And Laura studies business at Boston University. Two ambitious ladies."

Laura and Bunny talked briefly, but Clay was surveying the room, and when he found Allison he focused on her with a brooding look. He can't still believe he wants her, Laura thought, but she realized she hardly knew Clay anymore. Once, before he moved to Philadelphia, she had asked him where he got the money to date as much as he did. "I only spend what I earn at Felix and Leni's," he replied.

"Clay, you aren't stealing, are you? You told me you weren't."

"Shit, Laura, you know I'm not. Who do you think I am? Ben?"

"He's not stealing anymore."

"How do you know?"

"He told me in his letters."

"Sure."

Laura didn't pursue it. When Clay didn't

want to talk, it was impossible to get past his stubborn silence. She knew he wouldn't talk about Bunny Kirk either. If she asked, he would only say that she was a good friend.

And why shouldn't he? That's exactly what I tell him about the men I meet at college. The trouble is, it's always true: they're just good friends.

A toss in the hay to keep the doctor away. As Ben used to say.

Owen had asked her, a year ago, if there were no young man she loved. They had been dining at his favorite restaurant, celebrating his recovery. "You've spent enough time on a cardiac patient over eighty," he said. "You need men your own age, and other kinds of love."

"I'm happy with the way I am," she said. But she'd known he was right.

She remembered that as the sounds of her party rose and fell rhythmically around her and she thought of Paul Janssen. *He's not here. He isn't coming. Not on time, not late, not at all.*

"Champagne for the hostess." Thad Wolcott was beside her, replacing her empty glass with a full one. "A dreaming hostess, I see."

"I was remembering when Owen got well," Laura said. "We had a private celebration at

Loch Ober's and he gave me a lesson in how to know good wines."

"One of his many talents."

Laura looked at him. "Why do you always talk about people as if you're making fun of them or don't like them?"

"I like all the Salingers."

"You didn't answer my question."

"I complimented you on your dress. Was I making fun of you?"

Laura shrugged, then caught herself. *Ladies don't shrug their shoulders, my young miss.* That was the hardest habit to break. "I'm never sure how you feel about anyone," she said. "I suppose I'd have to know you as well as Allison does."

He smiled obscurely. "Allison doesn't care how well she knows me; she only wants to reform me."

"I didn't know you needed reforming."

"If I didn't, Allison wouldn't want me. Even if I were perfect—which I must admit I am not—I would pretend to have faults so Allison would want to make me her project."

Laura knew he was making fun of Allison and she looked around, wondering where she was.

"One thing you might remember," Thad said. "I can make her happy. She'll take me in hand and I'll turn out very well. She'll be proud of me and so will you; I promise you that."

"You should be making promises to Allison, not to me."

"That's too easy; she expects them."

"Sometimes the easy things are the hardest to do."

He looked at her with an alert eye. "What does that mean?"

"It's easy to love," Laura said coolly. "But to do it well, you have to think of someone besides yourself. And that's something you haven't learned how to do, isn't it? Now if you'll excuse me, I should be taking care of my guests."

She glimpsed his startled look as she made her way through the crowded room. For a brief moment she was proud of herself for thinking of a sharp, clever remark at the right time, just like Allison and her friends. But then she thought about Allison. I have to find out if she knows how Thad talks about her. She moved among her guests, smiling as they praised her apartment and her party and Rosa's hors d'oeuvres, but not pausing to talk until she reached Allison.

"Laura, did you hear?" Allison asked. "One of Mother's bracelets showed up—from the robbery, you know? Just this afternoon, in a pawnshop in New York. Isn't that incredible? After all this time . . . Oh, let me introduce my friend from school; his father's a lawyer in New York, and he knows a private investigator who's been hanging on to our robbery for years . . ."

Laura did not hear his name. *Ben is in Amsterdam. How could he pawn a bracelet in New York?*

". . . and they're looking for other pieces. Of course, it could be months or years before they show up—"

I just got a letter; he didn't say he was coming to New York.

"—but they think now they have a chance to find the thief. Wouldn't that be something? They might even find him before he sells Mother's necklace, which would be the most wonderful—"

Ben, if you ruin everything I have, I'll never forgive you; I'll never have anything to do with you again.

"I'm sorry I'm late," a voice said just behind Laura. "I really wanted to be on time but something came up."

She turned. Paul Janssen had come to her party.

CHAPTER 7

EVERYONE stayed and stayed. "Great party!" they exclaimed to Laura. "So different!" Clay and his girl left early, but the others lingered, eating and drinking, shifting from one group to another until the noise level rose so high no one could hear the music, and Ferdy, stacking dessert dishes in the dumbwaiter, paused to turn up the volume.

Laura had to escape the noise. Allison's words echoed in her mind— *pawnshop . . . bracelet . . . a chance to find the thief*—and she fled to her bedroom to catch her breath and try to think. But when she turned to close the door, she found Paul standing there. "If you want to be alone I'll leave," he said before she could speak, "but if you only came in for some quiet, I'd like to share it."

He was taller than she, and Laura looked up to meet his eyes, dark, probing, quizzical. She had thought about him so often over the past three years that now it was as if her thoughts had somehow come to life, dimming the fears that had seemed so terribly important just a moment before. I'll think about all that tomorrow, she thought, stepping aside, and when Paul walked into her room she closed the door behind them.

"Much better," he said, grinning at her in the sudden silence. "That's a noisy group; you've done something they're not used to."

"What have I done?" she asked defensively.

"Mixed up completely different kinds of people, given them a chance to have conversations they don't usually have. It's like a tossed salad out there. Those students never mix, you know."

"You mean my classmates don't mix with Allison's."

"Not in the normal course of things. And they never socialize with the others you invited —Owen's landscaper, who's out there talking to a very high-toned poet, and my mother's favorite cabinetmaker, who's drinking scotch and exchanging profound ideas with one of Harvard's top law students, or the fascinating greengrocer from the corner whom I talked to—"

"You're making fun of them. Those are my friends."

His eyebrows rose. "On the contrary. I'm admiring your courage. You invited the people you wanted instead of taking the easy way and having only Allison's friends, who know all about each other since they're together at every party all year long."

"Courage," Laura repeated. A mischievous smile touched the corners of her mouth. "More like fear, probably. I was afraid I wouldn't have anyone to talk to."

He chuckled, admiring her swift change from prickly defensiveness to sophisticated self-mockery. Another contradiction, he thought. "Tell me how you've gathered such a wide circle of friends."

"You mean peculiar," she said coldly. "You wouldn't ask that if my friends all lived on Beacon Hill."

"It wouldn't be a wide circle if they did." He stood relaxed in front of her, his hands in his pockets. "Are you always armed for battle, even when someone asks you an innocent question?"

"That wasn't innocent. You were saying I must be different if I have such different friends."

"You are different; that's why I'm here." He reached out to take her hand. "Could you invite me to sit down for a few minutes? It's difficult to get a friendship going standing up."

Involuntarily Laura glanced sideways at her bed. It seemed to be oozing in all directions, looming huge and inescapable, filling her room. And Paul seemed to be bigger, too, taking up more of the private space she'd never shared with a man. She shivered slightly with anticipation and apprehension; all she could think of was Paul and her bed, a few feet apart.

"I said friendship."

She looked up and saw his amused smile. Stung, she turned without replying and led the way to the wing chairs flanking the fireplace. They weren't really close to the bed; they were fifteen feet away, and their high backs blocked Laura's and Paul's side vision like blinders on a horse. The two of them sat facing each other in a circle of amber light, a small table between them, the shadowed room like a retreat as sounds of the party drifted through the closed door.

"I've been hearing about you for three years," Paul said conversationally. He sat relaxed in his chair, an ankle resting on one knee, watching her almost lazily. "And I should have spent some time with you last summer; I'm sorry I didn't. You've become a real member of the family. I assume that means you like us."

"I love you," Laura said. She flushed. "I mean, I love Owen and Allison and Leni and Barbara—they've all been wonderful to me."

"I don't hear my uncles Felix and Asa on that list."

She shrugged, then caught herself. "I don't see much of them."

"A careful answer. They're not easy men to get along with, although Asa can be pleasant when he gets out of Felix's orbit. Don't you miss your own family?"

"No. I mean, Clay is here and . . . he's all I've got."

"No one else? I didn't realize that. It must have been hard, then, to leave your friends in New York."

"It's always hard to leave friends." Laura's

face was smooth. "But I like meeting new people; it gets dull having friends who know all about each other since they're together at every party all year long. Rosa says you've been traveling for the past few years."

Something wrong there, Paul thought. She'd used his own words and they'd rung false. He wondered what was forbidden territory: her friends, or New York, or leaving New York. "Europe, Africa, India," he said. "It keeps me out of trouble."

"And what else do you do?"

"I take pictures."

"And sell them?"

"No, why should I? I do it for pleasure."

"Some people might need the money," Laura said dryly.

He nodded. "I'm luckier than most. My great-uncle Owen set up a trust for me when I was still crawling around his study and charming him with my baby wit. I probably looked as restless and unambitious then as I am now and he took pity on me and ensured my future. I did go to college; does that make me sound a little less frivolous? And now and then I do think about taking photography seriously. I'm told you're in college. What will you do when you finish?"

"Something in hotel management; that's what I'm studying. And maybe some acting in my spare time." At his look of surprise, she said defensively, "Why shouldn't I? Other people have hobbies. I've had parts in four plays and everyone says I'm very good."

"And you like it?"

"It's wonderful. To be somebody else and have all your lines written so you never have to worry about what you might say—because playwrights use words more beautifully than the rest of us."

He pretended he had not noticed her abrupt shift in mid-sentence. "I thought your hobby might be making friends. You were going to tell me how you met all those people out there."

"Oh. It's nothing special; I don't know why you think it is." She was frustrated because instead of talking about himself the way most men did, he kept trying to find out about her. But she realized she wasn't angry, as she usually was when people asked prying questions; she was more concerned with saying the right things and keeping that warmth and interest in his eyes. And she knew why. Because he was the most attractive man she'd ever met; because he had an aura of excitement about him, something she might share if she could be clever and quick enough; because he was like a magnet, pulling her closer, making her want to talk instead of running away.

It's dangerous to get close to anyone who makes me want to talk.

"You were saying?" Paul prompted.

I'll be careful. I won't say too much. "I like to listen. People love to talk about themselves; all they need is somebody who's interested and they'll go on for hours. And I guess I'm interested in just about everybody."

He smiled. "You'd be good in the hotel business."

"That's what Owen says."

"Does he? He doesn't say it to many people. Has he offered you a job at the Boston Salinger?"

"Yes," she said, adding almost defiantly, "and I'm going to take it."

He looked at her thoughtfully. "Doing what?"

"Assistant to Jules LeClair. The concierge."

When he made no response, she said, "You don't know him?"

"I don't pay much attention to the hotels. When do you start?"

"On Monday. Full-time for the summer and then part-time when I go back to school."

"To study hotel management. Why don't you major in theater since you like acting so much?"

"Owen wants me to learn the hotel business."

"In case you don't make it as an actress?"

"He calls acting a hobby." She smiled, almost to herself. "And he says anyone who manages his hotels has to be good at acting and have dozens of other skills."

Paul's eyebrows rose. "His hotels?"

"I could do it," Laura declared.

"I'm sure you could. But Felix and Asa handle the management of the chain."

"Yes, but Owen was talking about his own hotels—the four oldest ones that aren't part of the family corporation. He has some plans for them. He says Felix and Asa aren't interested in them."

"Don't fool yourself; they're interested in

every dust ball in every Salinger hotel. And Owen knows it. What kind of plans?"

"I don't know much about them; they aren't put together yet. What do you photograph when you travel?"

Skittish and secretive, Paul thought. What the hell did she have to hide? And what were she and his uncle up to? "Animals and people and sunsets. Have you convinced Owen to start a new hotel chain?"

"I haven't convinced him of anything! I'm learning from him, not telling him what to do!"

"Hold on," he said softly. "I wasn't accusing you of anything. I just thought an active, discerning man might think up a new project with an attractive young woman as a clever ploy to keep her close to him for a long time."

Laura's anger disappeared; her eyes danced. "You mean you think Owen behaves the way you would."

Paul laughed aloud. In some ways she was like a child, he thought, feeling her way around a strange house, pretending she knew what she was doing, quick to anger when she thought she was being suspected of something. But in other ways she was a woman of beauty and spirit, and a cache of secrets. A challenge, Paul reflected; it had been a long time since anyone had seemed so interesting to him.

"What do you do besides photograph when you travel to all those countries?" she asked.

"Read a lot, hike, ski, bicycle cross-country, and wonder what's over the next border."

"Don't you ever want to stay where you are?"

"No. Do you want to stay where you are?"

"Yes." *Safe with Owen, forever.* "If I could, I'd stay here and do all the things I want . . ."

"You can't want many things if you can do them all in one place."

"I do! I want so many things! And I suppose I can't do them all here . . . everything I need to do to be special and secure—" She bit off her words. "I'm sure that sounds foolish to you but I never had a trust fund—I never even had a bank account when I was younger—and I have to make my own safe place. It's what I most want in the world." She stood up. "I'd better get back to my party."

"Stay a little longer," he said. "Your party can roll along for hours on its own steam." He stood up with her. He was surprised at the feelings of tenderness she had aroused in him. She had sounded so ingenuous about being special and secure—whatever that meant—that he wanted to comfort and reassure her. "Listen to me," he said and put his arm around her shoulders, pulling her to him like a child. "You're already special. You're a lovely young woman with nothing to stop you from doing whatever you want or being anything you want." He felt the slender bones of her shoulders beneath the satin dress, her silken chestnut hair brushed his cheek, and desire surged through him. He tightened his arm and turned her toward him. "I'll help you; we all will. There's nothing to stop you. It's not as if you're alone, or have some dark past to live down, or— What is it?"

She had pulled away, her eyes wide, her face pale. "I have to get back," she stammered. "I'm supposed to—"

"What the hell are you afraid of? Me? Because I held you? For God's sake, Laura—"

"No, no, it's not that; it's not you; it wouldn't ever be—I'm sorry, I really am. I'm not being very smart about this—"

"What does being smart have to do with it? Come here, sit down, just for a minute. I'd like to understand. . . ." He looked about for some way to change the subject. "Tell me about your room. I like what you've done with it."

Giving her time to calm down from whatever was bothering her, he studied the country French furniture he remembered from Iris's rooms, newly reupholstered in ivory and apricot silk, and the ceiling moldings and carved fireplace surround, all painted in soft ivory against the palest of mint green walls. "Dawn," he murmured, almost to himself. "Clear, cool, and warm, all at once. Depth and intimacy. My God, what wonderful light." He smiled at Laura. "You've given this place life. It's been in the doldrums ever since I can remember. Perfect colors—you have a good eye."

"Thank you." She was looking at him in surprise, seeing a different Paul Janssen. No longer the careless playboy with no ambition or direction, he was absorbed, intense, an artist who cared deeply about color and light, whose praise was generous, whose smile was warm and intimate. And at that moment Laura knew she would be with him as much as he wanted her to. It might be risky to be close to him, but she was drawn to his intensity, and she wanted more of his praise—and his smile.

He was standing before a shelf of books near the fireplace, running his fingers along the spines. "Where did you get these?"

"A friend named Cal Hendy gave them to me. Left them to me, really: he owned a bookstore and when he died he left me the ones he knew I loved the most."

"A good friend." He took one down and leafed through it. "Do you have any idea what they're worth?"

"No, why should I? I'm not going to sell them."

"You might want to someday, and this one could be worth a good bit: there can't be many first editions around of Washington Irving's *Legend of Sleepy Hollow*. Would you mind if I had it appraised?"

"If you'd like. It's really not important, though; they were a gift from Cal and I loved him and I'd never sell them, no matter what."

" 'Never' is a long time. Anyway, you ought to know what you have. I'll bring it back in a week or so." He put the book on the coffee table, then moved a few steps to gaze at a large framed black-and-white photograph Laura had hung over the mantel. "Where did you find this?"

"In Owen's library. I was admiring it one day and he said I could hang it here. You don't mind?"

"Photographers never mind seeing their work displayed." He studied the three children in the photograph as if he had not spent hours watching them one day on the beach at Wellfleet, photographing them again and again. And then he had spent a week in his darkroom to get a set of prints that satisfied him. That had been five years ago, when he was twenty-three, and it was because of those prints that he had decided that if he ever took anything seriously, it would be photography.

Owen had bought four of the prints after Paul gave him the first as a Christmas present. The one Laura had chosen showed the little girl and her two brothers quarreling over a sand castle they had just built: the girl had made a flag from her hair ribbon and wanted to fly it from the highest tower; her brothers had insisted on flying their own skull and cross-bones. Paul had printed the photograph with high contrast to intensify the emotions; the children's eyes flashed, in the background dark waves broke in a stark white froth onto the sand, a white gull was brilliantly outlined against a deep, cloudless sky, the sand castle was scored with long, angular shadows.

"Why did you choose this one?" he asked Laura. "Most people prefer softer prints. More fantasy, more like a dream."

"This is the dream," she said without hesitation.

He looked at her curiously. "Why?"

"Because the castle is finished."

His eyes moved back to the picture. No one else had ever said that about it. "And you have a castle somewhere, waiting to be finished?"

"Everybody does, don't you think? Or do you have everything you want?"

There was a small silence. "I have everything I want," he said reflectively. "But sometimes I wish I wanted more."

She shook her head. "I don't understand that."

"Well, neither do I," he said carelessly. "At least not most of the time." He moved to Laura's side and took her hand. "But I do want to see more of you. Will you have dinner with me tomorrow night? Better yet, we'll start early, with one of Rosa's lavish teas, and then go out for a late dinner. Can you arrange that?"

"Yes," she said. She did not hesitate or wonder about it after she agreed. He might be dangerous, but he was someone she could love.

The bracelet found in a New York pawnshop had been bought in Austria by Leni Salinger's grandmother as a gift for her thirteen-year-old daughter, to ease her sadness at leaving home to make a new life in America. It was solid gold, with a monogrammed locket that sprang open to reveal a picture of Leni's grandfather. When the police returned it, and Leni held it in her hand, looking at the tiny picture of her smiling, curly-haired grandfather, she began to cry. "I know it's silly; so many terrible things could have happened, far worse than losing a bracelet, but it seems so important to have it back and not in some stranger's hands . . ."

"It is important," Felix said. He fastened his cummerbund and reached for the cuff links he wore only with his tuxedo. "But mainly because it will help us find the son of a bitch who took it."

Leni was sitting at her dressing table in a long satin slip, waiting for her maid to arrive and help her into the intricately draped gown she had chosen for the opera ball, the last of the season before everyone left town for the summer. "I'm not sure anymore," she said. "I did want to punish him, whoever he is, but now . . . do you know, Felix, the only thing I really care about is getting everything back so it can all go to Allison and then, someday, to her daughter. That's why I want the necklace most of all; my father got it from his grandparents in Denmark and gave it to my mother, and she gave it to me . . . and Allison knew it would be hers one of these days. That's what means something to me. I don't like jewelry that's just stones and gold or silver; I want it to have meaning and a history so we don't lose touch with our past, and how else can that happen except by being passed down from one generation to the next?"

"Yes, that is a pleasant romantic view," Felix said, struggling with his cuff links. "Can you help me with these? But romance is irrelevant in this case; I would hardly indulge in it when it comes to punishing a criminal—"

"You never indulge in romance," Leni murmured.

"—and when he's found I'll see to it that he suffers. The bastard invaded my home and took my property, and no one does that to me and goes unpunished."

"He did it to all of us," Leni said quietly. "And after all, he is unpunished, isn't he? It's been three years and this is the first clue we've had."

"There will be more; I guarantee it. That's fine, thank you. I don't know why I still have trouble with cuff links after all these years. Will you be ready soon? We'll be late."

"We're never late. You are the only man in the world who times arrivals to the second." She slipped the stem of a diamond earring through the neat hole in her ear and fastened it. "I hear Clay Fairchild is doing very well in Philadelphia."

Felix glanced at her, then reached for his jacket.

"Isn't it odd," she said, "how I think of Clay and Laura every time we talk about the robbery? It's very wrong of me—poor things, it's not their fault they started working for us that awful summer. Thank heavens they didn't get scared off and leave. Owen adores Laura, and she's so good for him; I've never seen him happier. He got her a job, Rosa says, as one of Jules's assistants, and in their spare time he teaches her about running hotels—"

"Why?" Felix's eyebrows had drawn together. "He's using her as his secretary—I can't imagine why, when there are a dozen at the office he could have any time he wants— and I knew she was working with Jules, and she's at the university. What more does she need?"

"She wants to be more. All young women today want to be more than whatever it is they are, don't you think?" Leni's voice murmured through the bedroom like a quiet stream and Felix leaned down to hear her. "And she gives as much as she gets from us. She gave that lovely party last night for Allison; she even insisted on paying Rosa for the food. Owen stopped by and said it was very lively. Paul was there, too, he said, and very attentive to Laura. That won't go anywhere, of course—their backgrounds are impossibly different—but it does seem a good thing for her to take an interest in the hotels. She'll have to earn her living and it's good for Owen to be able to help someone . . . to nurture, in a way. He hasn't had anyone, you know, for such a long time. You and Asa weren't exactly cuddly and loving, Rosa says; you kept Owen at arm's length. So he lost Iris and then he lost you, and I think it's wonderful that after all these years he's found someone like Laura who's smart enough and loving enough to let him help her. And Clay, too. I'm so glad you got him that job in Philadelphia when Owen asked you to; he'd never have gotten it without help. And maybe he'll think of some ways to make the hotel better. Poor old thing, it's gotten quite shabby— you said so yourself—and you won't put money into it. Owen says you want to sell it, but of course he never would do that. I could have told you he wouldn't: it's his, and he loves it— that one and the other three he started with— and if Clay can bring some new ideas to it and learn the business at the same time, isn't that a fine thing?"

She fastened her other earring and picked up a matching necklace. "Felix, would you do this for me?" She closed her eyes, fighting the shock of desire that ran through her at the touch of his fingertips on the nape of her neck. It has nothing to do with Felix, she thought.

It's because I don't have anyone to hold me.
No lust, no love . . . and I've got to have one
or the other. I'll have to find someone; it's
been so long since I sent Ned away . . .
"What?" she asked.

"I said, when is your maid coming? I don't
like being nervous about the time."

"She'll be here any minute; we have plenty
of time. There's no reason for you to be nervous." She watched him pace. "You're not nervous, you're excited."

"Nonsense."

"No, I can tell . . . It's my bracelet, isn't
it? You've been this way ever since they
brought it back. You think they'll find the
thief, even after all these years." She shook her
head. "I don't. It seems impossible."

"Not anymore. Not when there's a new development. They know what they're doing.
They're relentless—when they're dedicated,
that is. They don't give up; they don't forget.
And they'll track the scum down, and his ac-
complices, too. Whoever they are, they don't
have the brains to understand that people like
us don't allow anyone to invade our lives and
upset the order we've made. Sometime, sooner
or later, they'll be cornered, however many

there are, and if I have anything to say about it, they'll be kicked into a hole, like the filth they are, and kept there until they're old or dead. Pity we have to waste money and feed them; they ought to be shot. The only good they'll do is be an object lesson for anyone who thinks there's something glamorous about burglaries; they might change their mind when they know we'll have them rotting in jail."

The room was very quiet. Seated at her dressing table, her tall, lean body slanting away from her husband, Leni watched him straighten his jacket, tuck a silk handkerchief in the front pocket, and stand at the pier glass to examine himself for imperfections. When he let out a long breath of approval, Leni knew he had found everything in place, everything correct. Hidden behind the impeccable Almaviva white-tie tuxedo was a caldron of hatred and rage and implacable vindictiveness—but the world would not see it. The world would see only perfection.

Leni stood as her maid arrived with the freshly pressed gown. How amazing, she thought, that my hands are as cold as ice. I don't know why I still have trouble accepting Felix for what he is, after all these years. It's not as if I don't understand him or remember why I stay with him.

She raised her arms and let her maid slip the silken dress over her head. There's no reason to be upset, she told herself. Whatever Felix does about the thief or thieves who robbed us, it won't have anything to do with me. I just want my jewels back; after that, if he wants some kind of revenge, he can do what he likes. It won't touch me or the rest of us; we're too far from it. We won't even know when it happens.

Clay had been calling Laura for three hours before she answered. "I even called Rosa," he fumed. "She said you were out."

"I went to dinner with a friend. Why are you so angry? I didn't get mad when you weren't there this morning when I called. And I left a message at the hotel, but you're just now calling back and I'm not—"

"I got your message. What friend?"

"Just a friend. We had tea here and then went to a place called Julien's. You'd love it, Clay, it's very elegant—"

"Which friend? You sound different. *Happy,*" he added accusingly.

"What's wrong with that? Clay, what's the matter with you? Don't you want me to be happy?"

"Sure I do, it's just that—oh, fuck it, Laura, you know I hate it when things happen and I don't know about them . . . when I'm *outside* . . ."

"But you can't be in the center of everything," Laura said gently. "Even if you still lived here, I wouldn't tell you everything I do."

"You'd tell me more. What did you call to tell me?"

"They found some of the stolen jewelry."

"They what?"

"In a pawnshop in New York. What do you think we should do?"

"Shit, I don't— What did they find?"

"One of the bracelets."

"Just one?"

"That's all they told us about. They—"

"What else did they say?"

"Nothing much. They don't know who pawned it but—"

"But the guy who owns the pawnshop! He must have said something!"

"Clay, if you'd let me talk . . . He said it

was a young man with blond hair and dark
glasses; nothing unusual—"

"But the receipt! They always sign a receipt!
The police must have seen it!"

"It was signed Ben Franklin. With a fake
address."

"And that's all they have? Nothing else?"

"Aren't you even surprised at the name?"

"Yeah. Real cute of Ben. Is that really all
they have? No other clues? Not even where to
look next?"

"They say they don't, but I don't suppose
they'd tell me if they did. Clay, I can't think
of—"

"You're sure they didn't say anything else?
Some little thing you might have missed?
Damn it, think about it! Are you sure the
owner didn't spot something? How come he
called the police?"

"He recognized the bracelet from the description the police sent out. Clay, I can't
think of anything to do. Can you?"

"No. Stay out of it. We're not involved; nobody thinks we are. How come Ben's in New
York, anyway? I thought he was in Europe.
You're the one he writes to; did he tell you he
was going to New York?"

"No, I didn't know anything about it. You'd think he'd call if he was this close."

"You told him not to."

"Well, I know, but if he really wanted to see us . . . Sometimes I think it would be so nice to see him."

There was a silence. "Yeah, it would," Clay said finally. "He was really great . . . most of the time. Like, remember the time we did that job in Brooklyn, and the people came home early and we had to get out through the attic and across the roof? We were so scared, and Ben kept telling us jokes and he took us to a movie and afterwards we had hot dogs and ice cream. Shit, I have ice cream all the time now, but it tasted better when Ben bought it. Except—Christ, if he gets us in trouble . . ."

There was another silence. "I'd better go," Laura said. "Owen expects me in a few minutes. I'll talk to you in a couple of days. But call me first if you think of anything we should do."

"Just keep cool and quiet. And call me if anything else happens. Take care, now."

"I will. I love you, Clay."

"Me, too." Clay was scowling as he hung up. Fuck it, he thought. Things were going pretty good; he was starting to make plans; now this had to happen. Three years, for Christ's sake; you'd think any decent pawn-shop would throw away police descriptions of stolen goods when they hadn't been heard of in three years. What was wrong with those idi-ots; didn't they ever throw anything away? You couldn't count on anything these days. You thought you were all set and then—

"Clay! You playing with yourself in there?" He shot up as the manager's voice bellowed from the front office. The son of a bitch could still scare him, even though he wasn't making any noises about firing him. Clay knew they didn't like him but, what the hell, why should they? He was a kid of twenty who'd never worked in a hotel in his life, and he'd been foisted on them by Felix Salinger, telling them this was their new assistant desk clerk, whether they liked it or not. What were they supposed to do? Cheer?

They didn't cheer, but they didn't make too much noise, either. They were old and shabby, like the hotel; they'd been around forever, like the hotel, and they knew Felix wanted Owen to sell the hotel and build a fancy new one on a bigger lot, which would mean the end of their jobs. They didn't know why Owen hadn't done it, but they didn't ask: they kept their mouths shut and hoped nobody would pay attention to the Philadelphia Salinger. It may have been fading and shabby, but to the old-timers it was home.

None of which, Clay reflected, prevented them from treating him like shit, scheduling him for night shifts and talking around him when he was in the room. But lately he'd begun to win them over. Owen Salinger liked this old hotel for some reason, and Clay figured if he played his cards right he could someday replace Willard Payne as manager and run it himself. Laura kept saying there was a future for them with the Salingers, so why shouldn't he be a hotshot executive? After all, if Ben could be a security expert, for Christ's sake, in a hotel in Europe, why couldn't Clay do better than that with the Salingers in America?

"Sorry," he said as he walked into the manager's office. "I was talking to my sister in Boston. She sends you her love and says thanks for keeping an eye on me."

Willard Payne adjusted his steel-rimmed glasses. "Bullshit."

Clay grinned, man to man, and sat on the

corner of the desk, leaning close to the old man's hearing aid. "What she said was, I should listen to you. I was telling her you worked the hell out of me and she said it was good for me because I need settling down, and I could learn a lot from somebody who's been in the business as long as you. And I guess she's right."

Willard nodded several times, his loose jowls flapping softly. "A smart young lady, your sister; you could learn from her. Age is wisdom, young man; age is wisdom. You're young, you're impatient, you learn that age is wisdom and you'll be getting smart." He pushed back his chair. "You take over. I'll see you tomorrow."

"It's awful late for you to be here," Clay observed. "Almost midnight."

"I'm checking something," Payne said vaguely. "See you in the morning."

Alone, Clay reclined in Payne's chair, his feet on the desk. "Checking up on *me*," he mumbled. "Treating me like a goddam high school kid." He knew he was young; it drove him crazy that he wasn't silver-haired and smooth, like a politician or a Mafia don. He wished Laura were there; she'd have said

Payne was jealous because Felix had done Clay a favor, and that would have made him feel better. She always could make him feel better; that was one great thing about her. But here he was alone in Philadelphia in a run-down hotel and he hadn't found a girl yet and nobody gave a damn about him. Ben was gone, and Laura had Owen and some guy, whoever he was—took her to *Julien's,* for Christ's sake; it probably cost a pile—and who else was there? Nobody.

Shit, nobody in the whole goddam world was as alone as he was.

I need a drink, he decided. The office can take care of itself for half an hour.

He waved at Terry Levonio as he walked into the crowded Brass Ring Saloon, just off the lobby. Terry grinned back beneath the handlebar mustache that had become part of Philadelphia lore. The Brass Ring was a hangout for newspaper and television people, it was listed in Philadelphia tour guides, and it was the only part of the Philadelphia Salinger that consistently made money.

"Midnight, the hour of melancholy," Terry observed as Clay took the last empty stool at the bar. "And you are in need of a small friend." With dextrous fingers he mixed Clay's favorite scotch and soda. "A companion to cheer night's darkest depths."

"Cheers." Clay drank it off and held it out for a refill. "Was Payne asking about me?"

"The usual. How much time do you spend in here, how much do you drink, do you ever talk about the Salingers, why are you here? Same old stuff. Take this one slowly; I expect customers to let my perfect drinks slither down like a caress, not a fucking Niagara."

"Why not." Clay sipped the drink. "Nice cuff links," he said, eyeing the jet and diamond rectangles on Terry's starched cuffs.

"A gift."

"Who from?"

"Me to me." He left to serve two women standing at the curved end of the bar; Clay recognized one as a news anchorwoman, the other as the host of a noon talk show. Where did Terry get the money for jet and diamond cuff links? he wondered idly. And the Porsche he drove. And Brioni ties and a Loewe wallet. Taken singly, they were expensive but not impossible; Clay had some Brioni ties, too. But taken together, Terry's lifestyle was a hell of a lot flashier than Clay's. And Clay knew his salary and could guess at his tips.

Only one way, he thought, finishing his drink. He's stealing it. He brooded over the idea. Shit, the guy's probably been stealing the whole time I've been here; something going on practically under my nose that I didn't know about. He can't do that to me; I'm assistant desk clerk; he can't play me for a fool. Another idea struck him. Shit, if there's money missing from anywhere in the hotel, who'd get blamed? Me, who else? Christ, just when I'm straight and making something of myself, this son of a bitch comes up playing tricks.

He did not look up when Terry returned and refilled his glass; he was thinking about how somebody could rip off a bar. The easiest way would be to pocket the money for every third or fourth drink and not ring it up on the cash register. That's what he's doing, Clay decided. He's too cheerful to be honest; he never stops smiling.

He began to watch. The hours passed; he kept his eyes on Terry's whirlwind fingers, pouring, mixing, serving, playing the keys of the cash register, collecting money and dropping it into the register's compartments without missing a beat. "Who's minding the store?" Terry asked a little after two in the morning.

"They'll call me if they need me," Clay said.

"Some wise fella said the mice play when the cat's not looking," Terry observed cheerfully.

Clay nodded. "I was thinking the same thing."

But he'd been watching for over two hours and whatever Terry was doing, it wasn't pocketing money or failing to ring the charges; he'd swear to that. So it was something else. I should have known, he thought; Ben told me plenty of times that smart thieves make their tricks look legal. He slid off the stool. "Put it on my bill," he said to Terry. "I'll see you tomorrow. What time do you get here?"

"Three o'clock, as you well know since you check my time cards for my inhuman hours."

"You don't work them every day."

"Tomorrow I do. Shall I call you an hour from now to make sure you haven't fallen asleep at your desk?"

"I won't fall asleep. I know how to keep my eyes open." He waved as he left, and the next morning, when the bar was dark and the maids were all upstairs, he slipped quietly into the employees' room in the basement of the hotel and picked the lock on Terry's locker.

He felt like a detective solving a crime. But he felt a different thrill, too. Just like old times, he thought, reveling in the coolness of the metal pick in his hand, the feeling of power when the door swung open. Wait'll I tell Laura I can still do it. No, can't tell Laura; she wouldn't appreciate it. It's my own secret. Except for Terry, of course. Because if I find something, I'm going to stop him dead in his tracks.

Paul reached the top of the seawall and turned to help Laura. But she was already there, taking a smooth, high step to stand beside him, and together they looked out at the silver-blue ocean. This part of the shore of Cape Ann, a knob of land thrusting into the Atlantic north of Boston, was lined with enormous rocks dredged up by reclamation teams and wedged together in a wall that stretched as far as the eye could see. On the rocks gulls perched in small congregations; farther out, belted kingfishers wheeled above the ocean's waves, diving to snatch unwary fish from just below the surface, then, their wings beating strongly, climbing straight up to vanish into the bright afternoon mist. Waves pounded the rocks below Paul and Laura, and when the wind shifted a fine spray blew across them, leaving tiny droplets in Laura's hair that shimmered like jewels in the afternoon sun. Paul touched one and then another, and they clung to his finger when he put his arm around her.

"You took those rocks as if they were a stairway," he said. "I never had a chance to be gallant. You didn't tell me you're a climber."

"I haven't been for a long time." She put her head back, feeling strong and free in the fresh salt air. "I used to climb on the rocks up the Hudson with my brothers."

"Your brothers?"

"My brother's friends." She moved away and sat on a rock, tightening her shoelace with shaking fingers. She felt angry and a little sick. She didn't want to lie. She never wanted to lie to Paul or any of the family again. She'd done so much lying she couldn't remember which lie she'd told to whom, and that scared her, but it was more than that. She and Paul had gone out five nights in the two weeks since her party, to dinners and concerts and piano bars where they sat and talked for hours, and she knew she wanted it to go on forever, just as she wanted everything with the Salingers to go on forever. And that meant being honest with them. It was as simple as that. But, still, if she kept making stupid mistakes . . . *How do I get out of a lie that's gotten so big and gone on so long?* She stood up but she stayed a little distance from Paul. "Can we walk along the rocks for a while?"

"Good idea. I haven't done it since I was a kid and my father brought me here."

"Your *father?*" She was taking a long step to another rock; when her feet were securely planted, she looked back at him. "You and *Thomas* jumped around here?"

He laughed. "My very quiet father was a champion rower and mountain climber until he did something to his back and had to quit." He took the step and joined her. "And who taught you to do this? Not Clay, I'll bet; from what I've seen, he isn't nearly as surefooted as you are."

"No, it was . . . someone in New York."

"A friend of yours?"

"For a long time he was the best friend we had."

She left him behind, jumping lightly from rock to rock, remembering how it had been to climb brick and graystone walls, clinging with callused fingertips to windowsills and drain-pipes and ivy. She speeded up, exulting in her strength. Tennis and swimming, long walks to and from the university, and exploring Boston had kept her muscles taut and responsive. *I could do it again if I had to. But I never will.*

Paul watched her slender body flowing in long, smooth lines. She reminded him of a dancer whose movements are so liquid there seems no break between them. Or a gazelle, he thought: elusive, wary, quick to flee when startled, beautiful to watch. He followed her, thinking that he knew more about her than he had known two weeks earlier, but still far less than he had expected. After two weeks with any other woman, he would have known about her past, her friends, her likes and dislikes, and the feel of her beneath him. He would have been able to categorize her. He hadn't realized, until now, how predictable his affairs had grown, or how absorbed he could become in a woman who was so different: frustrating, annoying, fascinating, and enthralling. And fitting into no category that he could think of.

Some distance ahead, Laura had stopped and had bent down to pick something up. "It's a tiny ring made of stone," she called, the lilt of her voice carrying over the crash of the waves below them. "Or maybe it's bone. Isn't this amazing?"

He caught up to her and looked at the tiny ring in her palm. "Crinoid. Distant cousin of the starfish and the sea urchin." He took it from her palm. "It's a fossil, probably about three hundred fifty million years old."

Laura stared at him. *"Three hundred fifty million?"* He handed the fossil back and she touched it with her finger. "It's so hard to comprehend; it's like touching infinity." She smiled. "You'd think, if something can survive this long and this perfectly, love affairs and reputations could, too."

He laughed. "Well put. It makes us sound fickle and hopelessly short-lived."

She was still rolling the small ring in her palm. "What did it look like?"

"It probably had arms, like plumes on top of a stalk. A paleontologist would know for sure."

"Starfish . . . sea urchin," she whispered

as if the words conjured magic images. "Incredible . . . so many marvelous things waiting to be discovered." She tucked the fossil into the pocket of her jeans. "Wouldn't it be wonderful to have a collection of things like this? Then when something bad happened we could take them out and remember that some things are perfect and don't disappear and if we keep trying . . ." She flushed, then gave Paul a quick smile. "Of course, lots of people wouldn't need that."

He put his hand under her chin. "You have the strangest notion that the world is full of people who have no problems. I don't know where you got it. Even this crinoid isn't perfect; after all, it died."

Laura broke into laughter. "You're right. I'd better find something else to envy."

"No." He held her face between his hands. "There's nothing and no one you should envy. My sweet girl, you outshine everyone; if you'd just learn to trust yourself as much as everyone trusts you—"

"Thank you," Laura said quickly. She felt dizzy, as if all of her were being drawn to the warmth of Paul's hands and she could scarcely feel her feet balancing on the rocky ledge.

"Don't you think we should turn back? Isn't it getting late?"

He shrugged, feeling purposely misunderstood, and followed her as she made her way along the rocks. She was moving quickly, almost flying, and as he kept up with her, Paul began to lose his annoyance and respond to the beauty around them and the exhilarating harmony of his body. The ocean had quieted, its waves lapping at the dark rocks that seemed to change color from moment to moment beneath lengthening shadows and a copper sun low in the sky. The air was warm, but a breeze brought a hint of evening coolness. When he saw the parking lot, he was regretful; it was almost like leaving childhood.

"I'm glad you suggested that," he said to Laura as they sat in the car. "You brought back my youth and made it better than it ever was, even in my memory." He backed out of the parking lot. "I don't know when I've had a better day."

"When you photographed the beautiful women in the marketplace at Avignon," Laura said mockingly.

"Did I say that was wonderful?"

"One of the best days you ever had."

He smiled. "It was, in its way. But I wasn't with you, so it can't have been as wonderful as I thought. In fact, the memory is fading fast; I can barely remember it."

She laughed. "Can you remember where we're eating dinner?"

"The King's Tavern at six-thirty. Are you hungry?"

"Famished."

"So am I. We'll be there in ten minutes. Maybe less."

The King's Tavern was built on a small rise overlooking the main street of Gloucester and, beyond it, the crowded wharves where salt-encrusted fishing boats swayed and creaked in the light breeze. At the back of each boat, rope as thick as a man's wrist and heavy nets stiff with ocean salt were wound on huge drums or coiled on the deck; gulls swooped in to strut on them and perch on the prows where names generations old were boldly lettered. Beside the harbor, the shops and restaurants on the main street were of wood darkened by the sea, making the small town seem rooted in earth and ocean and sky, tolerating the modern cars of tourists but unchanged by them.

Laura savored it all, especially the sense of

timelessness that reminded her of her favorite neighborhoods of Boston, and then Paul had parked at the King's Tavern and they were being shown to a small room at the back. Somehow he had arranged with the owners for a place where they could wash up and dress for dinner: a spare room at the back of the restaurant with two chairs and a tiny bathroom. Laura went first, carrying the overnight bag Allison had given her. "Dress simply," Paul had said, but she had agonized over what to take. In the tiny room at the King's Tavern she pulled off the jeans and khaki shirt that smelled of the sea, washed as well as she could in the small basin, and dressed in white polished cotton, full-skirted with long sleeves and a deep V neck. Around her throat she fastened a turquoise necklace she had found in a small shop in Provincetown, on the Cape. There was nothing she could do about her hair: the damp air turned the loose waves into long chestnut ringlets that would not comb straight, and so she left them, even the tendrils that curved onto her cheeks and forehead. Not sleek and sophisticated, she reflected, but there wasn't time to worry about it; she had to let Paul have his turn in the room. But she did pause when she took a final look in the small mirror and saw her glowing face. I look too happy, she thought, too excited. He likes cool, clever women. He'll think I look like a Girl Scout. But she didn't know what to do about it, and after a moment, since no one was watching, she shrugged. *This is me. He'll like me or he won't.*

He was waiting for her in the bar, looking out over the town and the wharf, where crews were unloading the square, white lobster pots they had just brought in. Laura watched him for a moment. His face was somber, almost severe, and for the first time she wondered about his secrets instead of worrying about her own.

He turned and saw her and smiled, his eyes glad and admiring. "You're lovely and you put me to shame; I feel like a grubby rock climber. I ordered wine for you; I won't be long."

She sat at the table where his half-finished drink still stood and gazed, as he had, at the purposeful activity of the sturdy men on the wharf. Gloucester. Cape Ann. A coast less than fifty miles north of Boston where one could climb on rocks and dine on fresh-caught lobster and still get back home before midnight. If one wanted to get back home. She pictured in her mind her overnight bag and felt again Paul's fingers touching the droplets of water in her hair, and his arm around her shoulders. If one wanted to get back.

Happiness surged through her and she put her hand to her cheek: she thought she must be blushing, she felt so hot. This is silly, she thought; I'm acting like a virgin. But in a way she felt like one. The quick, furtive couplings in the back seats of cars when she was in high school and the brief affairs at the university had left her untouched; her body had moved in all the expected ways, but she hadn't ever been able to care about what she was doing or even feel it had anything to do with her. It had been as if she stood apart, watching. She helped the panting, insistent boys who mounted her because that was what she was supposed to do. But each time she'd gone home to Beacon Hill feeling cheated and bewildered. Why did people go to so much trouble to do this?

Now, sitting in the King's Tavern, filled with a happiness as heady as noon wine, more rare than sex, more difficult to find than passion, she began to understand. *My sweet girl, you outshine everyone.* Her body seemed to lift out of itself, toward whatever they would find together.

The scene on the dock had changed. Fishermen and their families were arriving with floats they were finishing for St. Peter's Fiesta, when the fishing boats would be blessed. It was a tradition that went back hundreds of years. I'd like to be here for the parade, Laura thought. But then I'd like to be everywhere: Europe, Africa, India, finding crinoids at Cape Ann, marching with the Portuguese fishermen of Gloucester, shopping with the women at the market in Avignon. I wasted so much time stealing and dreaming, and now I'm twenty-one and how will I ever have time to do everything I want to do?

She felt Paul's hand on her shoulder and looked up, meeting his dark eyes. I have time for Paul, she thought.

The words settled inside her as they sat at dinner in the soft light of ship's lanterns. Around them was the murmur of voices and the soft clatter of dishes on polished wood tables, while they spoke in low voices, their hands brushing as they turned to each other to share a smile, letting desire build. Only once was the spell broken, halfway through dinner. "You're the only woman I know," Paul said, "who can crack open a lobster without turning her plate into a disaster area. You'd make a good magician. Or a pickpocket. Would you like more wine? I'll order another bottle."

"No. This is fine." She sat still, looking at the bright red tail and neatly split claws on the plate before her, the white lobster meat lying beside them in long smooth pieces. She hadn't even thought about it; her fingers, trained and sensitive, had done the job while she had talked to Paul and thought her thoughts.

Paul, the joke already forgotten, was talking about visits to Cape Ann when he was a boy, staying for weekends with a school friend whose family had a home in Marblehead Neck. "The backyard sloped to the bay, and we'd have races to see who could roll fastest down the grass and into the water. After a while his parents got the idea it wasn't the safest playground for kids, and they put up a fence. It was one of my first experiences of someone telling me what was best for me."

Laura laughed softly. Her happiness had returned, and she felt lighthearted and at ease.

"Is that why you travel all the time—because you hate fences?"

Surprised, he said, "I don't know. I'll have to think about it. You're right about my hating them; I always want to jump over instead of using the gate. Do you? You must be good at it, the way you climb rocks. Are you good at jumping fences?"

"Yes," she said boldly, wanting to share it with him, "but I haven't done it for a long time."

"Neither have I. We'll do it some day, shall we? Pretend we're kids and leap a fence?"

"And convince ourselves we can't be kept out?"

"And convince ourselves there's nothing we can't do."

Laura smiled. "I like that."

"Better yet, do you believe it?"

"Yes," she said simply, and they smiled together, and then sat quietly, listening to the music that drifted up to them from the wharves where people were dancing, and gazing through the huge windows that encircled the room. The moon had risen, turning the fishing boats to ghostly shapes gently swaying in the harbor. Paul took her hand in his. "I'll take you back to Boston, if that's what you'd like. Unless you'd rather stay up here."

"I'd rather stay."

He lifted her hand and kissed the palm. "My friend's house is empty. He only uses it on weekends."

She nodded, not asking how often he had used it when it was empty, not caring. Each of them had a past they would never share with the other.

The house was at the end of Marblehead Neck—a cluster of gray shingled mansions strung on a narrow curve of land jutting into Marblehead Bay. Across the water Laura could see the lights of the town of Marblehead, but in front of them everything was dark as Paul turned into the driveway. "I didn't call ahead; there won't be anyone here to pamper you and fix breakfast."

Laura smiled in the darkness. "I was counting on you for that."

"Trusting woman. How do you know I can cook?"

"It doesn't matter if you know how to pamper."

He chuckled and slid out of the car, reaching into the back seat for their bags. "Hold on while I find the key. It's here somewhere . . . on top of the lamp post as I recall . . ."

He hasn't been here in a while, Laura thought, then remembered she didn't care when he'd been here last.

The house smelled faintly musty when the door swung open and Paul walked through the living room, switching on lights and opening windows. "The kitchen is through that door. What would you like? Something to eat? Or drink?" Laura tried to think of something to say. She was nervous, trying to retrieve the pulsing happiness that had glowed within her at the restaurant. *I want you to love me. I want you to tell me what to do. I want everything to be simple and wonderful.*

"We'll go upstairs," he said. His arm was around her waist and they walked up the curved stairway with matching steps, into a long room that was white with moonlight. When Paul turned her to face him, it was as natural to put her arms around him as it had been to walk into the house at his side, as if they belonged together. "Two weeks," he murmured, his lips brushing hers. "An eternity."

"Not for me—" she started to say, but his mouth was on hers, opening it, and she tasted

the sharpness of cognac on his tongue. It was a
long kiss; he held her mouth with his and her
body in the tight clasp of his arms until she felt
there was nothing but the two of them in a
small enclosed place that roared with a pounding that was like the surf. It came from her
own heart but it shook her with a force like the
ocean's.

Paul lifted his head and she took a tremu-
lous breath. "I'd better sit down."

He laughed softly. "There's a bed." Holding
her hand he led her the length of the room,
along a silver ribbon of moonlight, to a high
four-poster bed hung with white curtains and
covered with a worn patchwork quilt. A small
mahogany step stool was beside it, and Paul
kept Laura's hand in his as she climbed the
three steps and he followed, bending over her
as she lay back, his mouth covering hers again,
his hands holding her face. "My lovely girl, my
darling Laura . . ."

Laura was burning. She had never wanted
anything the way she wanted Paul's mouth, his
hands, his body joined to hers. When he
pulled off his sport coat, her urgent fingers
were unbuttoning his shirt, and then he was
opening her dress, slipping it off her shoulders

and lifting her to pull it down and toss it aside, and all the time her hands were touching him, curving, stroking, learning the feel of the hard muscles in his arms, the dark hairs on his chest, the yielding at his waist, until he drew back and tore off all his clothes and came back to lie on her.

Moonlight flooded the room. The bed canopy and curtains glowed like sheltering moonbeams, lightening his dark skin, turning Laura's pure white. "My God, you are so beautiful," he said, the words like a long flame against her breasts. Laura's body moved of its own accord; she couldn't lie still. "I'm sorry," she whispered, ashamed of her eagerness. "Don't!" he responded sharply, then said quickly, "I didn't mean to snap at you. But don't apologize. Ever. My darling girl, we do what we want because we want each other, because we have joy in each other . . ." "Yes," she said; it was no more than a long breath. "Yes, we do. Yes." With her hands in Paul's hair, she brought his mouth to hers, drinking him in, and felt his hardness between her legs. Yes, she thought, the word chiming within her. We have joy in each other. And she let herself become part of the joy; she let herself want everything: to do everything, feel everything, taste everything.

Paul raised himself and slipped his hands beneath her underclothes, pulling them off, and as the cool air and his warm hands embraced her she gave a small cry that pierced the quiet room.

He took her breast in his mouth; her nipple tightened beneath his lips and tongue, and a long sigh that was his name broke from her at the pleasure radiating through her. As his mouth held her breast, his caressing hand slid along the curve of her waist and down her thighs, opening her flesh with his fingers, sliding into the wet darkness within, and even as she cried out with longing her hands were following the harder curves of his body until she raised them and again took his head between her hands, fiercely kissing him, taking his lower lip between her teeth, then, still hungry, still moving, sucking and biting the smooth skin of his neck, tasting the fragrance of the soap they had used when they changed before dinner.

Abruptly, Paul stopped caressing her and raised himself on his elbow, holding her still with one hand as he looked down at her. Until that moment, he had accepted her desire without questioning it. He was accustomed to having women desire him, and he had let his hands follow the skillful patterns he had used with so many of them for so many years. But Laura was not like any of them; she was sexual but almost clumsy, demanding but unsure, not a virgin but oddly inexperienced. An urgent woman and an unschooled girl. The fleeting thought came to him that he wasn't sure it was just a man she wanted, or him.

"What is it?" Laura asked. Her breath trembled and she tried to see his eyes, but they were shadowed in the moonlight; his face was almost a mask. "Paul, I want you, I thought you wanted me, I thought you felt this, too—I never knew I could feel it—this wonderful wanting . . . I never knew what it was like . . ."

"My God," he said roughly and lay on his side, pulling her against him. He kissed her long, tangled curls, her smooth forehead, the delicate eyelids that hid her large clear eyes. His hands explored the curves of her body as if she were the first woman he had ever known, and he felt himself aroused and absorbed by her in a way that startled him. "So much a child, so much a woman . . ." he said, and then he was as urgent as she, almost savage in his need to be part of her. He turned, and turned her with him so she was spread beneath him. Laura's hunger flared again and again, flames fed by the flint of his body; she opened her legs wide and pulled him inside her, deep, thrusting, filling her. He raised himself on his hands and they watched his shaft, hard and glistening in the moonlight, disappear deep inside her, then slide up and thrust down again, while her hands moved over his chest and down his hard stomach, and held him when he pulled out of her before thrusting down once more. Then his weight was upon her again, his hands raising her hips, his tongue meeting hers, and Laura felt an overwhelming sense of wonder—that need and desire and joy could merge and become one, in one instant, with one man. And the wonder buoyed her up as Paul's closeness buoyed her, his lips murmuring her name against her mouth, their bodies moving together, and within her the rhythmic thought that everything was perfect, and would be forever.

CHAPTER 8

IT took Clay a month to figure out what to do with the television remote control he'd found in Terry Levonio's locker, and then he waited another month to make sure he was right. It was so simple he was filled with admiration. Who'd have thought Terry the grinning bartender would have the brains to think it up?

He finally tried it out one night in the quiet hour before dawn while the night staff sat staring fixedly at magazines or television in a desperate effort to stay awake. The lobby was empty, the restaurant closed, the bar dark and shuttered.

"Going to the bathroom," Clay told the

back of the night manager's head nodding in front of a John Wayne movie. Around the corner from the lobby, he unlocked a back entrance to the bar and slipped inside. The bottles were put away, the glasses washed, the bar wiped clean. Thorough, careful Terry. Clay stood behind the bar, holding the remote control he'd taken from Terry's locker a few minutes earlier. Pointing it at the cash register, he pressed buttons at random until he heard, in the silent room, a distinct click.

How about that, Clay marveled. If somebody planned to skim a nice living from a bar, he'd fix up a little electronic thingamajig that would temporarily disable his cash register when he wanted it to. He'd push his little button—out of sight, under the counter—and when he rang up the price of a drink, so that anybody watching could see him do it, *it wouldn't register.* Something like typing without a ribbon. And he pockets the money. And when he goes home, he'd have—how much? How much would he have in his pocket?

He left the bar, locking the door behind him, and went downstairs to the employees' room where he replaced the volume control exactly as he'd found it in Terry's locker.

At the end of his long hours he'd have skimmed maybe ten percent of the night's booze. We do sixteen, seventeen hundred bucks a night in that joint. At least that's what the cash register says. Which means we're probably doing closer to two thousand and friend Terry takes home a couple hundred each and every night. No wonder he drives a Porsche.

"Everything quiet?" he asked the night manager when he returned.

In response he heard a gentle snoring. Shit, Clay thought, this place needs a good shaking up.

He sat on his high stool behind the reception desk, and thought. He could tell Terry what he'd found, and that would end it—no more danger that Clay Fairchild would be blamed if. somebody else found out. But he ought to be able to do better than that. He ought to get a medal for saving thousands of dollars for the hotel. For the Salingers. He ought to get a promotion.

Why not? he thought. Laura had gotten close to them, and look where she was. If he made a big thing of this so they'd think he was God's gift to the Philadelphia Salinger, he'd be in as solid with the Salingers as she was. Then wouldn't she be proud of him for really getting ahead!

Goddam, he thought, sitting straight on his stool. That's where the future is. It's a pain in the ass that it has to be a job, but if it's a big job . . . And the Salingers are as big as they come: they could find a neat place for me if they wanted to.

Shit, he told himself with a grin, if we're smart and take our time, there's no reason why Laura and Clay Fairchild can't end up right in the middle of the Salinger empire. And then let anybody try to take anything away from us.

The next morning, as soon as Willard Payne walked into his office, Clay knocked on his door and said he wanted to talk to him about a serious problem in the hotel.

Laura's desk was dark gray steel, crammed in a windowless room with gray steel filing cabinets and typewriter tables and three other assistants at their own steel desks. Sitting beneath the unsparing glare of fluorescent lights, it was hard to believe that just beyond the closed door was the elegant lobby of a grand hotel. "Someday we will make this place beautiful," Jules LeClair said vaguely once or twice a month, but he never got around to it; he was very busy.

"The concierge of a great hotel must do everything—exquisitely," he had instructed Laura when she first arrived. "He is the eyes and ears and the mother and father of the hotel. A guest also once called me the mayor of the lobby. He was, of course, exactly right."

Jules LeClair, wearing a perfectly cut black suit and red brocade vest, his mustache clipped, his silver hair precisely waved, ruled from his carved walnut desk set at an angle in the most prominent corner of the lobby. Fresh flowers bloomed in his Waterford vase every day, his pencils were sharpened before he arrived, the heavy glass protecting the desktop was polished until he could see his reflection— a satisfying sight he permitted himself before plunging into the day's work.

"The hours are 7:00 A.M. to 5:00 P.M., four days a week," he told Laura. "You may, of course, work longer; it is the only way to learn, to become a true concierge. There is, naturally, someone always at this desk, around the clock, but the truly crucial times, when we are absolutely indispensable and everything would crumble without us, are seven to seven. Therefore, I, Jules LeClair, work those hours. Anyone who dreams of being as superb as I will work those hours at my side. We allow ourselves exactly one hour for lunch. The remainder of the time it is our delight to please our guests so that they return and also tell their friends how well it is here. Each day we hand them their room keys, of course greeting them by name. If they have been here before, we arrange for their favorite drinks and flowers to be in their rooms when they arrive; we remember whether they will want tickets for the theater or the symphony or the basketball. And they think we are wonderful. And they are exactly right. Are you always so quiet, like a little mouse? This is excellent; this means you will learn."

Each day Jules gave her a different job to do, and soon Laura had her own private file of information about the city, the hotel, and returning guests. "There are always times to rely on other people," Owen told her, "but not on their information. You must have your own. If you don't, you'll always be an assistant, never an authority. You'll always have to rely on others."

"I won't," Laura said. "Not on Jules, not on anyone."

Owen smiled. "Very good," he said, and did not point out to her that she had already taken the first step away from his tutelage. She'll do just fine on her own, he thought, and he was pleased.

Mornings began for Laura before Owen left his room. Rosa had breakfast waiting for her at six-thirty and she was at the hotel twenty-five minutes later, while Arlington Street still seemed to sleep and the lobby of the Salinger Hotel was hushed and waiting for the day to begin. "Good morning, my good staff," Jules said amiably and perched on the corner of Laura's desk. "Here is the first work of today." He handed out folders with assignments. "Laura, for you I have a special task: you will arrange for a yacht for the Countess Irinia, for two weeks from today, for a period of five days. Use our check to reserve it; the countess's secretary will naturally reimburse us when they arrive. Insist that the company assign chef Louis; the countess commended his *crème brûlée* last year. When this is done, you will write to that effect to the countess; I of course will sign the letter. Also, Madame d'Allessio wishes to visit the Dior showroom when she is in Paris next week; this I will take care of myself because it is very sensitive, keeping my good friend in Paris happy so he does us these favors, but you will please write to madame and tell her we are delighted to arrange this for her. That letter also I will sign. Now, a few other matters . . ." He went over them rapidly while Laura nodded and said nothing, annoyed because Jules, possessive of his status and the enormous tips he received, always refused to let her deal directly with the wealthiest guests.

The door from the lobby opened and Jules looked up. "Yes, yes?"

"May I see you," Felix said. It was not a question.

"But of course," said Jules, his small careful mouth clearly showing that he would allow no one but someone of Felix's importance to take him from his work. "Laura, you will sit at my desk. Make no decisions; simply hand out keys, write down requests, and smile often. I will not be long. So," he said cheerfully to Felix, "shall we sit on the couch beside the window? From there I keep an eye on my desk and my very pretty assistant."

Laura watched them sit together. She had smiled at Felix when he came in, but he had barely acknowledged her presence and she wondered, as she always did when she saw him in the hotel, what he thought of the fact that Owen had bypassed him to get her the job with Jules. She looked up as the first of the morning joggers stood before her, asking for his key. Drops of sweat dripped on Jules's immaculately polished glass. "Good morning, Mr. Starrett," Laura said, smiling as she took his key from the board in the top desk drawer and handed it to him. "Would you like me to have pecan rolls and coffee sent to your room?"

"Right." He peered through the cascade of sweat that blurred his vision. "You're new here. I'd remember you."

"I usually work in another office."

"Smarter to have you out here. You're a hell of a lot prettier to look at than that Frenchified little dandy they usually have. You knew my name, too."

Laura smiled again, thinking that even if her memory were terrible, the loud Dallas twang and the many demands of Wylie Starrett would be impossible to forget. "We remember our favorite guests," she said and picked up her telephone. "I'll order your breakfast. And let me know if you need a driver for your appointments today."

She had made the call to the kitchen, and greeted six other joggers, when a small, pale man, fussily folding a handkerchief in his hand, appeared before her. She tried to think of his name and failed. She couldn't even recall seeing him before. "If I may help you?" she asked warmly to make up for her failure.

"Security Systems Incorporated," he said. "I have an eight o'clock appointment with—"

Laura missed the next few words in the pounding of her heart. But as swiftly as the fear had gripped her, it was gone. What was wrong with her that she still jumped when she heard someone say 'security' and even when she saw a policeman walking in her direction? Nobody was after her; there was nothing to be afraid of. And then she smiled to herself. *Except not being able to tell a security man from one of the Salinger's wealthy guests.* "I'm sorry," she said, "who is it you want to see?"

"Mr. Asa Salinger."

Laura called upstairs to confirm the appointment, gave him directions to Asa's office, and had only a moment to wonder what security problems Asa was worried about before she was caught up in a rush of early-morning guests who needed information or wanted tickets for events that evening. As she responded to each of them she jotted down their names and their requests, and when Jules and Felix returned she handed Jules the list. "Ah, excellent. You see?" he said to Felix. "My little Laura is as efficient as she is pretty. I have written to Mr. Owen Salinger to thank him for sending her to me. But, Laura, I have returned. My chair?"

She relinquished it, hiding her reluctance beneath a cool smile. "I'll be in my office."

"Laura," Felix said, "I'd like you to have a cup of coffee with me."

Masking her surprise, she looked at Jules. He was less successful; his curiosity clearly showed as his gaze flicked rapidly from Felix to her and back again. When he could learn nothing from their faces, he sighed and nodded. "For a brief time. We are, of course, extremely busy."

Laura was smiling as they walked away.

"Is there a joke?" Felix asked.

"I was thinking about Jules. With his red vest and the way he moves his head, he reminds me of the ruby-throated hummingbirds at the Cape."

He gave a small smile. "I hadn't thought of that." Clever, he thought; I hadn't given her credit for being clever. And damned attractive. He gave her a sidelong glance, approving her pearl gray suit, her white blouse buttoned to the throat, and the dark blue silk scarf, worn like a man's tie, with an ivory stickpin in the center. Vaguely recalling the ordinary, gawky teenager who had come to work for them three years earlier, he wondered who had taught her. Allison, he supposed. She was always taking somebody in tow: stray animals, stray people, even friends and family members who she thought needed her help. Damnedest thing how she always had to help people. Like her mother, he thought. She gets it from her mother. Not from me; I leave people alone. If they need something badly enough, they'll ask. "We can sit here," he said, coming to a stop. "They'll bring coffee to us."

Laura sat on the striped sofa. *The president of Salinger Hotels Incorporated can have coffee*

brought to him in the lobby. Why can't every-
one? If I had my own hotel . . .

"—understand you're learning everything
about hotel management," Felix was saying.

"Everything Owen and Jules can teach me.
I suppose between them they know just about
all there is to know."

"And you're studying it in college?"

"Yes."

"And what will you do with all this knowledge?"

"Use it." Laura watched the waiter from the
hotel's Bostonian restaurant arrange cups, a
pot of coffee, napkins, and a basket of croissants on the table before them. *He should have
brought fruit; I'll remember that.* As he filled
the cups, she said, "Owen wants to help me
find a job when I graduate."

"You have a job. With Jules."

"I want more than that. Someday I want to
manage a hotel."

"Only one?"

She smiled. "One at a time."

"But you've thought of others."

"I've thought of possibilities," she said carefully. She studied him, wondering why he had
changed toward her. His face was expression-

less, but his voice was warmer than at any time in the three years she had been with his family. "Was there something special you wanted to ask me?"

"Not special, no. I simply thought it would be good for us to talk. Jules is pleased with you; Owen says you're a quick student; my daughter Allison calls you her best friend. And I hardly know you. Leni tells me all young women want more these days; she was speaking of you and it seems she was right. Which hotel do you expect to manage?"

"I don't expect anything. We haven't talked very much about it. I'm sure it will be a small one, but it's up to Owen to decide."

"An older one, I assume."

"The older ones are the small ones." They were sparring now and Laura was tense. Whatever he claimed, he did want something from her, and she didn't know what; and she was afraid she wasn't quick enough to keep up with him. At that moment she saw Owen crossing the lobby, and instinctively she stood.

"What the hell—" Felix began, not used to having people interrupt a conversation before he was ready; then he followed her gaze and saw Owen, who was smiling broadly as he joined them.

"Laura, my dear"—he took her hand, holding it for a moment—"and Felix, and breakfast. An irresistible combination." He sat in an armchair beside Laura's, but he spoke to Felix. "This is fortuitous; I came in early to find you before your busy day began."

"Is something wrong?"

"Not to my knowledge." He took the cup of coffee Laura had poured for him. "Thank you, my dear. I try to keep up, Felix; you know how interested I am, and retirement has not changed that."

"We send you weekly reports."

"So you do. Can you tell me a little more about the new hotel we are building in St. Kitts?"

"What about it?"

"The rooms are small."

A tight defensiveness pinched Felix's face and he bent forward, explaining in clipped words why they had chosen to put money into the conference rooms and golf course instead of larger bedrooms. Laura watched him: the small but urgent gestures he made with his hands, the ramrod back inclined toward Owen, his anxious eyes, and suddenly she felt she was seeing him for the first time. He's desperate for Owen's approval, she thought, astonished at the humanity of a man she had always thought of as unfeeling. For a moment she pitied him. But then, as Owen made a comment about gracious surroundings, impatience flashed over Felix's face and his grating voice became even harsher. "Just because you like nineteenth-century bedrooms it doesn't mean our customers do. They don't. They want frills: swimming pools, exercise rooms, golf courses, marble lobbies, French chefs. And we give them all that, but it costs money. It makes money, too. What other reason is there to do anything, unless you're stuck in a swamp of sentiment? The way you're hanging on to those old hotels of yours—being romantic about bricks and mortar—when any fool could tell you we should be tearing them down and building new ones . . ."

Owen slowly shook his head. "Romance is the only magic we have left, and I have plans for those hotels." His somber look settled on Laura. "One of these days you and I will see what we can do with them. I've always wanted to, you know, but we were busy building up the chain and the years passed, and so did much of my energy. But now, with someone young to stimulate me . . . well, we'll see what we can do. Otherwise, Felix will wait until I'm dead and then tear them down and build fancy high rises with swimming pools and tiny rooms."

"And profits," Felix said shortly.

"Those four hotels break even; they've never lost money." Owen contemplated his son. "Why does this bother you so much? Four hotels, Felix, out of fifty-eight Salinger Hotels in this country and Europe."

"Four of the top markets in the country— New York, Chicago, Philadelphia, Washington —where we don't have modern hotels because I can't go into competition with you by building new ones. Four cities where the Salinger name means shabby and second-rate."

Owen nodded. "A good point. Our name should indicate excellence. And something will be done about it."

"How? You won't let us touch those hotels; you keep them locked in your own damned private corporation, separate from the rest of the hotels. It makes no sense! It's not good business!"

"But it might be good romance." Owen smiled at Laura. "And maybe I'm not too old to try to mix a little romance with business. It's worth a try, wouldn't you say, Felix?"

Felix shrugged. "Whims," he muttered. "If you'll excuse me, I have a busy day. Someone from Security Systems is supposed to be here and I want to see him."

"He's here," said Laura. "He asked for Asa and I sent him upstairs."

"Problems with security?" Owen asked.

"Not a big problem yet, but it might be. Two guests in the past month have had their pockets picked in front of the hotel. We hired a detective and he stood around for two weeks, but the second incident occurred five feet from him and I've got to find a way to prevent any more from happening."

"Yes. Good God, people will see us as unsafe; it has to be stopped. You're hiring more detectives?"

"I'll hire a dozen if I have to. I want to get some suggestions from an expert first."

"Why don't you have your detective sit down?" Laura asked.

Owen and Felix frowned at her.

"I mean," she said nervously, "standing up

is no good; his eyes are at the wrong level. If he's sitting down he's looking at pants pockets and he can see better."

"By God!" Owen roared, causing nearby guests to turn in disapproval. "Wonderful! Who would have thought of that? Eh? Felix, get a chair for your man!"

"He'd attract considerable attention," said Felix dryly.

"What about that?" Owen asked Laura.

Warmed by his praise, Laura ignored Felix. "Put him in a wheelchair."

"With a tin cup!" Owen exclaimed. "And a monkey!"

"Let's not overdo it," Felix murmured, but for the first time his interest was caught. "It might work."

"It's worth a try," Owen said. He grinned at Laura. "It takes a creative mind to think like a pickpocket. Thank you, my dear—"

A woman screamed.

It cut like a sword through the morning crowd. For an instant the lobby froze. Then it came to life. Everyone was milling and talking at once, as if a film had speeded up and might soon be out of control.

Felix had shot out of his chair and was gone.

"I must go," Laura said to Owen. "Jules will want me."

"Yes, yes, go." His bushy eyebrows were drawn together. "We've never had violence here. Never . . ."

Laura kissed the top of his head and quickly made her way through the milling confusion toward her desk. But before she got there she saw Felix bending over a woman sprawled on a love seat; he looked helpless and enraged. "Can I help?" she asked.

His mouth was tight. "She won't say what happened. She doesn't want a doctor; she doesn't want the police."

The woman's hands were clasped tightly beneath her chin and her eyes were closed. Late fifties, Laura thought, too much makeup, bleached hair, expensive suit, fine pearls. Her nails were manicured and she was crying. Jules arrived but held back as he saw Laura bend over and gently push the woman's hair from her eyes. "I've ordered tea for you," she said quietly. "Can you sit up?"

Her eyes still closed, the woman shook her head. Laura gestured to Felix, who struggled briefly with his desire to ask her who the hell she was to be giving orders, then decided a peaceful lobby was more important. "Jules," he said, "get tea. And something to eat."

Jules went through the same struggle, then turned furiously on his heel and marched away without a word. "I'm going to help you sit up," Laura said, her voice low. "If you can't manage it, we'll have to carry you to the lounge until we know how badly hurt you are."

"Not hurt." The woman struggled to sit up. She opened her eyes and looked at Laura. "Knocked around, but I should be used to . . ." She closed her eyes, then opened them again. "Do you work here?" Laura nodded. "Well. Sorry I made a noise in your lobby." The nonchalant pose failed and she closed her eyes again. "My God, my God, what will people say?"

"That doesn't matter."

"It does, it does, you don't understand, you're too young." She sat up with Laura's arm around her, once more opening her eyes, and her tears returned, spilling over and leaving wavering tracks in the thick powder on her face. "I'm sorry, I'm so sorry. I knew I shouldn't come. I told myself a hundred times I was better off in Dallas not knowing what he was up to, but then I just found myself here, and of course he had her in his room after he promised he wouldn't see her again, ever . . ."

"I don't think you want to talk about this here," Laura said firmly.

"She was in bed—nude, the little slut—waiting for him to come back from running." The woman laughed harshly. "Good healthy activity, first thing in the morning. Nobody ever said Wylie Starrett doesn't take care of himself. He's in top form, they say. . . . Oh, God, what got into me that I had it out with him here, in the lobby, when I knew he'd use his fist; he always uses his—" She bent over in a fit of coughing as Jules and a bellhop arrived with a tray.

Laura smiled absently, as if it were perfectly natural for Jules to wait on her. "Thank you . . . if you'll just put it here . . . Oh, good, you brought something to eat." She filled a cup. "I want you to stop talking, Mrs. Starrett, and drink this and eat some biscuits. And then we're going to put you in a room upstairs. I assume you have luggage."

She nodded, her eyes startled. The puffy half-moons below them were streaked with mascara, and Laura wiped them gently with

her handkerchief. "Drink your tea, Mrs. Starrett," she said softly.

"It's Virginia. Ginny. I want you to call me
Ginny."

Laura smiled. "I'm Laura Fairchild. Will
you wait here while I get you a room? We can
talk later, if you like, when you've had a chance
to clean up and rest."

"I want to talk. You'll take me to my room."
The authoritative voice contrasted oddly with
her red eyes and tear-streaked face, but it was
obvious that she was used to giving orders.

"Of course," Laura said, standing up.

She saw Jules make a quick gesture. His staff
went only where he directed. Laura looked at
the woman on the couch and spread her hands
slightly so Jules could see she had no choice.
"I'll take care of your room," she said to Virginia Starrett, and crossed the lobby to the reservations desk.

"Very efficient," Felix said to Jules. "You're
lucky she was here."

Behind him, Owen had been watching. As
he saw Jules's face darken, he put a friendly
hand on his shoulder. "You've trained her well,
Jules. She does you credit."

"Ah." Jules let out his breath and reorganized his thoughts. "It is, of course, difficult, the responsibility for shaping a good and trusted staff. But your protégée, Mr. Salinger, is a fine young woman. She learns well from Jules. I am proud of what she has learned."

And all three men, each pleased in his own way, stood guard over Virginia Starrett as she drank her tea in the midst of a discreetly murmuring lobby that had returned to normal.

After dinner in the kitchen bay of Owen's house, Laura told Paul about her day and finished with a performance of Jules LeClair in action. "I am proud of what she has learned," she finished with a small precise bow, her French accent perfectly mimicking Jules's, her voice just deep enough to sound like his.

"Exactly," Paul said as they laughed together. "It's exactly Jules. You're wonderful."

"How do you know? You told me you don't pay attention to the hotels."

"I'm paying more attention now. I've stopped by a few times, just to make sure your working conditions are acceptable."

Laura smiled but her eyes were serious. "What would you have done if they weren't?"

"Taken Jules by the scruff of the neck, dropped him into the bay, and fed him to the lobsters."

"And been lynched by the lobstermen for changing the taste of Boston lobsters. Paul, you wouldn't have done anything."

He shook his head. "I just wanted to be able to picture you in your job when I think about you during the day. I do that quite a bit, you know. Go ahead, finish your story. How did you hear Jules congratulating himself for your skills if you'd gone off to get a room for the lady in distress?"

"I walked very slowly; I wanted to hear what they said."

"Wise woman. Always know what's going on behind your back." He poured coffee for her. "You had a good time, didn't you?"

"I loved it. Jules doesn't let me work with people very often; I got to Ginny Starrett just before he did. If I could do that kind of thing all day it would be wonderful."

"You wouldn't want a steady stream of crises," he said, amused.

"Why not? Solving them is what makes heroines."

He laughed. "You're already a heroine to

me." He looked more closely at her. "You don't really want to be a heroine to Jules Le-Clair."

"No, to myself. To know I'm perfect at a job."

"In this job?" he asked. "What happened to being an actress?"

"That was only an idea I had. Acting is a hobby."

"Wasn't Owen the one who said that?"

"I'm saying it. I can mimic people, and it's fun, but it's different to try to make it a whole life, and I haven't got time to find out if I really could or not. I can be successful much faster this way, and I do love it; it's something I can talk about and not hide—" She stopped. "It's something I can be proud of."

"Hide," Paul said musingly. "Why would you have anything to hide?"

"I hope I don't," she said, tossing it off. "But what if I tried to be a famous actress and failed and then turned to a life of crime?"

He smiled and shook his head. "You couldn't do it. You won't even pick up something in a department store to look at it, much less make off with it." He wondered what she really had meant. He wouldn't force her to tell him—she had a right to her own secrets—but it was a curious thing for her to say. "Anyway, let me help you become a heroine. Shall I register at the hotel and demand some exotic service and say you're the only one who can provide it?"

"We don't provide that kind of service," she said with à straight face. "The international concierge association forbids it."

He burst out laughing. "Good for them. Well, then, you'll have to make it on your own; it's foreign territory to me."

"You mean a job is foreign," she said. "Any job."

"Probably. I've never had one, but I suspect I'd feel like a foreigner if I had to satisfy someone else's fantasies instead of my own."

"But you can satisfy your own fantasies; you have your photography. Why don't you do something with it?"

"I don't need to."

"I didn't mean money. I meant doing something with your life, giving it a direction."

"Laura, my life is fine. Nothing is missing."

"You said—that night at my party—that you have everything you want but you'd like to want more."

"And you said you didn't understand what I meant."

"But now I think I do. You have all the things you want but there's no center, nothing that makes all the rest mean something. You don't have anything important in your life—"

"You're important."

"Can't you take me seriously?"

"I am taking you seriously."

"No, you're not. I'm talking about the Paul Janssen who does nothing all day but sports or sailing with friends or reading or taking pictures when he feels like it but usually not even developing the negatives, or . . . whatever else you do before you pick me up at work. You don't do anything that has a beginning and a middle and an end; nothing has a shape or a meaning; you can't look back at night and say, 'I did something good today that I'm proud of, something that will last.'"

There was silence in the kitchen. "You're a passionate and wise lady," Paul said at last. "But you're talking about something I don't need. I find my shape, as you call it, in my own ways, and I'm perfectly satisfied. But what does that matter to us? If we don't agree about work we'll talk about other things. Would you like more coffee?"

She hesitated as if about to say something more, then changed her mind. "Yes. Thank you."

Paul filled their cups, then turned away, looking beyond Laura at the fading streaks of a russet sunset, and at Owen's garden, dark in the shadow of its brick wall. He didn't want to argue. He'd learned long ago, from his father, that if one could avoid controversy and tension, almost everything eventually came out all right. It was quarrels that confirmed people in their ways, making them cling more tightly to ideas they might have shed or modified if they'd been left alone, turning them inward to protect the beliefs others were challenging. Nothing is worth a quarrel, Thomas Janssen had taught his son, and while Paul thought that probably was going too far, he wasn't sure what really might be worth the fervor and involvement of controversy.

"Let's leave it alone," he said to Laura. "And maybe we'll end up agreeing with each other."

She smiled and began to clear the dinner dishes. She didn't think it was that easy, but she didn't want to quarrel. Everything was so wonderful between them; why think about disagreements? She moved back and forth between the table and the sink. Around them the house was quiet, the rooms dark and empty. Owen and Rosa were at the Cape; the housekeepers were on vacation. All the Salingers had finally left that morning, later in the season than usual. Laura would join them on the weekends; the rest of the week she would live in Owen's town house. This was the first night she would be there alone, and she was feeling uncomfortable. It was too big; it was too much. She felt like a fraud. What am I doing here? she thought; how can I have this whole house to myself when just three years ago I was living in a New York tenement and dreaming of a room of my own? Five floors, twenty-two rooms on Beacon Hill. I don't belong here.

"You're bustling," Paul said as she stacked and rinsed dishes and put them in the dishwasher. "You don't have to do that; the maid will do them in the morning."

"I can't leave dishes overnight," Laura said.

"Why not?"

Because of cockroaches and other things that crawl in the dark. "It's just not right."

"Is that what your mother taught you?"

"Of course. Don't all mothers teach that?"

"Did you do the dishes together?"

"Yes," she said. That was true; she could remember standing at the sink with her mother. But she couldn't remember what they'd talked about. It was all gone, drowned in the torrent of tears she had shed when suddenly she had no parents and there was only Ben, saying he'd take care of them forever.

"Then I'll do the same," Paul said and carried the coffee cups to the granite counter with its stainless steel sink. He kissed the top of Laura's head, enjoying the silence around them. There was a charming domesticity to the scene, he reflected; in Owen's home and Rosa's kitchen they were like two children playing house. But they weren't children, and as Paul watched the play of light on Laura's long chestnut hair he wanted her as if it were the first time, in that empty house in Marblehead Neck. That was new for him—usually his interest began to wane as the weeks of an affair passed—but the novelty wasn't important enough to distract him from his desire. "Laura," he said, his voice low, and she came to him and moved into his embrace.

"I was thinking"—her lips were beside his ear, her words as soft as a sigh of wind—"how strange it feels to be here alone. . . ."

His mouth covered hers and then, together, they left the dishes and went upstairs to her apartment.

That was the pattern of that golden summer. When Laura left work, Paul was waiting for her in his car outside the hotel, and they ate dinner at a restaurant or at the round mahogany table in the kitchen bay, where tall beeswax candles cast a warm circle around them. After dinner they went to a concert or a play, or walked through Harvard Square, browsing in the shops, watching the people, holding hands as they strolled, until desire sent them back to Laura's rooms, where they made love and slept and woke to make love again until morning, when they made breakfast in the kitchen, bright this time with sunlight. And then Paul drove Laura to work before going to his studio and darkroom because, as he told her casually one morning, he'd gotten interested in photography again and had begun to make a series of portraits of her.

On the weekends they went to the Cape, where Laura stayed in the cottage Owen had offered her just before the robbery and Paul stayed with his parents. "I can't spend the night with you with your whole family around us," she said when he objected. "It's like flaunting us in their face, and your father doesn't approve of me—"

"He approves of you. He likes you."

"He calls me your diversion and wonders how long you'll keep it up."

"How the hell do you know that?"

"Allison told me."

"Allison should keep her mouth shut."

"Shouldn't I know what your family thinks?"

"If it matters. It doesn't."

"You love your father. You care what he thinks."

"Unless I know he's wrong. Laura, they know I stay with you in Boston."

"I don't care. I just can't walk out of the door in the morning as if I'm saying to all of them, 'Look, we just got out of bed.' "

"It would be honest."

"Sometimes it's better not to be honest."

He shrugged. "Whatever you want." But he had seen the sudden flash of worry in her eyes, and with a quick grin he put his arm around her. "Do you know how remarkable you are? For the first time in my life I find Boston in July so attractive I stay there five days a week."

They laughed together, and by the end of the summer Paul had come to believe she was right: why force the issue with his family when there was nothing to gain? He had Laura's passion, whether all night in Boston or for the early part of the night at the Cape; he had his own fascination with her, growing deeper each day; and he had her love. Even if he hadn't been sure of that, Allison confirmed it.

She and Thad were traveling in Canada but she telephoned almost every day, talking to her family more often than when she lived with them. When she called others in the family she talked about scenery and weather; she and Paul talked about each other. "She adores you," Allison said when she called one morning from Lake Louise. "You must know that. She doesn't exactly hide it. You do know it."

"Yes," he said. "But I like hearing it from you. Are you having a wonderful time?"

"Didn't I send you a postcard saying I was?"

"You did; Laura and Owen got them, too. But you also told us you wished we were there and we got the impression that you meant it."

Allison gave a short laugh. "I did. Why didn't you come dashing up to Canada and join us?"

"Dear Allison, if you can't enjoy a vacation with Thad, how can you marry him?"

"A good question. Are you going to marry Laura?"

"I haven't thought about it."

"Bullshit."

"I've thought about it but there doesn't seem to be any rush. Did Laura say something when you talked to her last week?"

"No, but according to everybody else it's been a hot and heavy summer. I'm sorry I'm missing it."

"According to everybody?"

"Well, Mother said you're very attentive and more settled down than you've been in a long time. Daddy said he sees you in front of the hotel every day, picking Laura up—does he spend most of his time peering out of his office windows? And a few of the cousins mentioned long walks on the beach, and boat trips to Nantucket and the Vineyard, and nuzzling on the veranda of the cottage. You two aren't invisible, you know. Do you love her?"

"Do you love Thad? As I recall, you're marrying him in October."

"Well, I don't think I will. Or I'm not really sure. Anyway, I won't have a wedding that looks like a coronation. If I decide to marry Thad it's going to be very quiet and maybe at the last minute."

"Will I hear about it beforehand?"

"Of course you will; I want you there. And Laura too. I wish you'd talk about her. Are you angry because I asked if you love her?"

"Dear Allison, I couldn't be angry with you." His voice was oddly gentle. "If I can help with your dilemma, will you call me? And when I want to talk about Laura, I'll call you."

"She's good for you. You're a lot nicer these days. Not as impatient. And it's such a novelty having you with us for more than a week or two at a time. Paul, I love Laura and I love you; I don't want you to hurt each other. And I don't want to have to take sides. So be nice to each other, will you?"

"That's one of the things we do best." He was smiling as he hung up.

Nearly everyone in the family tried to talk to Paul about Laura to find out how serious he was. But Owen said nothing until September, when everyone was preparing to return to the city, and then he talked to Laura.

They were packing the books he wanted for his library in Boston, and he leafed through each one before putting it in a carton. "What an interesting summer this has been," he murmured casually while studying an engraving in a history of Rome.

Sitting cross-legged on the floor beside him, Laura smiled. "Yes, it has been. I've learned so much from Jules; I can't thank you enough for getting me that job."

"I didn't mean Jules," Owen said, peering at her. "But if you want to talk about him I won't argue."

"I'm sorry," she said, ashamed. "I knew you meant Paul. But you've never asked me about him, so I thought you approved of us."

"Of your sleeping together or being in love?"

At Laura's quick look of surprise and embarrassment, he rested his hand on her head. "Did you really think I didn't know? I may be in my declining years, my dear, but my powers of perception are intact. Also, Leni told me."

Involuntarily, Laura smiled. "Does everyone talk about us?"

"Of course they do; can anyone resist talking about young lovers who walk around oblivious to everyone else? I did think you might come to me and tell me about your feelings."

"I'm sorry," Laura said again. "I wanted to, but I thought you'd disapprove."

"Of your sleeping together, you mean." She nodded. "Well, I confess it is not a form of courtship I can speak about from experience. Leni says all young people do it these days; I find that surprising, but I don't pass judgment. Customs change, and it takes time to know whether for better or worse. But I have some nostalgia for the time when I was young, when a decent man wouldn't even try to kiss a young woman until they were engaged. Even then he asked her permission. He didn't always get it, either."

"Did you ask Iris's permission?"

Owen smiled. "As I recall, we both had the idea at the same time. There wasn't a great deal of discussion."

Laura's smile met his. "And then you asked her to marry you?"

He gazed across the room at a photograph of Iris standing beside a gnarled tree at the Cape. Her hair blew straight behind her; she was shading her eyes with her hand and laughing. "You know, I don't recall asking. One night we were sitting in her living room—we could see her father through the open door to his study; he was reading and I remember he held his newspaper in front of his face so we could kiss —and we just found ourselves talking about where we would live."

Laura's face grew wistful. "Did you always have ideas together?"

"A goodly amount of the time." Once again Owen put his hand on her head, this time stroking her shining hair in long slow movements that matched his recollections. "More and more, the longer we were together. I was a little wild at first, not yet a man, and Iris was a woman who knew what she wanted. She didn't try to change me—at least not that I could see —but she was determined to shape her own life in a way she thought was good and important, and after a while I had the same ideas. I never knew what magic she worked, but suddenly I was a family man, coming straight home from work, raising children, building up my hotels for my wife and sons instead of just for myself, and buttoning myself into tuxedos two or three times a week because my beautiful wife liked fancy balls."

He looked down at Laura. "She once told me," he said softly, "that she liked me best with nothing on, and next best in blue jeans and a lumberjack shirt, and then in a tux. I thought it was wonderfully daring of her to say that."

"It was. You must have had such fun together."

"You know, we never called it that. But you're right; we had fun. Oh, my dear, what we had was so joyful and good; it was as if a lantern lit our way through the years and it was always bright. When she died the darkness came. I stood beside her coffin and I couldn't see her because the light was gone. I could only see her in my memory, smiling at me when she lay beneath me, laughing as she danced through the house on Beacon Hill for the first time, nursing our baby in a rocking chair in our bedroom while I lay on the bed beside her, sharing the peace and beauty of that moment. Ah, my dear child, if I could make you feel what we had . . . A man can sow his seed, he can build an empire, and none of it is worth a damn if he can't bring it to a woman he cherishes and say, 'Take this from me; I did it because of you and now it is yours.' Iris was my life, the center and also the boundary, all I ever wanted."

He stopped and cleared his throat. "And then she was sick. Such a short time, we barely had a chance to say good-bye. And she died . . ." His voice fell into a long sigh and he closed his eyes. His hand still on Laura's head, he cleared his throat again and again, but still he was hoarse when he went on. "I wandered through that house and I reached out for her but my hands were empty, as empty as my life. I got angry and I shouted at her clothes hanging in her closet. *'Damn you to hell for leaving me when you know I love you and need you!'* For a while I was so angry I didn't mourn. And then the anger left and I had nothing. That was when I stopped paying attention to anything. For two years I didn't go out; Rosa took care of Felix and Asa—she took care of everything—and I sat in the house reliving the years with Iris, because those were the only years I cared about. Rosa would stand in the doorway with her hands on her hips and tell me it was time I found someone to give me companionship and perhaps love, but I couldn't do it. I ached, I hurt, and I wanted the darkness because Iris was in the dark."

The room was silent. Laura took his hand as it rested on her hair, and when she kissed it Owen felt the tears on her cheek. "She had a way of smiling," he said, "as if everything was new. As if everywhere she turned she made wonderful, exciting discoveries. You smile the same way; your eyes light up the same way. I almost see Iris when you smile. And her hair was the color of yours; a bit darker, but not much. And it was long, though she wore it pinned up in some complicated way. And sometimes she had a faraway look in her eyes, as if she could see something the rest of us couldn't see . . . no, it was more; as if she had a secret, something that was hers alone. You have the same kind of look."

Startled, Laura looked up at him. "As if I have a secret?"

He nodded. "It was the first thing I saw about you that day on the beach, and you still have it. Mystery. It made me want to know what lay behind that faraway look. Iris was the same. She had mystery and she had beauty. And you always had beauty, in your eyes and smile, before the rest of you caught up." He paused, but Laura was silent. "Well, for those two years I sat in my chair reliving my life with Iris, and then one day for some reason I started thinking about the hotels. And even though I tried not to care, because it was more important to think about Iris, I did care and I couldn't stop caring. And that was when I started paying attention again. And went back to work." He paused again. "So you see, dear Laura, I care a great deal about love and sex, and also marriage. And I care about you. So when you have an affair and I have some concerns about it, I must speak up."

Surprised, Laura said, "Concerns? About Paul?"

"About you and Paul. I love that boy, but I see him clearly and I know he has the wandering urge of a hungry coyote."

She gave a small smile. "Couldn't you find a nicer comparison?"

"There is nothing wrong with coyotes. They've gotten a bad name, but the fact is they're strong and handsome, sharp, creative, good to their families, and superb survivors. They also move around a great deal, and they've been known to forget what they leave behind."

Laura turned away and reached for a new stack of books.

"My own great-nephew," Owen said. "I've loved him since he was a baby. He used to totter around my study, and nothing was safe from him; he had an insatiable curiosity and stubbornness. It was one of my greatest pleasures to introduce Paul to the wonders of the world; he cared about learning, he responded to beauty, and he wasn't stingy. He knew how to take life in his hands and enjoy every bit of it. I'm afraid I spent more time with him than I spent with my own sons; with Paul I was having fun. But then he grew up and started wandering around the world, picking up projects and dropping them and then moving on. I'm told he does that with women, too. I would not like to think he would do it to you." Silent, Laura looked through the window at leaves tinged with gold and red. "I don't want you hurt, you see. Of course, I don't want you angry at me, either."

Laura kept her eyes on the trees. "I'm not angry. But I don't think you should criticize people in your own family."

"Horsefeathers. I see people clear and straight, whether I want to or not. After I hit seventy, I couldn't fool myself anymore, couldn't pretend people were kind or good-hearted or fascinating when I knew damn well they weren't. I can't even pretend I love my own sons, and that hurts, but I don't ignore it. So why shouldn't I be honest about my great-nephew when I love you as much as I love him and worry about you more? Damn it, girl, I don't want you hurt!"

Laura looked at him over her shoulder. "What if someone had warned you about Iris?"

"I wouldn't have listened. In fact, I'd probably have run him out of town for saying anything against her."

She turned, kneeling before him. "Were you smarter than I am now?"

"I knew more about the world."

"But you said you were wild. Not yet a man, you said."

"Damn it, young woman, who gave you permission to use an old man's words against him?" But he was grinning, and he leaned forward to kiss Laura on her forehead. "Well, perhaps I should stop. I may be wrong, though I haven't been very often. But I'm getting old, and maybe Felix is right; maybe I should stay out of people's lives."

"I don't want you to stay out of my life; I want you to share it. I'm so happy. I've never been so happy."

He looked at her shining eyes and felt, oddly, like weeping. "I do know something about happiness. And maybe you'll be good for Paul, settle him down. If you work the same kind of magic Iris worked on me—"

Laura shook her head. "You and Iris were married. Paul and I aren't, and we're not talking about it." *He hasn't even said he loves me.* "I have another year of college, and then I'm going to work—you said you'd help me find a job in a hotel—"

"I'll do that whether you and Paul are friends or roommates or husband and wife. As long as you want to work, I'll help you. But"— his voice grew wistful—"you will stay with me until you finish college?"

"Yes, of course; I couldn't leave. I want to stay with you as long as you'll have me. And you said I could help you with your plans for your hotels . . ."

"To revive them and make them grand again." He smiled. "And we'll do it together.

Well, it sounds like a fine year. Now bring the sherry and we'll have a drink together before dinner. Or are you going out with your young man?"

Laura rose and went to the tall wine cabinet wedged between overflowing bookshelves. She took out a bottle of amontillado and two glasses and put them on the table beside Owen's chair. "We planned to; do you mind?"

"If I did I'd keep it to myself. I can't dictate your schedule or keep my eye on you, out of bed or in."

"You wouldn't want that," Laura said, her eyes dancing.

"Ah, but I might. Think what I might learn: Paul's more a man of the world than I ever was." He peered at her. "Now I've made you blush. I beg your pardon." He sighed. "You've become so lovely, my child, and you have a quick mind and a good imagination. If you trust yourself and give yourself time, you'll be a strong woman and a fine executive. And if you ever needed to, you could have your pick of half the men on the eastern seaboard."

"What about the other half?" she demanded.

He grinned. "They're after Allison, or they

would be if she'd get rid of that solipsistic, preening peacock she's decided to marry, God knows why." He sighed again. "Well, you'll all do whatever you want. I might as well keep my wisdom to myself. I spent a lifetime accumulating it, and who's interested?"

Laura laughed and kissed him. "I am, and you don't feel half as sorry for yourself as you pretend."

"True." He took her hand between his. "I feel privileged because you do listen, and proud because I've helped you change from a scared little girl to a happy woman, and I feel loved, which is the most profound feeling of all. As if you brought back the lantern I lost when Iris died."

That was what he thought about later, after Laura was gone. She reminded him of Iris and she had made his world bright, but she was also distinctly herself: warm, loving, enchanting, unique. He'd hoped she would someday trust him enough to tell him her secrets, but she'd given no sign that she even wanted to, and there was no way he could tell her how unimportant they were. Of course she had a right to guard her secrets for as long as she wished, but he knew they were burdensome,

and he would have liked to make the load easier by sharing it.

Maybe someday, he thought. He refilled his
glass and then sat quietly, watching the light
fade over the water and letting memories fill
his thoughts, less painful than before, but no
less vivid. *Iris, I wish you could be here; Laura
is the daughter we never had.*

CHAPTER 9

IN the unusually hot May sun, the black robe clung like a blanket, and Laura tried to think cool thoughts as the commencement speaker droned on. Pay attention, she told herself. Enjoy the ceremony. You'll only graduate from college once, and it took a lot of work to get here. But she was too hot to concentrate; her thoughts kept drifting to Paul, who was sitting with Allison and Owen in the first row of the Nickerson Field stands. Clay had called from Philadelphia at the last minute to say he couldn't be there. "Willard's got the flu, and ever since I became a hero and assistant manager after they fired Terry, I'm stuck if he's not around. I'm sorry; I really wanted to be there."

"It's all right." A year ago she would have been upset, but by now Paul and Owen and Allison were her family, too, and she wouldn't feel alone. "I'll tell you all about it."

"And I suppose your handsome *beau* will take lots of pictures."

"I hope he will," Laura replied calmly, refusing to be drawn into an argument about Paul. It was foolish of Clay to worry about her loving one of the Salingers, saying things like, "Sex makes women drop their guard," and after a while she got tired of telling him that neither passion nor anything else would lull her into giving them away because she'd shut the door on the past.

It had been four years since the robbery. None of Leni's jewelry had been found after the bracelet in the pawnshop, and except for increased security in their houses, the Salingers behaved as if it had never happened. And that was almost the way Laura felt about the first eighteen years of her life: they were like a dream. She was twenty-two now, and a different person. As if I were born the night of the robbery, she thought. It was fanciful, but most of the time it seemed almost true, because she had been with the Salingers long enough to see changes in them, and only when we share change are we truly connected to someone or something else.

In the past year, Leni had begun to spend increasingly more time in New York. She was on the boards of hospitals and museums there as well as in Boston, and Felix frequently remarked, with a tight smile, that he'd given his wife to charity. But Laura saw that as long as Leni was at his side for major galas and business functions, he never suggested she spend more time at home, or with him.

Allison had left college and married Thad, but after a four-month honeymoon, and three more months to settle into a condominium on the harbor, they had an erratic schedule that reminded Laura of an employment agency: Thad tried one occupation after another while Allison, anticipating his boredom, would already be looking for another. They socialized every night, usually with new acquaintances; their old friends were uncomfortable with the silences between them, like heavy gray fog.

Laura didn't pay attention to most of the family gossip; she knew whom she loved and she knew what she believed about them. She looked at them as she stood on the commencement platform, meeting their smiles, and she raised her hand in a quiet greeting as the speaker ended his peroration with a long quotation in Greek that almost no one understood. The applause swelled hugely from universal relief that he was done, and then the graduates received their diplomas, and a few moments later Laura stood on the artificial turf of the field with her family. "Just a minute," she said as Allison and Paul reached out to embrace her, "I have to get out of this robe."

"I thought you must be melting," Allison said.

"I am." Laura dropped the robe and, with Paul's arm around her, took Owen's hands as he held them out to her. "I'm so glad you were here."

"How could I miss it? You were my pupil at home before you ever came to the university. Do you know Jules wanted to come today? I had to tell him you could only get three tickets."

"He really wanted to come?"

"He wanted to take credit for you; he thinks he's taught you more than your professors have."

"He's right. But you've taught me more than anyone."

Owen chuckled. "I won't tell Jules you said that." He reached into his pocket and took out a small velvet drawstring bag. "Your graduation gift, my dear. With my love."

Laura pulled the tiny cord to open the bag. Her fingers felt the cool metal and the sharp point of a pin before she took out a piece of jewelry and held it in the palm of her hand. It was a single iris of blue-violet opal with a gold center. She gazed at it for a long moment, then looked up at Owen, her face glowing. "Was it Iris's?"

He nodded. "I had it made for her on our first anniversary. It was very special to her."

Laura put her arms around him and kissed him. "Thank you, thank you . . . it's very special to *me* . . . how can I tell you—?"

"You don't have to. I saw it in your face." He held her away from him. "And you looked so much like her, excited and full of wonder . . . Well, now. Time for you to go. Allison is driving me home; you and Paul go off on your honeymoon." At her startled look, he struck his fist against his forehead. "Vacation. I meant to say vacation. Go on, now; you've worked hard; you deserve some play." He held her close. "I'm very proud of you, my dear."

Laura kissed him again. His drooping mustache was feathery against her cheek, and it struck her that Owen had aged. She'd been so preoccupied in the past weeks with final papers and exams and keeping up with her job that she hadn't really looked at him; now she thought he looked almost ethereal. His cheeks were more sunken than she remembered, and his face was crinkled with webs of fine lines, like ancient parchment. His eyes were as bright as ever, but they seemed more deep-set, his thick eyebrows overhanging them like wild grass on bluffs on the Cape. *He's eighty-three, but he's never seemed old; he isn't old, not really; he has so much vitality.* "Are you all right?" she asked him.

"I'm fine; why shouldn't I be?" He put on a scowl. "I mixed up a couple of words; that doesn't mean I'm falling apart. It's hot, that's the problem, and you're keeping me here in the sun when Allison and I could be eating lunch. I thought you were in a hurry."

"Good-bye," Laura said softly. "Don't try to be fierce with me; I'm not fooled." She took Paul's arm. "We've been dismissed."

"About time," he said with a grin, and they left Owen and Allison standing together as they walked through the tunnel beneath the stands and out onto the street. "I want to make love to you," Paul said conversationally as they reached his car in the next block.

"Here?" she asked. "Or shall we stop at a more private gas station along the way?"

He laughed and they kissed in the front seat. "If those are the only choices, I prefer your cottage at the Cape. Would you be willing to wait a couple of hours?"

"I would always wait for you," Laura said, her voice low, and he glanced at her quickly before turning onto Commonwealth Avenue and driving toward the turnpike.

They had learned to be leisurely in their lovemaking. After the storms of their first weeks together, when it seemed they could never satisfy their hunger, they began to come together more slowly. And when they could stay together for the whole night, they took even longer, talking as they caressed and laughing together, even as their passion grew. When they finally fell asleep, their hands were clasped between them, and in the first moments of waking, before opening their eyes, they turned to each other and lay full length together, encircled tightly in each other's arms. Their legs were twined, her lips against his chest, his on her forehead, as they slowly came awake to the light in the room and the small, fluttering movements of their bodies. Each morning they held each other for a long quiet time, drifting in warm silent closeness until desire flickered and then grew, like a small ripple far out in the ocean that gathers force and becomes, at last, a thundering wave. And as desire built they moved even more slowly, learning to hold back, to find new forms of pleasure, to draw arousal out like the long ripple moving to shore until passion overtook them, and together, one voice, one heart, they rode it to its crest, and together drifted back to the somnolent embrace in which they had begun.

In Osterville, they had the summer compound to themselves; they almost had Cape Cod to themselves, since few visitors came in May. They spent the days out of doors, sailing on the sun-sparkled water, picnicking in cool pine forests, climbing barefoot in the sand dunes, leaving footprints that overlapped as they walked closely, hand in hand. And they walked by moonlight along the beach, laughing at the clownish gait of sandpipers hopping just ahead of them, and speculating about the long-ago women who had paced the widow's walks atop gray shingled houses overlooking the sea, waiting for their husbands, the whaling captains who had gone to seek the ocean's riches and instead were taken by the ocean to invisible graves.

"Two weeks," Paul said on their last day. "Not enough. Let's extend it; we need at least another month to ourselves."

Laura buttoned her shirt. "I wish we could. But what excuse do I give Jules for not being there first thing tomorrow morning?"

"I'll call and tell him his chief assistant concierge has been kidnapped." He swept her long hair to the side and kissed the back of her neck. "I'll say I need her to help me clear the dinner dishes because it's not right to leave them until morning."

Laura laughed and reached for her hiking shoes. "Jules would say you're mad. He doesn't clear the table at his house."

"And if I tell him I dry while you wash?"

"He'd say that isn't man's work."

"Well, it shouldn't be yours, either, while

you're working full-time. We'll need at least two maids to run our house."

Laura's fingers stilled, then, slowly, she resumed tying her shoes. "I couldn't tell a maid what to do," she said lightly. "I've never had one."

"I have. I'll lay down the law and all you have to do is give praise when it's due. A perfect partnership."

She gave a small smile. "It sounds like it."

"Of course, it depends on where we're living." Paul was bent over, tying his boots. "If we stay in Boston, Mother or Leni will find us the perfect maids who already know everything, and we won't have to worry. Or Rosa will send over one of her dozen or so nieces to take charge of our household. If we're not in Boston, then we're on our own. Do you think we should stay in Boston?"

"But Owen—" Laura's heart was racing and the words caught in her throat. "Don't you remember I told you Owen may want me in Chicago?"

"Is that definite? When?"

"Not for a while, I think. I'll stay with Jules until . . . until something is settled."

"Well, it doesn't matter; we can live very

well in Chicago. I have friends there; you'll like them. I'll be one of those husbands who happily follows his wife from job to job and greets her at the door every night with a martini. But you don't drink martinis."

"No." Laura's throat was choked. "But if you could find a nice red wine . . ." Tears stopped her and she turned away, blindly reaching for a tissue.

"My God, what have I said?" Paul got to the box before she did and wiped her eyes. "You don't want me in Chicago? You don't want me at all? For God's sake, why would this make you cry? It all seems so natural—"

"Oh, hush," she said. "Please stop talking. Of course I want you in Chicago. I want you anywhere. I don't know why I'm crying—"

Paul kissed her, and then they held each other for a long time, while her heart slowed. And she felt his slow, too. "This was all serious," she said, drawing back to look at him.

"Did you doubt it? Of course it's serious; it's the most serious thing I've ever done. I should have done it long ago; I've loved you for so long I can't remember what it's like not loving you. But why would I want to remember? I'll never have to live that way again."

"No. We'll always be together." She put her head on his shoulder, feeling the sinewy muscles of his arms beneath her hands. It was all right now. Everything was all right.

She was safe.

They stood quietly until Paul tilted up her face. "Laura, my love, what are you thinking about?"

"Owen," she said with a small smile. "I asked him once how he proposed to Iris, and he said he didn't, really; one night they just found themselves talking about where they would live."

"Did he? I never heard that. But Rosa always said they were perfect together. Now she'll have us to talk about. And she can make our wedding cake; ever since I finished college she's told me she's been waiting to make one, whenever I decide to settle down. Is next week all right—here at the Cape? There's a wonderful old church in East Dennis; I always thought I'd like to be married there. And I'd like the family to be with us. You would, too, wouldn't you? It will make it seem more official."

Laura's words were soft. "Of course I would. And next week would be wonderful."

But Leni declared it impossible. She needed time to make a proper wedding; it would have to be in August. In private, she told Owen she had serious doubts about the whole affair. "They're so very different, their backgrounds are different, Laura has no money at all and Paul doesn't even know what it is to work, and whatever she earns will always seem like pin money next to his fortune—"

"It's the best thing that could happen," Owen said firmly, omitting all mention of his warnings to Laura the year before. "Leni, this girl has made the past years a joy for me, and she's going to make her mark in the hotels; you just wait and see what she and I are cooking up. And look at Paul; have you ever seen him stay with one woman or in one place for so long and so happily? And Allison says she feels as if they're sisters. My God, if Laura weren't marrying into the family we'd have to adopt her!"

Leni smiled. "She's delightful, I don't deny it, and I'm very fond of her; I just don't know what to predict with the two of them."

"How were your predictions when you married Felix?"

"Wrong," she said briefly. "And that reminds me. Felix is extremely angry; he says Laura is a fortune hunter. That's why I'm giving them a splendid wedding."

Owen chuckled, but when she had left, his eyes grew somber. I'm eighty-three, he thought, and, no question about it, a little more shaky than I used to be. I have one of the world's great hotel chains and two sons. But—

What does a man do with the work of a lifetime when he doesn't like what his sons have become?

There was no one he could talk to; the only confidante he was comfortable with was Laura, and he couldn't bring her into this. Nor anyone else. He had to work it out alone.

He sat in his library through the early part of June while the family prepared to leave for the Cape. Often he saw the sunrise; he slept badly and would leave his bed to sit in the high-backed leather chair in his library and watch the stars or the setting of the crescent moon. In the afternoons, he would doze in the same chair and waken when he heard Laura come in from work. But mostly those days he wrote, filling page after page with his bold, sloping handwriting, summarizing the plans for his hotels he and Laura were working on. He had thought about them for years without any sense of urgency; now he knew the project had become a way of saying he wasn't really old, wasn't anywhere near death. How could anyone be close to death when he was making such grand, far-reaching plans?

"Nearly done," he said on a Friday evening when Laura sat across from him at his desk. It was a massive two-sided piece of furniture made by Chippendale the Younger in 1804. Leni had bought it for Owen years before, envisioning Felix and his father sitting cozily across from one another, working together. But it was Laura who sat there; Felix had taken advantage of the double width only a few times and not at all after Owen retired. Owen had thought of giving the desk to Thomas, who admired it, especially after he discovered a flaw in it: there was a crack in the wood behind one of the drawers where papers got stuck and seemed to disappear forever when the drawer was too full. But he didn't want to hurt Leni and the crack wasn't serious; he just used other drawers. Later he was glad he had kept the desk. Some of his happiest times came when he and Laura faced each other across its gleaming mahogany, each having what amounted to a full desk with drawers and cabinet doors flanking the kneehole opening that went through from one side to the other.

"Nearly done," he repeated with satisfaction, handing four manila folders across the desk. "New York, Chicago, Philadelphia, Washington. We'll keep them separate for now, for accounting purposes, so we know what each of them costs to renovate and furnish, but we'll buy for all four when we purchase supplies."

Laura nodded, feeling little jolts of pleasure every time Owen said "we," making her part of every step in the plans for restoring his hotels.

"Of course we'll begin with Chicago," he said, "since that's the one you'll manage."

"If I'm ready."

"You will be. My dear, you learn more quickly than anyone I've ever known, and you have at least another year to prepare. You'll be far more ready than most managers; my God, Willard Payne was a bellhop straight out of high school when I bought the Philadelphia hotel fifty-odd years ago, and he got to be manager just by outliving everybody else. Of course the hotel was fading by then; we were so busy buying new ones, building new ones, expanding to other countries . . . I let those old ones slip badly, I fear. And then none of the young hotshot managers wanted them; they wanted the glamorous modern ones." He paused. "You see, Felix is right in a way. Everyone does want only the most up-to-date of the important things. We'll find guests who like my kind of antique charm, but every one of them will demand modern plumbing and television and this new beeper system I understand they're putting in some of the Hyatts. So we have to give them both. Yesterday and today."

He gestured toward the folders. "Well, it's all there; we've talked about most of it. I've added a few more ideas; Felix won't like them —too expensive and risky—but he won't like the whole project, which is why I've always kept my small corporation separate from the family one: he has nothing to say about what I do or don't do with those four hotels. Now, what else? Ah, Clay. I'd like him to be assistant to a professional manager for a few years; then if we both decide he's ready, we'll find a hotel for him to manage. Is that satisfactory?"

"You know it is. You're wonderful to both of

us." Laura walked around the desk and kissed his forehead. "I'll read through these later. You're having dinner with us, did you remember?"

"I never forget invitations from people I love. Is it just the three of us? Or do I need a tie?"

"You don't need a tie; it's just us; I'm cooking at Paul's apartment. And he's doing the dishes. We'll see you at seven."

"Laura." She turned at the different note in Owen's voice. "You haven't told Paul about these plans, have you?"

"No; you asked me not to until we were ready to start."

He nodded. "There's a chance it might get to Felix; it will all be so much easier if he isn't trying to create obstacles. Does that bother you, to keep it secret?"

"I'd rather tell him, but if it will please you I can wait."

"Thank you. And my dear—" He paused and pulled his sweater more tightly around him. He always felt chilled these days, even in June; he didn't know why. "I've written you a letter with all our plans—financing, renovation, everything—in one document, instead of four folders: a summary of them, really, and an explanation of some things that I've done, so everyone will understand. I want you to have it in case you have to handle the project yourself."

"But why would I? You can manage everything far better than—" Her eyes widened and quickly she returned to his chair. "Is something wrong? Are you ill?"

"No. But neither am I young. A wise man thinks ahead, and if I am not wise at eighty-three, when will I be?" He held out to her a long envelope with her name on it. "Take it; put it away somewhere for safekeeping. You may not need it but I want you to have it."

"Keep it in your desk," Laura said. "Do you mind? I'll always know where it is but I'd rather you kept it." *I don't want to think about your dying; I don't want to have anything that reminds me I'm going to lose you.* "It's yours until . . . until I need it."

"If it makes you feel better." He dropped the envelope into the top drawer of his desk. "Now I'm going to take a nap so I can be scintillating at dinner. Go on, my dear; I'll see you at seven."

Laura left the house slowly and walked down

Beacon Hill, crossing the Arthur Fiedler footbridge to the promenade that ran alongside the Charles River. It was one of her favorite walks. On one side of the grassy, tree-shaded strip of land was the wide river dotted with sailboats; on the other was a narrow finger of the river; and just beyond glowed the soft red brick of old Back Bay houses. Their blunt shadows enfolded her in that special aura of sedate age and fixedness that was what she loved best about Boston. Nowhere else, she thought, would she have been able to feel so secure, with the past wiped out so completely. And nowhere else would she have felt protected enough to write to Ben about her engagement. He was still in Amsterdam—that job seemed to be lasting—and she had written to him about her graduation and her plans for marriage and a job in Chicago. She had told him most of it—but she had not told him Paul's name. There was plenty of time, she thought; once we're married, he'll keep his feelings about the Salingers to himself. Maybe he'll even change the way he feels. There's time for all of that.

Paul's apartment took up the third floor of one of the old four-story apartments in the

Back Bay, a block from the river. He had taken the basement for his studio, and Laura found him there, reorganizing photographs; old ones, she saw; he hadn't made any new ones, except pictures of her, in months. He turned and kissed her. "I set the table this afternoon, but I regret to tell you that dinner is not ready."

She laughed. "I wasn't expecting miracles. Anyway, it's going to be simple: fish chowder and salad." She leaned against him within the circle of his arms. "I'm so grateful for you. For finding you and loving you, and knowing you love me."

"And whom do you thank?" he asked with a smile.

"The fates," she said gravely. "The three daughters of Zeus. They spin the web of life, and measure it, and cut it out."

"And brought you to our family four years ago?" She was oddly silent and he said, "Well, whoever did it has my deepest thanks. He or she or they changed my life. All our lives, when you think about it. We'd all be different in some ways if you weren't here."

"Shall we take a walk before dinner?" Laura asked.

"If you're up to it after a full day with

Jules." Something had caused that sudden silence, he thought; something from her past. He wondered why she didn't understand that nothing mattered but the present and the future they would make together. He took her hand as they walked along Fairfield to the corner, coming upon the crowds of students from the colleges housed in the old buildings along Commonwealth. "Was it a good day?"

"It was a wonderful day; we pleased the Countess Irinia. I told you about her last year —the Romanian exile who wanted a yacht for a week, and we got the yacht and her favorite chef. This year she wanted ideas for a different kind of party, and I thought of a resort Jules had checked out about six months ago and raved about. It's called Darnton's and it's on its own island in Lake Champlain, and I called the owner—Kelly Darnton; she and her husband run it together—and arranged a week for the Countess and her party, with entertainment, and then Jules leased a private train to take them there. She was so pleased, like a little girl who gets to show off for her friends; she kept telling me how wonderful I am."

"She's right." Paul put his arm around her

shoulders. "Shall we go to Darnton's for our honeymoon? Or would you prefer Africa?"

She smiled. "Are those the only choices?"

"I thought of London and Paris and Rome but everyone goes there—"

"I don't."

He stopped walking. "I'm sorry; you've never been to Europe; of course that's where we should go."

"No, you choose a place you want. I really don't care, but I would like to see Europe someday."

"You'll see everything, my love. I'll make everything yours." They walked on, silent in the hazy sun that made their shadows long, thin figures trailing lazily behind them. Clusters of students and young executives coming home from work filled the sidewalks, but they barely noticed; they walked in a circle of silence, golden and dreamlike, until they were once more at Paul's building. But as they climbed the stairs to his apartment, the telephone was ringing, and when Paul answered it Laura could hear Rosa's voice, crying, saying over and over, "Mr. Owen . . . Mr. Owen . . ." and she knew he must be dead.

"No," Leni said as soon as they arrived at the hospital. "Not dead. But he had a massive stroke, and Dr. Bergman thinks he might not last the—" She bit off her words, as if saying them might make them true.

"Can we see him?" Paul asked. "We'll just look in the door . . ."

Leni was shaking her head. "They're not letting anyone in. Anyway, he's unconscious; he has been since Rosa found him . . ."

The waiting room was crowded with family members who arrived as they heard the news and then, as the hours passed, came and went, bringing food and coffee, trying to read magazines, murmuring about Owen and how frail he'd looked lately and how they should have taken him to the Cape early this year. Every hour, Dr. Bergman stopped by and said he had nothing new to tell them. But at midnight, he said Owen was stable. "We don't know the extent of the damage; we'll know better in a day or two. I think you should all go home and get some sleep. We may be in for a long stretch."

"I want to see him," Felix said flatly.

Leni put her hand on his arm. "We'll be back early in the morning. I'm sure we can see him then."

"Perhaps," the doctor said, and the next morning he did let Leni and Felix spend a few minutes beside Owen's bed. He seemed to be strung up with wires and tubes, and Felix kept repeating, "Terrible, terrible"; he could not believe this was his dominating father, this frail-looking figure lying like a puppet with strings hanging lax all around him. But part of Felix's shock was a dizzying wave of anticipation so powerful he felt he could barely stand up. He had been expecting his father's death for a long time—any son would, he told himself, with a father over eighty—but the years had passed and Owen had begun to seem eternal. Everyone still saw him as the head of the Salinger family and the head of Salinger hotels, though for years Felix had been president and fully in charge, even when his father appeared at the office and asked questions or participated in executive meetings. But now Owen was dying. Felix knew it; this time he was certain, and the certainty unleashed all his expectations with a force so overwhelming it was almost more than he could bear.

He could not show it; he had to share the others' fears and grief with a calm dignity befitting the head of a family. But inside him expectancy flowered and spread, dominating his thoughts. He was fifty-five years old and for the first time in his life there would be no shadow over him. Asa would do what he said; there was no one else to gainsay his decisions. Salinger Hotels Incorporated would at last bear his mark, and his alone. In every sense of the word, it would finally be his.

"Felix," Leni said. Her hand was on his arm and she was leading him out of the room, thinking he was frightened or crushed by the inescapable fact of his father's mortality.

"I'm going to the office," he said. "I'll come back later." He left, almost scurrying, before she could respond. He had to get out of those long corridors lined with grotesque equipment, patients in wheelchairs, carts loaded with medicines, television screens with green lines peaking and undulating to show heartbeat, brainwaves, whatever they measured in that antiseptic hell. Felix was always healthy; he prided himself on his strength and energy and the force of his will that kept him calm, never losing his temper or feeling fear or panic. But he was almost running as he reached his car, and that afternoon he called Leni at the hospital and told her there was no way he could return that day; too much depended on him at the office.

Asa knew Owen's illness changed nothing in the daily business of the hotels, but he also stayed in the office: someone had to keep an eye on Felix.

So the women kept vigil: Leni; Asa's wife, Carol, and their daughter, Patricia; Barbara Janssen, Allison, Laura, and, frequently, Rosa. Thomas Janssen was on an inspection tour of Salinger hotels in the Midwest and flew in to Boston on the weekend, but the rest of the time Paul was the only man who sat with the women in the waiting room, bringing coffee, snatching meals with them in the cafeteria, and finally, after a week, walking beside the gurney as Owen was wheeled to a private room. His uncle could not speak or move his left arm or leg, but he was conscious and not about to die.

Two weeks later they brought him home. "As long as you have twenty-four-hour nursing, he might as well be there," Dr. Bergman told Leni. "There's nothing we can do that all of you can't do, and he's probably better off in his own home. Make sure Laura spends a lot of time with him; he responds best to her."

Laura would have been with Owen anyway: she didn't want to be anywhere else. She took an unpaid leave from her job and spent her days beside Owen's bed, reading to him, talking to him even when he made no response, describing the sunrise and the sunset, the hummingbirds in the garden, nannies who pushed baby carriages and strollers along Mount Vernon Street, boys on skateboards, young girls on bicycles, their hair flying behind them, couples with clasped hands and rhythmic footsteps on the cobblestone walk.

And one day, in the middle of July, Owen smiled. And a few days later he began to talk.

At first only Laura could understand the slurred and misspoken words. Then, as he grew angry at his clumsy tongue, Owen tried to form each word separately, and others were able to decipher much of what he said. Still, it was easier for Owen and the rest of the family to let Laura repeat his words in her low, clear voice, as if she were translating a foreign language. And so when he suddenly asked for a lawyer, it was Laura who called Elwin Parkinson and greeted him when he was shown to Owen's room.

She stood up from her chair beside Owen's bed. "Do you want me to leave?"

"If you don't mind," Parkinson said.

"I'll be glad to stay and help you understand—"

"No, no. We'll get along just fine." He closed the door behind Laura and then sat in her chair and put his head near Owen's.

"Will," Owen said. He went on, one wrenching word at a time. "Meant to change it. Didn't. Do it now."

Showing no surprise, the lawyer took out a pencil and a pad of paper. "We can write a codicil; is that what you want? You're adding a new bequest?"

Owen told him what he wanted. Parkinson frowned deeply, but he wrote it down; then he moved his head so he was directly in Owen's line of sight. "This is a radical decision to make on short notice. It would perhaps be prudent to give it more thought; wait until you're better, more yourself—"

A harsh sound came from Owen's mouth and it took a minute for Parkinson to realize it was a laugh. "Don't have time. You fool. I'm dying. Last chance . . ." Suddenly his words burst out, clear and firm. *"Do it!"*

"Yes, of course, if you insist. I can have it for you to sign—can you sign it?" Owen nodded. "I can have it in a week—"

"God—!" His face contorted with rage, Owen tried to raise himself in the bed, and Parkinson, terrified that he would die and everyone would blame the lawyer who was with him, said quickly, "Tomorrow. Is that all right? I can have it for you tomorrow."

Owen's face grew calm. Closing his eyes, he gestured toward the door.

"Until tomorrow," Parkinson said, and scurried out. He saw Laura come down the stairs and slip into Owen's room as he left, and wondered where she had been while they talked, and whether she had overheard them. But he was in a hurry and did not pause in his rush down the stairs and past the library where he glimpsed members of the family having tea. Damned odd, he thought, as he drove back to his office through the afternoon traffic. He's had years to think about changing his will. If he really wanted to do it, why didn't he take care of it sooner? That had always been his way, of course—take a long time to make up his mind and then rush ahead to accomplish whatever he'd decided—but he was a top-notch businessman, and he knew that important decisions should never be made in the midst of a crisis. He could barely talk, barely move, barely think straight—but still he insisted on this radical bequest to a person none of them really, even now, knew anything about. It was damned odd. One could even say it made no sense.

For Owen Salinger's own good, Parkinson told himself solemnly, it behooves me to learn more about this young woman, before it is too late.

The family was again at tea when Parkinson returned the next afternoon and went directly to Owen's room. Once again Laura left the two men alone, and as soon as the door closed behind her, the lawyer began speaking in an urgent whisper. "Owen, I have information about that young woman—it will change your mind—it will change everything—I've found out she has a—"

"Will," Owen said, the word almost strangled in his throat.

"Yes, yes, I have it; it was finished before I got the call from New York, but you mustn't sign it—you won't want to when you know who she is—"

"*Shut up.*" Owen's eyes were glaring at Parkinson, his mouth was twisted as he tried to speak through his fury. "Will. Read it."

"Why? I'm telling you, you won't want to sign—"

"*Read!*"

Angrily, Parkinson pulled a single sheet of paper from his briefcase and read it. The instant he finished, Owen said, "Pen. *Pen!*"

"Wait. *Listen to me.* This woman is a thief, a convicted thief; she preys on old men—"

Owen's lips worked. "No."

"It's true, I have the information, I spoke to a police officer in New York—"

"No! No . . . it! No . . . difference. Fool." A ragged sigh broke from him. "Witness. Get Laura."

"I didn't understand what you said."

"*Get Laura.*"

"I want to know what you—" Parkinson saw Owen's face twist and he sucked in his breath, thinking once again that the old man was about to die. He will die, he thought, but not with me in the room. I've done my best; the hell with the rest of it. "We need someone else," he said. "A beneficiary in a will cannot be a witness to its signing. But the nurses will do. If you'll wait just a minute . . ." He crossed the hall and brought them back.

"I've asked you to listen to me," he said rapidly to Owen. "I've done my best to make you listen. No one can blame me—" He saw Owen's eyes and clutching fingers. "Yes, yes, yes." He placed a pen in Owen's fingers.

"Help . . ." Owen gasped, and the nurses lifted him to a sitting position high enough to see the document Parkinson held on a book on the mattress. Owen wrote, his sloping handwriting barely recognizable in the shaky scrawl he left on the bottom line. Then he gave a long sigh that was almost a moan. "Nearly missed," he said with a shadow of a grin at Parkinson as the nurses signed as witnesses. "Last victory." He closed his eyes. "Laura," he whispered.

"I did warn you," Parkinson said through tight lips. He slipped the document into an envelope and returned it to his briefcase. "I hope someone believes that."

"Laura," Owen whispered again. One of the

nurses was arranging the blankets and the other was unrolling the cuff to take his blood pressure as Parkinson left the room.

He found Laura on the landing, near the door. "He wants you," he said shortly. At the cold anger in his voice, she looked at him with startled eyes. "He's a sick man," he snapped, but as he said it he saw Laura's eyes change; there was a sadness in them so deep he almost felt sorry for her. But he caught himself. More likely she was just waiting for him to leave.

"Good-bye," Laura said and went into Owen's room, closing the door behind her. The nurse was rolling up the blood pressure cuff; both of them left as Laura sat beside the bed. "He's a peculiar little man," she said to Owen's closed eyes. "He seems to be angry about something. Did you shout at him?"

Without opening his eyes, Owen made the sound that Laura knew was a laugh and held out his hand. She clasped it between hers and he gave a slight nod.

"Do you want to take a nap?"

He nodded again. She rose and pulled the heavy velvet drapes across the windows overlooking the walled rose garden. The room was dark and somber. "Do you want me to stay?"

"Here."

She sat beside the bed. "What would you like?"

"Tell you." His eyes were still closed, his face ashen. "Dearest Laura. Left you a . . . little something . . . in . . . my will."

Laura's eyes filled with tears. "Don't talk about it. You're getting better. I saw you move your other hand this morning—"

"No." He opened his eyes and it was as if he were looking at her from deep within himself. "Love you, my child. Gave me such joy." Laughter trembled in his throat. "Sometimes . . . wished I was Paul. Paul's age. So much love."

Laura was crying. "Don't go. I love you, Owen. I'll take care of you, I'll make you well, I promise. I love you. Don't leave me, there are things I want to tell you . . . please, please don't go . . ."

Her head was bent over him, and Owen raised his hand and touched her tears. His fingers rested on her wet cheek. "Dearest Laura. Finish . . . our plans. Yours now. I wish . . . I could see . . . them . . ." His eyes closed. ". . . finished." His fingers slipped down her cheek. Laura grasped his hand before it could fall and took it between hers. She kissed it and held it against the tears that streamed unchecked down her face.

"You gave me my life," she said through her sobs. Her head drooped until her lips brushed Owen's still face and felt the irregular, frail breaths that barely stirred his mustache. "Everything I am. You made me proud of myself. I didn't thank you enough; I didn't even tell you the truth about myself so you'd know how much you did for me. I wanted to tell you; I want to tell you now . . . can you hear me? You gave me my life; you're part of it; part of me . . . Please say you can hear me; I haven't thanked you enough, I haven't made you understand how much you did and what it means to me . . ."

The room was hushed and dark. Laura wept, her tears falling onto Owen's cheeks so that he seemed to be crying, too. "I love you," Laura whispered at last. "I know you can hear me, because we can always hear when someone gives us love. Can't we? Dearest Owen, I love you."

The next day, without awakening, Owen Salinger died.

CHAPTER 10

FELIX was in his office when Parkinson called. "I've been trying to speak to you for three days—even today, in the cemetery—but I felt uncomfortable about discussing business there."

"My secretary says you told her it's something about my father's will," Felix said impatiently.

"More accurately, it's about Laura Fairchild."

Felix sat straighter. "What about her?"

"I'd rather tell you in person. I can be there in half an hour."

"Just give it to me now."

Parkinson felt a flash of longing for Owen's

old-world courtesy. Briefly he considered telling Felix what he thought of him. But he knew that would be unwise: the Salinger account was vastly bigger than Elwin Parkinson's pride. "Well, then. She has a record, in New York, for theft. She and her brother Clay."

"Theft," Felix repeated tonelessly. "When?"

"Seven years ago. She was fifteen; her brother was fourteen."

"And the parents?"

"According to the police report they were killed in an auto-truck accident the year before. It isn't clear who was their guardian; most likely their aunt. They were released in her custody after the arrest. Melody Chase."

"What?"

"I know it sounds improbable, but that was the name I was given."

"Probably a fake. What else?"

"Two years later, when she was seventeen, she was named in a will filed for probate—a bookseller named Hendy. He left her ten books."

"Anything else?"

"I wouldn't treat that lightly; it may be significant, especially if the books had value."

"Why?"

"Because the day before he died your father changed his will; he added—"

"He what?"

"He added a codicil leaving two percent of Salinger Hotels Incorporated and one hundred percent of the Owen Salinger Corporation to Laura Fairchild."

"Two percent? To that woman? You knew he was going to do this and you didn't tell me?"

"A lawyer doesn't talk about his client's decisions to others."

"Not others, you damned fool! His son! What the fuck were you thinking about, letting him do this? Are you out of your mind? His corporation, too? With those four hotels?"

"And his house on Beacon Hill."

"Goddam son of a bitch! He broke up his estate? And you didn't try to stop him?"

"I did try—"

"Not very hard! Not hard enough!" Felix felt as if his insides were twisted into knots; his stomach was taut, his teeth clenched. "He was mad."

"I don't think so; he knew he wanted to sign it; he even argued with me about it. And he knew it had to be witnessed; he forced me to bring in the nurses. His mind was very clear." Parkinson paused; it was time to make himself indispensable to Felix. "However, I did have a feeling—"

"What?"

"That he was very tired. And perhaps—of course one can't be sure—" He stopped.

"Fuck it, Parkinson, stop dancing around. Sure of what?"

"I did have the feeling he might have been under some kind of pressure."

The words reverberated in the air. Felix let them settle slowly into a new idea, and his muscles began to relax. "You mean someone was influencing him."

"Someone might have been."

"Someone who had a habit of getting old men to change their wills."

"I didn't say that."

"No," said Felix thoughtfully. "But if you were asked for your opinion . . ."

"I would have to say I had the distinct impression that Owen Salinger was highly agitated and acting under some kind of coercion or persuasion. I might add that I was alone with him in his room on two consecutive days, having asked Miss Fairchild to leave before we talked, and on both occasions, when I left I found her hovering outside the door."

"Thank you, Elwin," Felix said softly. He sat for a moment, hearing the slight whine of Parkinson's breathing on the other end of the line. "We've set the reading of the will for next week; you'll probably hear from me before then." He hung up and walked to his corner windows to look across the Public Gardens toward Beacon Hill. And his thoughts began to churn again. Left the house to that woman. And his hotels. And part of the company. My company. Insane. Vindictive. Making me look like a fool. At the last minute, when we couldn't stop him . . .

But I will stop him. He's dead and I'm alive, and I'll tear that woman apart; I'll tear his fucking codicil apart. We'll make the old will stick. It was good enough for him when he made it; it's good enough now. Everything else gets destroyed.

Looking at the Gardens, he felt a sudden alarm. Maybe there was more than the will. What else did the old man dictate or write? What other secrets did he have? What else needed destroying?

He had to find out. He couldn't wait; he had to know.

At seven he telephoned Paul. "I thought we might have dinner together, just the two of us. It's late, I know, but I've been tied up."

"How about lunch tomorrow?" Paul asked. "Laura's here and she's so upset, after the funeral this morning, I don't want to leave her."

"Fine. My secretary will call you in the morning."

And having made sure they were both away, he went to Owen's house.

"Good evening, Rosa," he said, walking past her and starting up the stairs. "I'll be in my father's study. You can go to bed; I'll let myself out."

Rosa bristled. Never in fifty years had Mr. Owen sent her off to bed. "Would you like coffee? Something to eat?" She sent her voice up the stairs after him. "Or I might help you find something? I've been doing a bit of cleaning—" She turned away to swallow the sudden tears that were always near the surface these days.

But Felix was already crossing the upstairs foyer to the third-floor stairway. "I can help myself," he said over his shoulder, and as he took the stairs two at a time he repeated the words to himself. I can help myself.

Owen's study was lovingly dusted, the books that had been scattered on tables and the floor made into unnaturally neat stacks, the papers on his desk aligned in perfect piles. Felix switched on the lamp on the Chippendale desk and began to go through the papers on top and then in the drawers. It took only a few minutes to find the envelope with Laura's name, and to read the letter inside.

Beloved Laura,

It is a fine day outside, as fine as I feel. But at my age a prudent man contemplates his mortality, and the things he may never have a chance to finish, and so today, while my mind is clear and my hand still strong, and my heart perhaps steadier than ever, I am writing to put in concise form the plans you and I have made together, for my hotels, because you know better than anyone what they mean to me. But first I want you to know that I am planning to change my will, leaving to you a small part of the family company, and this house, and all of my own corporation. This means the hotels will be yours when I die, and therefore you will be the one to oversee their rebirth if I cannot.

Felix stopped reading. There were ten pages, closely covered with his father's bold, sloping handwriting, but now that he knew what they were, he could not read them: he couldn't stand hearing his father's voice, through his written words, saying he preferred Laura to his own son. His hands were shaking and he realized he was holding his breath. Bastard, he thought, letting it out in an explosive burst. To do that to me. Telling the whole world you didn't care about me; you cared about *her;* you were giving her what I wanted. Only a sick man would do that to a son.

Sick. Under pressure. Coercion.

With a surge of energy he went through the papers on top of the desk and pulled everything out of the drawers, searching them for phrases, sentences, odd words that would show a mind unhinged. And then, in the midst of his frantic reading, both hands full of papers and envelopes, he heard the front door open, and voices from below: Rosa, loud and pleased, then Laura, then Paul. He couldn't make out their words; they were two floors below. What the hell were they doing here? Why weren't they fucking in bed?

He shoved the papers into the top drawer, stuffing them to the back so he could close it. No, damn it, some of them had been on top. Neat piles. He remembered. Pulling out papers at random, he put them squarely on the desktop and forced the drawer shut. Something was jammed at the back, and he gave a final push as Rosa's voice reached the other side of the closed door. "—got here about an hour ago; he said he'd be in his father's study."

There was a knock at the door. "Felix," Paul said, but Felix was moving silently into his father's adjoining bedroom. He heard the door from the hall open. "Sorry to bother you, but Laura needs—" There was a pause, and Felix heard him say, "He's not here."

"My goodness," Rosa said. "And I never heard him leave. I must be getting old. Though Felix always was very big on creeping about and surprising people. Well, we won't be bothering him, that's clear. Can I help you find something, Laura?"

"No thank you," Laura said, her voice almost inaudible. "We just came for a few of my things; I'm going to stay at Paul's for a few days."

Felix crept into the hallway from the bedroom and then down the carpeted stairs. *Creeping about.* That stupid woman would be fired as soon as he could manage it. He eased open the front door and closed it quietly behind him. Staying at Paul's, she said. There would be plenty of time tomorrow to come back for the letter and anything else he could find.

Unless that was what she'd come back for.

He cursed himself. He could have taken it instead of shoving it back into the drawer; what in God's name had gotten into him? He stood beside his car, torn between getting away before they saw him or waiting until the house was dark and then going back to find out for sure. He had his own key; he'd never used it but this was the time.

He waited. He had to know.

Half an hour later, he saw Laura and Paul leave. It took another two hours for Rosa's light to go out. And then he waited another hour before returning to the house and using the key he had had made after Owen's heart attack four years earlier.

He felt his way in the darkness up the two flights of stairs and into the study, closing the door quietly behind him before turning on the same lamp he had used hours earlier. And then he opened the drawer and rummaged through it, looking for the letter.

Which wasn't there.

He yanked the drawer out of the desk and turned it upside down, but only a single invoice was still in it, caught in a crack on the side. He went through the papers on top of the desk. Not here, not here, not here. She took it. The bitch took it. Conned a sick old man, then stole papers from his desk.

She didn't con him. The letter proves it.

Rage flooded him; his throat was filled with bile. He stood beside the desk, breathing in ragged gasps, trying to think.

He had to get it back. She'd use it to prove the old man wasn't sick and coerced, to show he knew what he was doing and did it on his own. Have to get it back, he thought; have to find it. Not let that bitch and that old man make a fool of me in front of my family and the whole world.

Have to think of something. And I will. I'm not the kind who panics and makes mistakes.

I'll think of something; I'll figure this out the way I always do.

I can take care of myself.

At the will reading, he attacked. He had thought of nothing new, and so he charged forward, as if the letter did not exist. Everyone in the family was talking at once and he stood up, to take charge. He stood behind the heavy library table with his hand on Parkinson's shoulder to keep him silent. When he had his family's attention, he spoke to Laura, who was standing in front of a window with Paul's arm around her. His voice was flat.

"He didn't know what he wanted. He was a sick old man who was manipulated and terrorized by a greedy, conniving witch, and for the entire month after his stroke—"

"Felix!" Paul's deep voice cut across his uncle's raspy one. "What the hell are you talking about?"

"You fucking bastard!" Clay bellowed, riding over Paul's words. "Who the fuck do you—"

"Keep your mouth shut," Felix snapped and went on, never breaking stride. "—entire month after his stroke was a helpless invalid who could neither move nor speak—"

"Felix!" Paul said again.

"He could speak!" Laura said. "He talked to me—we talked—"

"—neither move nor speak intelligibly, and it was obvious to everyone that he had lost his ability to think clearly. And that obvious fact was taken advantage of by this *girl*, who was only one of his whims until she wormed her way into his life and then, when he was dying, kept the nurses out of his room so she could be alone with him and manipulate him into changing his will—"

"That's enough," Paul said furiously. "God damn it, Felix, you're mad; what the hell has gotten into you? This is a goddam pack of lies—"

"Owen didn't want the nurses!" Laura cried. "He told me to keep them out!" Her tears had dried in streaks on her cheeks. "He didn't want strangers; he wanted me!"

"He didn't know what he wanted—" Felix began for the third time.

"Shut up!" Paul roared. "Let Elwin finish reading! And by God you'll explain this to me later; you'll apologize to Laura and to the whole family—"

Ignoring Paul, Felix put his head back, looked down his thin nose, and flung his voice at Laura. *"He didn't know anything, did he?* He didn't know that you're a criminal with a record, that you have a criminal for a brother, and that you lied to him—you lied to all of us —for four years while we took you in and gave you everything."

Her gasp ripped across the room and he knew she would lose.

"Four years," he repeated, hammering at her. "And we all know that four years ago, the summer you and your brother appeared at our door, our house was robbed of an irreplaceable collection of jewelry and—"

"We didn't have anything to do with that!" Clay shouted.

Everyone was talking at once, turning to each other in alarm, calling out to Felix to explain what he meant. But Felix spoke directly to Laura. "You don't think we'd believe that! From the evidence I now possess, I have concluded that you came here for one purpose only—to rob us—and then decided to stay when you saw you could wrap your tentacles around my father, *just as you'd done once before with another old man who left you a fortune before he died,* and then!"—he shouted above his family's rising clamor, with a glance at Paul—"then you wrapped yourself around a *young* man of wealth, because professional fortune hunters never miss a chance, do they, Miss Fairchild?"

"I'm not! I loved Owen!" Laura flared, but she sounded breathless. "I love Paul. You have no right to lie—"

"Don't you talk to me of *right!* You came to us with lies; you came to entrap, to ensnare; you wormed your way into our household . . . *and you robbed us of my wife's jewels and almost killed my father!*"

"It's a goddam lie!" Clay shouted. "We didn't do that job; we changed our—"

Triumph flashed through Felix. He saw Paul's arm drop from Laura's shoulder, saw Leni's look of disbelief, and saw Allison's shocked, angry stare. Good. Let her try to bring up her letter now; it was too late. He had her.

He looked at Laura with contempt. "*You changed nothing.* You're a couple of common criminals; you've never been anything else; and

I'm going to see to it that everyone knows it. I'm going to break that codicil in court; I'm going to see to it that you don't get a penny of my father's fortune. You'll leave the way you came, with nothing; you'll leave now, and you'll never have anything to do with any of us again!"

In the cacophony of the room he saw Laura put a hand against the windowpane; he watched her look up as Paul moved away, putting distance between them. And then he saw her eyes change, as if she remembered—

"Wait! Wait a minute!" she cried. "Owen wrote a letter . . . before his stroke . . . before he was sick! He told me about it—about what it said. I didn't force him to do anything —I can prove it—!" She turned and almost ran to the door.

"I'll come with you," Paul said. His eyes were dark with doubt, but he followed her and slammed the door behind them. "Will you tell me what the hell is going on?"

"I can't talk about it," Laura said. *He isn't sure; he thinks Felix might be telling the truth. How can he think that if he loves me?* "I just want to prove that I didn't force Owen to love me. He really did love me, God damn it, and I can prove it! And then I'll get out of here so no one—"

"Why?" He was keeping up with her as she sped up the stairs to the third floor. "If everything Felix says is a lie—"

Laura yanked open the door of Owen's study and ran to the desk.

"Is it all a lie?" Paul demanded.

She pulled the drawer toward her and sucked in her breath at the disorder within. "It never looked like this . . . I'll have to look through everything . . ." Sitting down, she pulled out all the papers and put them in her lap. The room was quiet. And when she finally looked up, Paul saw in her eyes bewilderment and then despair. "It's not here."

He looked at her, wanting to go to her but holding back, remembering.

Laura mimicking Jules. A superb actress.

Laura climbing, like a cat. "I used to climb on the rocks up the Hudson."

Her job as assistant concierge. "It's something I can talk about and not hide."

Her refusal to handle merchandise in department stores. As if someone might accuse her of trying to steal.

Her collection of ten perfect first editions

worth forty-five thousand dollars. Left her by an old man in his will.

"I asked him to keep it; I didn't want it," Laura was saying, almost to herself. "I didn't want to be reminded that he'd die, so I asked him to keep it and he said he would, and he put it in this drawer. I saw him."

"What did it say?"

"I didn't read it. He said it was an outline of all the plans we'd been making—plans for his hotels, the ones he owns separate from all the others."

"The hotels he left you."

"Yes, but I didn't know he was going to leave them to me."

"You had a letter from Owen and you didn't read it."

"I didn't need to. Don't you understand? It was only in case he . . . died. . . ."

"Was Felix lying about the rest?"

"Damn you!" Laura leaped to her feet. "Damn you, damn you, how can you ask me that? You saw me with Owen—you know how I was with you—*I loved you and I loved him!* Everything I did—everything you saw for a whole year—I did with love. And you know it! You're not a fool—you know what you saw, what you heard, what you felt . . . You know what you felt! It wasn't a lie! Was it? Were we lying—a whole year together—*were we lying?*"

"I wasn't." He was frowning as he looked at her, and Laura knew that for the first time he was listening to her as if there might be a double meaning in her words.

She held her head high and looked straight at him. "Owen believed in me. I gave him my love and my trust and he was proud to have them and he gave me . . . he gave me the same . . . so much I could never thank . . ." She swallowed hard. But her voice was husky. "He loved me, he believed in me, and damn you— *damn you*—for making me believe in your love as much as I believed in his and then not trusting me when Felix—"

She turned away. She was cold inside, and numb, and her eyes were dry. *I won't cry. I'll never let anyone make me cry again, not through love, not through pain.* Her back to Paul, she said, "Every day the world seemed new and wonderful because of you . . . and I thought you felt the same. But you pulled away from me, you cut us apart as soon as he started talking. You didn't believe in me enough to wait until we could talk . . . until we could sort it out. You didn't believe in our love . . . or in anything. Not even in your own feelings. Or yourself."

They stood without moving in the heavy silence. Laura's hands lifted slightly, then fell. Her back straight, her head high, she walked to the door.

"Was he telling the truth?" Paul asked.

"Yes," she said and left the room.

The family's voices stopped abruptly as she opened the library door. She saw Felix look at her hands and wondered why his eyebrows shot up. Why did he still pretend? He knew she wouldn't find the letter; he'd taken it the night Rosa said he was here. She looked around the room, her eyes moving impassively over Allison's bewildered, angry face, Leni's bleak sadness, Barbara Janssen's puzzled eyes, the confusion among all the others in the Salinger family. Her look reached Clay's scowl. "We're leaving," she said.

Rosa would send her clothes; she'd stay in Philadelphia, with Clay, until they decided what to do next. She had to find a lawyer, to see if they had any chance against Felix. But there's probably not a hope in hell, she thought. What judge would believe Laura

Fairchild, who had a police record in New York, against Felix Salinger, president of Salinger Hotels Incorporated and a prominent member of Boston society? She had to try, but it wasn't something to count on.

No one had spoken. She looked at Felix, and their eyes held for a long moment. *I'm going to do everything I can to ruin you. However long it takes, whatever I have to do, I'll make you pay for lying about Owen, and about me, and for taking those hotels and this house away from me when he wanted me to have them—and died thinking I would.*

Without looking back she and Clay walked out of the library, and out of the house, into the heavy heat of the August sun. Laura turned to look once more at the house, gazing at the red brick, the dark green shutters, Owen's windows on the third floor. *Dearest Owen . . . dearest friend. Godspeed. God bless you. I love you.*

Part III

CHAPTER 11

THE lawyer's name was Ansel Rollins. Rail-thin, with pale eyes, long jowls, and a few strands of hair across his smooth brow, he was the father of one of Laura's classmates at the university, and as firmly a part of Old Boston society as Felix's lawyer, Carver Cheyne. "I know Carver and I understand him," Rollins told Laura and Clay as they sat at a round table in his air-conditioned office. "A fine attorney. We don't know, of course, what kind of a case they think they have, but we do have a chance. Of course, they would not even start this fight if you could find the letter you say Mr. Salinger wrote: it would prove he knew what he wanted long before he had his stroke; it would establish irrefutably that you are entitled to this inheritance. . . ."

"I can't get back in the house," Laura said.

"Well." He pursed his lips. "Everyone knew how close the two of you were . . . we certainly have a chance."

Otherwise, Laura thought, you wouldn't have taken the case on contingency; working for nothing in the expectation of getting a third of what we win.

Rollins squared his yellow legal pad in front of him. "We have several decisions to make. First, we will of course request a jury trial."

"We're *entitled* to a jury," Clay said heatedly.

"Indeed. But you could waive it if you wished, in favor of a hearing by a judge. It would probably occur sooner and take less time than a jury trial but"—he surveyed Laura's face—"a jury would be more responsive to a beautiful young woman in distress than a judge sitting alone in his courtroom."

"How long must we wait?" Laura asked.

"Six months to a year—"

"What?" Clay was on his feet. "Laura gets cheated out of her inheritance and nobody does anything for a fucking *year?*"

"We will be doing a great deal," said Rollins. "Do please sit down, young man. I cannot speed the wheels of justice, try as I might."

Clay sat, and for the rest of the afternoon they went over and over the past five years. Laura and Clay told Rollins everything—but left out Ben. They had decided that together. Clay had been vehement about it. "He'd ruin us; he'd ruin our chances. We're okay now; nobody can prove we robbed them—"

"We didn't rob them!" Laura had exclaimed.

"Ben might say we did, to cover his ass. And they already think it. I just don't want him here! Keep him out of it!"

Laura, more quietly, had agreed. Telling about Ben would be admitting to another five-year lie, making them seem even more untrustworthy. So they kept Ben out of it while revealing everything else.

Rollins pursed his lips as they talked. "I see a number of dangers," he murmured, making notes. "But if we're prepared for them . . . All right," he concluded. "I'll call you soon and we'll plan the next step. I can reach you at this number, in Philadelphia?"

"No." Laura wrote on his legal pad. "We'll be here after tomorrow."

"Darnton's," he read. "Jay's Landing, New York. Darnton's?"

"A resort. We'll be there for a while, anyway. But we'll come to Boston whenever you need us; we'll do whatever has to be done. And we'll wait as long as we have to, but I hope you'll try to speed it up; it's very important to me."

"Money always is," he said dryly.

"I'm not talking about money." *I'm talking about revenge. And getting back what Owen gave me. And fighting, to help me forget I've lost a family, and what I thought was love.*

"What's our chances?" Clay asked bluntly as they shook hands.

"Fair to good," Rollins replied. "Assuming of course, that everyone manages to keep calm."

"Cold son of a bitch," Clay muttered as they left the office. He repeated it in the restaurant where they had lunch before leaving the city. "Cold son of a bitch. *He* doesn't have anything at stake."

"A lot of money," Laura said absently. Her thoughts were racing, from fury at Felix, to a hollow sense of loss over Owen and Paul, to uncertainty about the future. She knew, whatever Rollins said, that the trial was a long shot and that she had to make plans for afterwards.

Looking out the window beside their booth, she saw her ghostly image in the glass. I forgot makeup, she thought, and I need a haircut. And Rosa would tell me to sit straight. But Rosa was gone.

Her breath came faster, as if she'd been running; she was knotted up inside with anger and hurt. There was too much to think about all at once, too much to sort out, and no time to do it. They had to be on the move; they had to earn a living. I wish I had a quiet minute, she thought; I wish I could wipe everything out and start fresh and know what's ahead of me.

I wish I was somebody else.

Abruptly, she stood up. "I'll be right back," she told Clay and went to the powder room at the back of the restaurant.

For a moment she stood before the mirror, looking at herself. Then she took a small scissors from the manicure kit in her purse and started cutting her hair. She chopped and hacked, a few strands at a time. The ends were uneven, and the more she tried to even it the more ragged it became. But as it grew shorter it became more curly until finally she was left with a cap of springy hair with small ends protruding like tiny antennae. Her face looked smaller, her cheekbones higher, her eyes enormous.

Clay was paying the waiter when she rejoined him, and his mouth fell open. "What the hell did you do to yourself? Christ, I hardly recognized you."

"Good. I don't want to look the same."

"You were prettier before."

She shrugged.

As they drove away and headed north out of the city, he said, trying to sound casual, "Rollins said you'd need to be beautiful and pathetic on the witness stand."

"I'll be whatever I am. They'll believe me or they won't."

"Laura." Worriedly, he peered at her. "You're not giving up, are you?"

"No."

He was silent as he negotiated a traffic circle. "You'll be fine," he said, as much to himself as to her. "You'll be great."

She did not answer. How stupid, she thought, to try to change anything by cutting my hair. I have to change the way I think and feel and remember. Looking different doesn't mean anything; being different does.

She pushed her thoughts ahead, and tried to picture Kelly and John Darnton. She had never met them except over the telephone, but they had offered her a place to stay when she had called the week before, in desperation.

"You always have a place with us," Kelly had said without hesitation. "You didn't think I'd say no, did you? My God, lady, you sent us the Countess Irinia and a trainload of rich friends for a whole week—you practically saved our summer—and you think I'd say no? I wouldn't turn you down for anything you asked! I'd probably *give* you the place, if you asked for it!"

So they were still having trouble, Laura thought as she and Clay drove across the Massachusetts state line into New Hampshire and she began to look at the scenery. Until now, she had been careful not to look too closely at the forests and meadows, the marshes, the ponds with flocks of birds darting above them, because everything reminded her of long rides with Paul through just such countryside, but when the highway began to follow the Merrimack River, she looked up and let herself enjoy it. There were no memories in New Hampshire, nor in Vermont, and by the time they were driving through Montpelier, past its vast granite quarry, she and Clay were talking about the landscape, the neat houses and white New England churches behind long low walls of tightly fitted rocks that early settlers had cleared from the stubborn New England soil, and about Darnton's. "I'm not sure how successful they are," Laura said. "The countess told me she was very pleased, so it's far from shabby, but I have a feeling they really stretched themselves to impress her. I hope we can help them."

"Fuck it, we could have been millionaires, and instead we're on our way to rescue some people on the brink of bankruptcy."

She broke into laughter. "They're not on the brink, and they're the ones rescuing us, not the other way around."

"And we still have a chance to be millionaires. Right?"

"I don't know." She looked away from him, amused but a little troubled by his casual assumption that her inheritance would be his, too. She was glad it was his turn to drive; she could look at the Green Mountains that had suddenly risen up to surround them, as lush and bright as their name. They were her first mountains and she stared at their massive beauty, mesmerized by the way they enfolded the road and the car, making the rest of the world seem distant and unreal. A person could forget everything here, she thought, but Clay brought her back by pulling over beside a small lake in Waterbury.

"Your turn," he said. "I'm going to take a nap."

So she found Darnton's by herself, turning south at Burlington to follow the shore of Lake Champlain until she came to the small town of Jay's Landing, and the causeway Kelly had described, leading to the island. No guest cars were allowed on the island—"But you can drive over," Kelly had said. "Unload your luggage and let us make you welcome."

That was what greeted Laura when she drove up: Kelly's welcome. She rushed from the lodge and gave Laura a hug that made her breathless, then stood back, grinning, her red cheeks crinkling in her fair face.

Laura smiled back. Everyone, she would discover, smiled at Kelly Darnton, unable to resist the warmth of her black eyes, the halo of her long black hair that defied comb and brush to fly out in all directions, and her vigorous carrying voice that announced her arrival before she herself appeared. She was taller than Laura, and broader, and twice her age, but her exuberance made her seem younger, especially beside Laura's reticence.

"Hi," she said to Clay, who had emerged from the car. "Did your sister do all the driving?"

"Why should she? I drove my share."

"Good. We need a chauffeur. We don't allow guests to drive on the island, so we have a bunch of very classy vintage cars and we drive everybody to our golf course on the mainland and wherever else they want to go. Sound interesting?"

"God, it sounds terrific."

"I thought it might. Come on."

She had taken charge, and Laura watched with gratitude as she led Clay to the double row of garages behind the main lodge and introduced him to the head chauffeur. Clay was so young in so many ways; even working in Philadelphia hadn't seemed to make him grow up. Perhaps Kelly and John would find a way to help him get past his boyishness, as charming as it often was.

Alone, she walked up a small incline to get her bearings. Darnton's main lodge, a sprawling two-story white building with red shutters and a red roof, straddled a gentle rise at the far end of its own island, outlined against the deep blue of Lake Champlain and the pine-covered slopes of the Adirondacks in the distance. A pine forest covered much of the island itself, crisscrossed by horseback and walking trails, the trees giving way to a sweeping lawn in front of the lodge, tennis courts at the side, an outdoor pool to match the indoor one used mostly in winter, croquet and badminton fields, and a long flagstone walk leading to the marina and docks.

In the midst of one of the busiest resort areas in the country, Darnton's island was serene, wooded and beautiful. And the forests and beaches reminded Laura vividly of Osterville, on Cape Cod.

"Give a boy a bunch of cars and he's happy for a day," Kelly said, joining her. She gave Laura a sharp look. "What's wrong? Memories? I never asked why you wanted to come up here. Somebody died? Or betrayed you? Or kicked you out?"

All of the above. "Kelly, do you mind if I don't talk about it yet?"

"You don't ever have to talk about it. Come on and get settled. I fixed up a couple of spare rooms for the two of you; you even have your own sitting room. Dinner's in an hour. And by the way," she added casually, "I've done a fair bit of haircutting in my time."

Laura's hand went to her short, ragged hair. "It looks terrible, doesn't it?"

"Mostly amateurish." Kelly ran her blunt fingers through it. "It's not beyond repair. Maybe after dinner we'll give it some loving care."

"Thank you," Laura said. "Loving care would be wonderful."

That night Kelly trimmed her hair, helped her make the beds in the two tiny rooms, joined by a small sitting room, at the back of the lodge, and hung clothes in the closet as Laura unpacked. "Nice," she said, fingering the cashmere sweaters, silk blouses, and challis skirts Owen had insisted she buy. "I still have some of these left over from the days when I bought clothes instead of spending everything my parents left me on this lodge."

"But you're doing well here," Laura said, somewhere between a statement and a question.

"Surviving. Do you want some brandy? John was in such a hurry to get to the mainland we didn't offer you an after-dinner drink."

Laura shook her head. "It would knock me out. I haven't been sleeping too well."

"Tea? Darjeeling. Dark, soothing, good for a soul in turmoil."

A laugh escaped Laura's composed lips. "That sounds perfect."

They sat in armchairs in a lamplit corner of the great hall, drinking tea and talking late into the night. The room had a soaring pitched ceiling, walls of knotless pine paneling framing two massive stone fireplaces at each end of the room, a dark plank floor strewn with animal skins, and groupings of buffalo plaid couches and armchairs. Fur throw pillows, willow-twig rocking chairs, pewter lamps, and ceramic vases with arrangements of leafless branches of mountain ash still holding their red-orange berries, gave color and warmth to the rustic comfort of the room. It was, after all, completely different from the airy wicker and chintz of the Salinger homes at the Cape, and the velvets and brocades of Owen's house on Beacon Hill. It was a place where one could forget the past.

"We didn't do all the furnishing," Kelly said, taking one of the amaretto cookies the chef had served with their tea. "Most of it was left here by the oil baron who built it and then sold it in the middle of an acrimonious divorce. Trouble was, he and his wife hadn't been speaking for a long time, so they'd let the place deteriorate and there was an awful lot for us to do. Are you going to miss working at the Salinger?"

"I'll miss the job. I liked it."

"I have a couple you could handle whenever you're ready to work again."

"Do you really? I was hoping you might have something. I'll do anything, Kelly, any job you have."

Kelly smiled. "Whatever they are?"

"I need work. So does Clay. We have to start somewhere."

"How about assistant manager of Darnton's?"

"Assistant manager?" Laura repeated. "But

you must have one. You couldn't run the place without one."

"True. But you see, you have arrived in the midst of a crisis." Kelly held her cup with both hands and rested her feet on the edge of the glass-topped coffee table supported on four pine logs. "Last week my short-fused husband fired the assistant manager and two maintenance men for soliciting tips from guests—which, of course, isn't a hell of a long way from blackmail, so I agree with his decision, it's the timing that bothers me. End of August, almost Labor Day, just about the busiest time of the year, and we have close to a full house. We're desperate for help. You'd be doing us a favor."

"I can't believe it; it's so perfect . . . And you want Clay to be a chauffeur? He could do other things; he was a desk clerk at a hotel in Philadelphia and he'll learn anything you tell him."

"First we need a chauffeur. If he passes John's driving test, he's got the job. After that we'll find other things for him to do. Why not? My friend, you are manna from heaven. First you send us the countess and now you bring us yourself. Except, you know we only have a hundred rooms, Laura, a third of what you had at the Salinger. You might be bored."

"I won't be bored." Laura hesitated. "There is one other thing. We'll have to be in Boston now and then for . . . business . . . some things we didn't get to finish. If that makes too much trouble for you, maybe I ought to take a job that isn't so important."

"How long will you be away?"

"I don't know. We'd make it as short as possible."

"Well, we'll work it out. Is this business going to go on very long?"

"It may take a year."

Kelly gave a small grunt. "Sounds like lawyers; nobody else drags things out that long. Let me know ahead of time when you'll be going."

"Thank you, Kelly."

It was almost three months before they went back for pretrial depositions, just before Thanksgiving. They drove the opposite direction, through the Green Mountains, white and pristine this time beneath drifts of snow that had not yet turned to ice, then through the meadows and forests of New Hampshire and into Massachusetts. With each mile the scenes grew more familiar, and by the time they arrived in Boston and parked near the glass and steel building in the financial district where Carver Cheyne had his office, Laura was tense with holding herself in, trying to ignore the waves of memory and desire that swept through her.

Once in Cheyne's office it was easier: his window blinds were drawn, fluorescent lights glared, the furniture was dull brown. With Ansel Rollins and a court stenographer sitting beside her, and Clay waiting his turn in the reception room, she answered Cheyne's questions in a level voice, her face betraying no emotion, going over the same story she had told Rollins, in exactly the same way. But Cheyne was not Rollins: not sympathetic, not gently leading her step by step through her story. He was cold and deliberate, returning again and again to her relationship with Owen, asking how she began working in his library, how often they went for walks, how many meals they ate together, how often they were alone instead of with other members of the family, how many times she wrote personal letters for him that no one else knew about, how many of his business affairs she handled alone so that he had to turn to her and no one else when he wanted to refer to them.

"He didn't *have to* turn to me," said Laura angrily. "He wanted to. We worked together and he trusted me."

"Of course," Cheyne said smoothly. "Tell me again, would you, why he fired his secretary."

"He didn't fire her. I told you, she worked for the executive offices in the Boston Salinger, and now that I was with him he didn't need to take her from her other work anymore."

"Now that you were with him. Was it your suggestion that he fire his secretary and use you instead?"

"He didn't fire his secretary!"

It went on and on, but Laura and Rollins knew it could have been worse: Cheyne could have brought up her arrest and conviction in New York. "It's a good sign, that they didn't," Rollins said as they left Cheyne's office after Clay had gone through the same procedure as Laura. "It's obvious they're convinced it would do no good to bring it up in court; I'd be ready for them, and I'm sure the judge would not allow it; it has no bearing on this case."

"How sure?" Clay demanded.

"Sure enough," Rollins said shortly. "What happened today showed us what they have. You may have thought the questions were difficult, but they were what I expected. The whole purpose of depositions is to get information. And of course to make sure no one springs any surprises at the trial."

"Then why bother to have a trial?" Clay asked, recalling dramatic trial scenes in films and on television.

"So a jury can decide who is telling the truth," Rollins said dryly. "You were the one who told me that was your right."

Clay mumbled something and Laura asked, "We'll know everything everyone is going to say before the trial begins?"

"Unless something is discovered at the last minute, or witnesses change their stories."

A flash of fear went through her. "Why would they?"

"They might remember something they'd forgotten or be asked a question one of the lawyers didn't ask at the deposition. It doesn't happen often." He led them to the door. "I'll call you soon."

He called in December. Laura was in Kelly's office, and she went into her small one adjoining it and closed the door to talk to him. He had conducted his depositions in his office, questioning the Salingers, the doctor and nurses, and Parkinson. "Nothing startling," he concluded when he had related them to her. "But that gives me concern. At the moment they have a weak case, and I would expect Carver to have more than we've seen. He's very confident."

"You mean we should be worried."

"I mean we should be alert. You and I should meet several more times before the trial. We'll begin in two weeks; can you get here?"

"Of course."

"Good. Make sure your story is clear."

"It is clear, since it's the truth," Laura said coldly. "Didn't the doctor and nurses say everything was normal?"

"As I told you, they said as far as they could tell Mr. Salinger was weak, and frustrated by his limitations, but not unduly agitated. That was the most definitive they would get. Our best hope is Parkinson: he's a fine lawyer and he was absolutely straightforward in answering my questions. He wouldn't have prepared that codicil or allowed Mr. Salinger to sign it if he thought something was amiss; no reputable lawyer would. As long as he says Mr. Salinger knew what he wanted, I think we're in excellent shape."

"Is that all?" Laura asked after a moment. "Didn't . . . anyone else give a deposition?"

"You're thinking of Paul Janssen. No. I understand from Carver that he doesn't want to testify. No one wants a reluctant witness—you never know what you'll get—so at least for now he won't be called."

Laura was silent. She didn't know what Paul was thinking. I could write to him, she thought; but she didn't know what she could say. Are you reluctant because you still love me? But if you do, why not tell the jury I would never rob the family or take anything from Owen or try to make him act against his will? Or is it that you still believe I'm guilty of those things and you don't want to have anything to do with me, for good or ill?

She didn't want to think about it. Whether they won or lost in court, Paul was gone; he was making a new life, as she was. No court case would change that.

She concentrated on work, learning the business of running a resort. She had written to

Ben, telling him where they were. "Things didn't work out at the Salingers'," she wrote. She couldn't tell him about Owen's will and how they'd been forced out; it would only prove to him that he'd been right about the Salingers from the first, when he told her they didn't care about her and never would. So she sent him her new address, and a short note, and that was all. And then, with all the others, she pushed Ben out of her thoughts and buried herself in the large problems and small details of the resort.

She and Kelly had divided the domestic and business affairs, while John handled transportation, sports, and the physical plant. They all worked in harmony, especially as Laura took on more responsibilities. From her first tentative days at the job she had, over the months, grown more sure of herself. Everything she had learned with Jules LeClair about the whims and demands of guests, she used at Darnton's. She used everything she had learned from Owen about the organization of hotels and priorities of management; she used the case studies she had done at the university; she used everything Kelly taught her about the peculiarities of a resort. She worked all day and late into every night, studying the way Darnton's functioned, and how it might function better; and when Kelly or John urged her to relax, she thanked them but went back to work. If she won at the trial, she could relax. If she didn't, she had to earn a living while she tried to figure out a way to get back some of what was rightfully hers.

After Christmas the lodge suddenly was quiet, and the island seemed deserted. "We ought to close down and go to Florida," John said.

"Too much work to do," Kelly responded.

It was an old argument, and it flared and faded as the weeks passed and they made plans for the summer. The three of them coordinated the different staffs that worked on the island, made lists of equipment, and wrote schedules for tennis, horseback riding, swimming and aerobic classes, speed- and sailboat cruises on the lake, golf on their eighteen-hole course in Jay's Landing, card games, and first-run movies shown at night. And, since people judge a place largely on food, they spent extra time on the dining room and bar menus for more than two hundred guests, depending on how many families were at the resort at any one time.

"It's expensive so we don't get too many kids," John said as he and Laura walked back from inspecting the marina one morning in January. "I don't want them—too much trouble, and the doc on the mainland on call more often—but Kelly thinks we might fill more rooms as a family resort. Do you have an opinion on that?"

Laura frowned slightly. "I don't understand why it can't be a family resort and very expensive, too. Don't wealthy people take vacations with their children?"

He stopped walking and looked at her, a giant of a man with a ruddy face, high forehead, and a heavy black beard. "Possibly."

"Maybe you ought to make Darnton's so expensive wealthy parents will think it's too good to pass up. Then they could stop feeling guilty about leaving their children with a nanny while they go off to play."

"You think they feel guilty?"

"I have no idea. I would. I'd love to have a place to bring my children and know we could do separate things and still share a good time."

He smiled. "You should have children; you'd be a good mother."

Laura flushed. "We're talking about Darnton's."

"Okay," he said. "Darnton's with rich little boys and girls romping in the fields. I like it. You impress me, Laura; I like a woman who thinks we can have it all." They began walking again and he shot a glance at her. "What about you? When are you going to have it all, instead of working every night?"

"I'm doing what I want to do," she said. "I might ask you the same question. When was the last time you and Kelly had a night out on the mainland?"

"She doesn't want it. All she thinks about is this damn resort, making it pay, making it bigger . . . anyway, I was talking about you. What's the problem that you don't go anywhere or—"

"I said I'm doing what I want!"

"Hey," he said, stepping back and putting up his hands in mock fear. "Don't bite, Miss Fairchild, you've got a scared fella here—"

"Oh, fuck it, John, grow up." Abruptly she heard Rosa's voice: *Ladies don't swear, my young miss. Or lose their temper, as I've told you many a time.* "I'm sorry," she murmured, to Rosa or John, she wasn't sure which.

Clay liked John; the two of them spent hours with Darnton's fleet of vintage cars after John had Clay drive him around the island and pronounced him an excellent driver. From then on, when he wasn't on call to fill in as a desk clerk, Clay's passion was cars, second only to the young women who staffed the resort, especially a tennis instructor named Myrna, long-legged and experienced, the way he liked them.

His favorite car, just ahead of a 1920 LaSalle and a 1925 Packard, was a 1927 Silver Shadow Rolls-Royce that he polished and cosseted more than any woman he'd ever known. He knew absolutely—and was reminded each time he ran sensuous palms over its gold and mahogany fittings, leather-bound steering wheel, and soft upholstered seats—that he was definitely made for the finest things in life.

The trouble was, most of the finest things had eluded him lately. He no longer even had his own apartment, as he had in Philadelphia. "It would be okay for somebody who didn't know any better," he grumbled, pacing around the small sitting room that linked his bedroom and Laura's, and eyeing the sturdy furniture and cotton throw rugs. "But, shit, if it wasn't for that bastard, we'd be on Beacon Hill with everything we have coming to us. You know what we're doing? We're going backward, for Christ's sake! Living in a little place, the two of us, just like five years ago, above that garage in Centerville. We were doing better, and now all we have is this fucking little—"

"It's home and we're lucky to have it," Laura snapped. Then she put her arm around him. "I know you're disappointed, Clay, but I wish you'd just learn as much as you can while we're here and let me take care of the future. I'm thinking about it; I intend to take care of Felix one way or another. And you could help; a little cheerfulness would go a long way around here."

He dropped into a chair and stretched out his legs. He hated criticism.

Laura looked at the room. "Do you suppose the fireplace works?"

"I don't know; the housekeeper always took care of them at Owen's. How can you tell?"

"Make a fire."

"The place might fill up with smoke."

"Then we'll know it doesn't work."

Clay laughed and jumped to kiss her. "You're okay, you know? I really like being with you. I don't want you to think I don't appreciate what you do—making a home and —well, what the hell, you know what I mean. I'll get some firewood, okay? Be right back." He went outside, wishing he could tell Laura how great he thought she was without getting embarrassed. She really was clever, and nice, and she really cared about him. She'd been miserable the whole time they were in Phila-delphia, after that fucking will reading, and he'd been so furious at the family he hadn't done much to help her. He didn't even have a job; he quit the hotel before Felix could fire him. So there they'd been, the two of them, with their own problems, and he'd kept sound-ing off but Laura hadn't said much. She hadn't cried, either; her face had been like stone, and she'd spent a lot of time alone, just walking around the city.

She was miserable, and Clay knew it. But he didn't know what would be the right thing to say, so he left her alone. He knew she'd work everything out; she always did. She didn't seem to need other people very much.

She said she needed him, though, which was

why he was here. He'd followed her from the Cape to Boston and from Boston to this god-damned island—an *island* in the middle of some *mountains* when what he craved was New York!—because she said she needed him; he was her family. Well, what the hell. He'd stick around for now. There was Myrna, and the spectacular cars, and John Darnton, who liked him and said he'd give him a raise if they had a good season. And besides, they weren't all that far from New York; he might be able to get there for a weekend now and then.

Anyway, where else would he be but here? He wouldn't go to Ben; he didn't trust him. Of course he could go anywhere—he was twenty-one, strong, healthy and free, with the whole world to choose from—but he'd decided to hang in there with Laura for a while more. It wasn't so bad, having a family of your own.

"You want to tell me about those trips to Boston?" Kelly asked Laura one fragrant morning in March as they sat on the front porch. "And why you jump every time the phone rings in your office, like you're expecting something?"

"I'd like to, Kelly. And I will. But not yet."

"Quite a shell you've built around you," Kelly observed casually. "I'm here, you know, willing and able to listen."

"I know it. Thank you."

Kelly poured coffee from the thermos jug they had brought from the kitchen. "One thing, you do look a lot less peaked than when you got here. I hope we have something to do with that."

"You do," said Laura with a smile. "More than anyone or anything." She turned to a clean page on the clipboard in her lap. "We haven't gone over the wine list yet."

"Don't you ever quit? We could take a break; the management allows it."

"No, I'm fine; there's still so much to do."

"All work and no play," Kelly sighed, but she, too, picked up her clipboard. "Oh, what about linens? Did we finish with them yesterday? We did bed linens and restaurant stuff, but how about the health club?"

"It's on my list: fourteen towels and two dozen sheets for the massage rooms that should be replaced. I'm going into town this afternoon; I thought I'd stop at the laundry and tell them they have to be more careful."

"Good. I hate doing those things; I end up listening to their family problems and telling them not to worry about a few torn sheets. You're tougher than I am, my friend."

Laura thought of her sleepless nights. *Not as tough as I'd like to be.* "They tell me their problems, too," she replied. "But I know people can live with their problems and still do a good job."

Kelly made the small humming sound that meant she was thinking and didn't want her thoughts interrupted by someone changing the subject.

"Kelly's humming," John Darnton said, coming onto the porch from the great hall of the lodge. "What did I miss?"

"A fascinating discussion of the laundry," Laura said.

He chuckled and kissed the top of Kelly's head. "Girl talk." He leaned over his wife's shoulder and read the top page in her lap. "Wine. I forgot to tell you, I found a new supplier yesterday. He specializes in boutique American wines instead of French and Italian. I'll bring you his price list and then we'll decide." He took the clipboard from her hand and riffled through the papers. "Better add some new bar glasses; breakage was up last season. Season. Lousy word, isn't it? We thought this place would be year-round."

"It will be," Kelly said. "It takes a while."

" 'A while' seems to be going on longer than I expected." He was trying to sound playful, and as if the effort was too much, he returned the clipboard to her and straightened up, rubbing the back of his neck. "I'd call four years a meaningful amount of time."

"You've said that before," Kelly noted flatly.

"About three thousand times, probably. And it's still dead around here from December to May, except for Christmas week—thank God for Christmas week—and what have we done about it?"

"We're working on it."

"How are we working on it?"

"What is this, a quiz?" Kelly demanded. "You know perfectly well what we're doing, we work together. Or did you *again* forget that?"

"Hoo-ee, the lady is on her crusade again." He clasped his hands behind his head and looked down at Kelly. "One time. One fucking time I play around with somebody and you absolutely will not let go of—"

"Who'd believe that? If there was once

there was twice or a hundred. Young chicks come here to work and you follow them to the mainland like a dog with his tongue hanging—"

"Did I ever expect my loving wife to call me a dog?" John asked the cloudless sky. "Was I warned?"

"Don't talk about me as if I'm not here."

"I'll talk about you any way I goddam please."

Laura walked deliberately to the front door of the lodge. "I'll be in the kitchen," she said.

"Shit!" John exploded. He dropped his arms, his palms slapping loudly against his thighs. "I'm going; I interrupted a conference. Sorry we put you through this, Laura; can you forgive us?"

Without waiting for an answer, he turned to leave. As he passed Kelly's chair, he reached out to touch her shoulder, then jerked his hand back and kept going, down the steps and across the lawn.

"Damn, damn, *damn.*" Kelly's fist pounded the arm of her chair. "Why can't I be cooler about things, like you? Because I can't; I start boiling when I think of him tangled in the sheets with some cute unattached chick who hasn't been married to him for ten years and doesn't have to worry about a resort sucking up an inheritance and every penny of savings like a vacuum cleaner and still needing more." She took a long breath. "Sorry, Laura, you've heard this before. First John apologizes, then I do; we keep making you our audience. It's just that there isn't anybody else around here who listens and doesn't gossip, and sometimes things pile up and . . ."

"You've got too much to worry about," Laura said. "It makes you feel smothered. You have to lock some things up and only worry about one at a time."

Kelly looked at her and nodded slowly. "You really do that, don't you? Is that how you stay so cool? God, Laura, I love you and I love having you here, but you make me feel so *sloppy*, all my emotions hanging out while you're so smooth and *together*, like one of those fortune-teller's globes that doesn't have any seams. Don't you ever let loose and scream or cry?"

Laura clasped her hands. "No."

"Everybody cries."

"Maybe if you concentrated on the resort and let things settle down between you and John—"

"Okay, you don't want to talk about crying. Concentrate on the resort? John gets jealous—can you believe it?—if I pay more attention to it than to him. And if I concentrate on him"—she spread out her hands—"he's loaded for bear, that man. You saw it just now; talking along nice and easy and—pow!—we're fighting. Even in bed, one of us says a simple word—well, maybe not always so simple—and that's it, no lovemaking that night, just another argument. And I tell you, that is not much fun."

"I know." *But I don't think about that. I don't miss making love; I don't want it; I don't even remember what it was like to want it. I know I used to think it was lovely but I'm not interested anymore.* "Maybe if you went somewhere, just the two of you . . . this is only the middle of March—we have two months until we get busy—isn't this a good time for you to get away?"

Kelly tilted her head. "You trying to get rid of us, my friend? Itching to take over and run the place yourself?"

Laura laughed and shook her head. "I wouldn't even try. I was thinking of you, not me."

"But you must want to run your own place," Kelly said probingly.

"Someday. We all have dreams we tuck away for the future."

"It's one big headache, you know. You're better off staying with us. Lifetime security."

They laughed, but inwardly Laura said no. The only real security was earning her way in a place of her own. Then no one could ever kick her out again.

"Think about it," Kelly urged. "I'm serious. We'd make you a partner."

"I'll think about it," Laura said, "if you think about a vacation. I still say this is a good time for you to get away."

"It would be if we could, but we can't. Cutting expenses, you cut your own pleasures first. You know about that; you've cut down a lot." She gazed at Laura. "That's one of the jackets you brought with you—and it's a Ralph Lauren or I'll eat my non–Ralph Lauren hat—and you haven't bought anything since. And there's that closetful of clothes, and those old leather-bound books I was looking at the other day. . . . Not that I'm prying"—she saw the involuntary smile that curved Laura's lips—"well, I am, but only a little bit. Mainly I'm interested in size, not cost, and I'm envious: every time I look at you I dream of being size eight instead of fourteen."

Laura smiled again, liking Kelly's openness and affection, thinking what a good place this was, and how lucky she was to be here, for however long she stayed. And then the telephone rang, and it was Ansel Rollins. The trial was set for July.

CHAPTER 12

LENI Salinger sat on the edge of the wide, satin-hung bed, leaning back, gazing beneath heavy eyelids at the bright red hair of the young man kneeling before her, his head between her thighs. She let herself float on slow waves of pleasure as he played his tongue on her sensitive flesh and thrust deep inside her wet darkness, and small shocks of sensation swept through her like iced vodka and warm honey, transforming her lean white body to a fluid line of feeling. She sensed rather than saw the brocade and velvet room, and the hypnotizing glow of a single lamp, and then her eyes closed as the young man suddenly lay on her, forcing her back on the satin spread, and thrust inside her, hard and deep. He moved within her, then raised himself so the tip of his penis caressed her small, hardened flesh, and then he plunged into her again so their bodies locked, and he pulled out and thrust again and again until the threads of Leni's body gathered together in a knot and then flew apart, giving her a few seconds of the ecstasy she kept locked inside her, waiting until she could find the secrecy and safety to release it.

The young man's breathing was as rapid as hers, and she put her arms around his muscular shoulders, pleased that he had found pleasure, too. But then she turned her wrist to see her watch. "I have to go," she murmured, and immediately he moved away so she could sit up. In the beginning, months ago, he had tried to keep her with him, but no longer: he knew if he wanted to see her again, he had to follow her lead.

"Let me help," he said; it was one of the games they played. He pulled on her hose and half-slip, fastened her brassiere, buttoned her sheer blouse, and tied the bow at her throat. Her body cooling, Leni drew her skirt over her hips, fastened a red snakeskin belt around her waist, stepped into gray snakeskin pumps, and picked up her jacket.

The young man was buckling his own belt. "Will you be here next week?"

"I don't know." She picked up the red Hermès Constance handbag she always used when she came to New York, and slung it over her shoulder. "I'll try, but I have four board meetings and that doesn't leave much time. Besides," she added lightly, "if I don't give you some free afternoons, when will you get your homework done?"

"At night."

"You should be dating at night."

"I don't date."

"All college students date."

"I can't. I can't even look at anybody else—"

"Tor," she said with a note of warning. "I would be very distressed if you changed anything in your life because of me."

"Well—" As always, he said what he had to say to keep her from looking for someone else. "I do go out, lots, I just didn't think you'd like to know. That's no problem, finding girls . . ."

"Then do your homework in the afternoon,"

she said gently, liking him, enjoying his infatu-
ation more than she would admit to him or to
herself. She stood before the full-length mirror.
Pearl-gray shantung suit, white silk blouse,
pearl silk gloves, a cherry red Adolfo straw hat
tilted over one perfect eyebrow. Her mascara
and eyeshadow were unsmudged. She fresh-
ened her lipstick; the case made a loud snap as
she closed it. "I'll call you when I can get
away," she said and kissed him briefly. In another minute she was in the brightly lit corridor of the Waldorf Towers, two steps from the
elevator that took her to the lobby where she
was one of dozens of well-dressed women
spending their afternoons shopping, lunching,
and perhaps adjourning for a couple of hours
with a friend in the exclusive privacy of a high-
priced hotel room.

The late afternoon air was warm and still;
even the crowds on the streets seemed to move
more slowly in the June afternoon as the sun
slid lower in the sky. Leni stopped at Tiffany's,
then caught a cab to the airport in time for the
five o'clock shuttle to Boston. And by seven
she was sitting at dinner with Felix, the French
doors open, the blue and silver flowers on the
French wallpaper seeming to sway in the ocean

breeze. "I found the tie clip you wanted," she told him. "The last one Tiffany's had. It seems people now give gifts for Easter, especially jewelry."

"Good news for the merchants," he said absently, then, as if reminding himself, looked up and thanked her for the tie clip. "Did you have a pleasant day?"

"Very."

"What did you do besides shop?"

"I stopped in at the Waldorf."

His eyes took on a glazed look. "Ladies' lunches. I'm afraid I have no interest in what you did at the Waldorf. No matinee?"

"You mean the theater?"

"What else would I mean? Oh, concerts. There are none on Tuesday, as far as I know."

"Nor at the theater, either."

"Well, whatever you did, I'm sure you were able to amuse yourself. I assume you're amused; you're there most of the time, it seems, and it can't be for those deadly board meetings."

"They're not deadly; they make me feel useful." She took a second helping of veal and wild rice; she was always ravenous after a trip to New York. "How was your day?"

"Good. Very good. We saw a videotape of progress on the Elani in Honolulu; we should be able to open this fall. And I met with a group of bankers from Chicago about building a new hotel there, on the lake; we shouldn't have trouble financing it. They may even help us sell the old one; they think they know of a possible buyer."

"You can't sell that hotel; it isn't yours."

"It will be next month, after the trial. You wouldn't expect me to wait until then to make plans; I intend to be ready to move the minute that mess is settled."

Leni was silent.

"There's not much demand for small hotels —no real way to make them profitable—but some junior-college people are interested in Chicago, and a nursing home director in Washington. If things go well, all four of those relics will be off our hands within a couple of years."

She looked at him. "Owen took pride in those hotels."

"And so you're sentimental about them. He knew as well as anyone they can't compete with modern ones. I'm doing exactly what he would have wanted."

"That is not true," Leni said coldly. "He would have been extremely angry. He would have glared at you and called you a narrow-minded opportunist kicking aside the past just as you kick aside anyone who gets in your way." Her voice grew wistful. "And his mustache would have quivered like long wings on each side of his mouth, about to take off—" There were tears in her eyes. "I miss him. He was so alive. Paul said the same thing the other day, how much he misses that wonderful sense of life Owen brought to everything he did . . ."

Felix picked up the carafe. "More wine?"

"I suppose so. Yes."

"I didn't know you talked to Paul. Where is he?"

"Rome, I think. He doesn't stay anywhere very long; I've never known him to be so restless. I asked him if he was doing any photography and he said he'd met someone who wants to be a model and he's begun photographing her. I wish he'd find a woman he could love."

"He'd do better to find a job. He's been wandering around the world for months; nothing but a wastrel."

"I don't think so; I think he's trying to find

something to believe in. It's the same with Allison. I know her trip to Europe was my idea, but I didn't think it would turn out the way it has: the way she's going from country to country, and dragging Patricia with her, it seems more like she's fleeing. Both of them, Paul and Allison, acting as if they're trying to get over a bad love affair. It's astonishing that one young woman could wreak such havoc. . . ."

There was a silence. "I had some of my father's things moved over here today," Felix said.

Leni frowned. "You took things from Beacon Hill? You're not supposed to touch anything involved in the court case—"

"I would appreciate it if you would stop telling me what I cannot do. I've done it, and what anyone says about it is irrelevant. I decided it was time we get some use out of those things; they've been sitting in that house for a year, with nobody there—"

"Rosa is there."

"She shouldn't be; she would have been gone long ago if you hadn't raised such an incredible fuss."

"I want her to live in this house, with us."

"I will not have her here."

"Then she'll stay in Beacon Hill."

"She will not. As soon as that house is mine, I'm going to sell it."

"You won't. Felix, you may succeed in taking those hotels from Laura, but I won't let you—"

"I will take back what is mine! My father was terrorized into cutting me out of his will!"

"Don't be ridiculous. He left you almost everything he had."

Felix's fist was clenched around the stem of his wineglass, and it suddenly snapped in his hand. A ruby rivulet ran along the dark mahogany table, staining the snowy place mat before him.

"Did you cut yourself?" Leni asked with faint concern. "I'll ring for Talbot."

"It's nothing." He wadded a napkin in his palm. "My father would never have done what he did if he'd been in his right mind. He trusted me, he cared for me more than anyone, he wanted me to keep his name as powerful after his death as it was in his lifetime. He knew I was the only one who could do that; he depended on me. He would never make a fool of me in the eyes of the world. The hotels were meant for me; his stock in the company was meant for me; his corporation was meant for me. And so was his house."

"If you win the case, that house will be ours," Leni said bluntly. "And it will not be sold."

Felix tightened his fingers against the linen napkin, pressing it into his throbbing palm. What the hell had happened to her? She'd been changing ever since Owen died and that witch had been sent packing in disgrace. Sometimes he hardly recognized her; she'd lost much of that charming passive serenity she'd developed over the years to mask whatever dissatisfactions she felt. Now, when she didn't agree with him, she told him so.

He had always dominated Leni. He used her elegance and style to make him feel powerful —the envy of other men—but his hold seemed to be weakening and it occurred to him that after twenty-two years of marriage he did not know her well enough to have any idea how to get it back.

Once he thought he knew everything necessary to make her his and to keep her. That was when she was nineteen, in hot rebellion against her wealthy, shipbuilding, churchgoing, publicity-shy family. Felix had met her on a street in

Greenwich Village; she was with a man who glanced at him briefly, then, again, piercingly, and stopped him with his deep, gravelly voice. "By all the gods of the Salingers, if it isn't Felix the robber baron: Felix Salinger in the healthy and well-dressed flesh."

"Judd," Felix said flatly. He couldn't believe it: he never saw a familiar face in New York; it was an article of faith with him that the city made everyone anonymous. Yet here was Judd Gardner, whom he had long since wiped out of his thoughts, looking slightly seedier but otherwise not much different from years before. He would have walked away, but as he turned he got a good look at the girl whose arm was linked in Judd's. She was tall and spare, with tangled blond hair and sloppy clothes—and a way of holding her head, an elegance of style, that would have been at home in a palace. It was that elegance that caught Felix: he knew, with the same instinct that served him brilliantly in business, that a man who owned that elegance would have the power that came from the envy of other men. And he knew he would not leave. "How are you?" he asked Judd.

"Barely," Judd said with a thin smile. "I barely am. But I see that *you* very much *are*."

"Judd, I'm cold," said the girl.

The April wind was bitter; it whipped around the corner with a raw chill. Felix was conscious of the girl's bare legs and his own fur-lined coat, leather gloves, cashmere scarf. "Do you live nearby?" he asked.

"Around the corner."

"Then we'll go there."

Judd's eyes had been sliding from Felix to the girl and back again as he saw Felix's fixed gaze. "Sorry, how rude I am. Leni Van Gris, Felix Salinger. Felix is known for taking what he desires, Leni, so be on your guard. Or perhaps I should be on mine. What do you think?"

"I think we should say good night and go home."

"But Felix wants a reunion," he said. "We can drink to old times. Except that we haven't got anything to drink. We'll have to stop on the way and get some supplies."

"We don't need any," she protested.

"We always need any," Judd said, and Felix realized he was in that perpetual state of drunkenness in which alcoholics can function for long stretches at a time before one more drink tips them into incoherence or stupor. "And Felix will pay."

"Judd, let's go home. Alone."

"No, no, Felix will join us. Felix is Bacchus, god of wine. And here we are."

The store was small and Judd was known there. Felix paid for wine and whiskey, and soda for Leni, and they carried it to a nearby fourth-floor walk-up in a brick building with a dry cleaner and pawnshop on the street level. The apartment had three rooms along a narrow hallway, like a train car, and Judd sat down in the front room in one of three chairs around a folding table set with assorted china and a wine bottle with candle wax dripping down the sides. One window was filled with a piece of plywood where an air conditioner had once been installed; beneath it was a stain the shape of Africa. And everywhere, on the walls, the furniture, the floor, were bright posters.

"The idea is to go somewhere," said Judd. He poured two straight scotches and a soda, and handed a glass to Felix and one to Leni. "I'd like to take this lovely child away from here. But in case I can't manage it, we stare at exotic sights to swell our spirits with the wonders of a world where beauty is all that matters."

"Judd, shut up," Leni said nervously. She sat cross-legged on a cushion on the floor beside Judd, the overhead light casting a shadow across her face that emphasized her cheekbones and the angular lines of her head and figure. Felix stood, staring down at her, knowing overwhelmingly that he wanted her and would do whatever he had to do to get her. It wouldn't be the first time, he thought dispassionately, that he had taken something he wanted from Judd Gardner.

Without being asked, he sat in one of the chairs at the table, across from Judd, and took a long look at him. Tall, blond, his hair falling to his shoulders, he was still good-looking, though not as extraordinarily handsome as Felix remembered him from the days when he had envied those golden classic features, and wished he himself were less dark. Judd's voice was still rough, but his eyes and mouth, when he talked to Leni, were tender. "Where do you want to go?" Felix asked him.

"Paradise. Where I can pick the golden apples of the sun and the silver apples of the moon and give them all to Leni, because, poor child, she thinks I'm romantic, since I'm poor and we met in an art gallery one rainy afternoon, and now she thinks she loves me."

"I do love you," the girl declared. "And you love me."

"Ah, if I could love you, my sweet Leni . . . if only I could."

"You will," she said. "I'll make you love me. You'll marry me and stop drinking and I'll find a way to get my parents to help you start another company all your own and we'll be happy."

"I had a wife. You'll find this interesting, Felix." Carefully he refilled his glass. "I had a wife and son but my wife kicked me out because I was drinking. Oh, and stealing, too—mustn't forget that. You see, once upon a time I owned a company. Owned it with a friend, but half was enough for me; I was so goddam proud of it. But it wasn't enough for my partner, so he stole my half." Once again he drained his glass and refilled it, this time pausing to hold it up to the light to admire its amber glow. "My friend stole it. Or, to be accurate, my un-friend. He wanted it so he stole it. So I stole too. That was after I found that I couldn't get it back legally, or even steal it back; all I could do was steal like an ordinary thief: breaking in and lifting a few things I could sell or pawn to keep going for a while and give money to my wife and son. He's eight now, my son, and I take him bowling and to Coney Island . . . fatherly things. I'm not much of a man anymore, but I can pretend, even if I have to steal to do it—so I do."

"Judd." Leni put her hand on his as he reached for the bottle. "You promised me you'd stop. You said when you finished what we had in the house you'd stop. And now we have all this stuff"—she glared at Felix—"and you know I hate it when—"

"Damn it, leave me alone! Sorry, I'm sorry, sweet Leni, but I'm talking to Felix and you mustn't interrupt."

She stood up behind Judd's chair and put her arms around him. "Will you please go?" she said to Felix. "I don't know anything about you, but for some reason Judd's getting awfully excited and it would be better if you left."

"You don't know anything about me? You don't know," Felix repeated, astonished at his good fortune. He looked at Judd's once-golden features in the circle of Leni's arms and thought he saw the first stages of a gaunt, hollow-eyed drunk. "Choose your paradise," he said to Judd, "and I'll buy your ticket."

Judd's eyes narrowed. "You want Leni."

"I want to help you find your paradise," Felix said.

"But not if I take Leni with me."

"No."

"What are you talking about?" Leni demanded. She moved away from Judd and spoke to Felix. "What the hell do you think you're talking about?"

"He's talking about taking you away from me," said Judd.

"Well, he can't do it." Leni stood with her head back, her hands at her sides, looking at Felix with the air of an empress. "I asked you to leave; now I'm telling you. Get out. We don't want you here. Anyway I don't like you," she added, suddenly sounding like a child.

"Let Judd tell me to go," Felix said.

"I might," Judd responded.

"Might!" Leni's voice rose higher. "Might! Judd, what the hell is *wrong* with you?"

"I might even talk about my past," Judd went on. His eyes were somber. "What do you think, Felix? Should I do that?"

Leni looked from one of them to the other. "When did you know each other?"

"In college," Felix replied.

"We were roommates," Judd added coldly.

"It was a long time ago," Felix said. "I don't remember it very well. Do you?"

There was a pause. The two men stared at each other. "No," Judd said. "I could remember, if I didn't get any money, but if I got some and went somewhere, the memory would no doubt stay very fuzzy."

Leni was biting her lower lip. "Judd, if you take money from this man, I'm leaving you."

He nodded. "I know. But you would anyway. Don't you understand, my sweet Leni? You'd leave me anyway, one of these days, when the novelty of rebellion and poverty wears off. You'd leave me when you begin to want a young man with success ahead of him instead of a failed drunk who has nothing but bitter memories and a few lines of poetry to quote when you're hungry." Reaching out, he took her hand in his. "I have nothing to give you, and you deserve a kingdom. You don't belong here. I wish I'd had the strength to tell you that sooner."

"You needed a bribe," she said angrily.

"I needed a push. Someday you'll understand that."

She looked at him with the craftiness of a child trying to trick someone. "I warn you, if you leave me I'll go with him! That's what you'll remember: me and Felix. You'd hate that!"

"Yes. I would. But that's a choice you'll make for yourself." He looked at Felix. "How much?"

"If you go away by yourself, a thousand a month as long as you live."

Judd's head snapped back. "I'll be damned. I told you we should watch out for him, Leni. He just made our future."

"Not mine!" she cried. "Judd, I'm strong enough for both of us! I won't let you do this!"

He looked at Felix. "I need a six-month advance."

Felix pulled out his checkbook and unscrewed his pen.

"I wanted to take care of you!" Leni said furiously. "I wanted to make your life better. I wanted to make you happy!"

Judd stood and put his hands on her unyielding shoulders. "You can't remake people, Leni; you can't force them to be good or happy. I'm too full of hate to love anyone, but even if I could love, I'm not sure it would be you: you're quite exhausting to live with, my sweet."

Leni jerked away from him as Felix tore out the check. Judd took it and folded it into smaller and smaller squares. "But before my past blurred and I began to forget it," he said to Felix, as if continuing a conversation, "I told my son the name of the man who ruined me, what he did and how he did it. He'll remember; he loves me. And someday he'll get my revenge. Don't you think that was smart of me, Felix?"

"I would have gotten your revenge," Leni said frantically. It was obvious she heard only some of what was said; her eyes were blank as she tried to understand what was happening. "But you wouldn't tell me anything!"

"I was trying to protect you from my hatred. Find someone strong and powerful, Leni; someone who can use your strength. You'll be happy then." He smiled, so sweetly that Leni began to cry, and both men saw the frustration and love behind her tears. "Now get out," Judd rasped. His smile had disappeared. "Go back to Mommy and Daddy and give them my apologies for stealing you away. Go on! *Get out of here!*"

Felix took Leni's arm and pulled her toward the door. She was crying stormily and Felix never knew whether she heard Judd whisper, "Good-bye, my lovely Leni," just before he kicked the door shut behind them.

Felix held her up as they walked down the four dimly lit flights. "I'm going to take you home." He tightened his hold as she tried to break free. "You have to go somewhere and I'm not taking you to a hotel."

"Why not?" she demanded. "That's what you want, isn't it? You want to fuck me; that's all you care about, shitty, filthy, rotten—"

He clamped his hand over her mouth. "Do you always talk like a stupid teenager? You'll have to change that before we're married."

"Fuck you—" she spat against the hand over her mouth.

"We will." He grinned: one of the few times Felix Salinger ever indulged in a full and gleeful grin. "As much as we want. Of course I want it; I've wanted you since the minute I saw you. And you won't try to make me better, the way you did that fool back there; you're going to be my wife and I'll be the one to make you better. And that's what you want, too, you little idiot: you haven't been satisfied by that pathetic drunk; you want to be dominated." She shook her head fiercely. "You're not a rebel," he said contemptuously. "You're a romantic. Rebels take up with other rebels and try to change the world; romantics take up with losers like Judd Gardner and wait for someone to rescue them."

She pulled away from him. "Bastard—!"

He kissed her. But it was a battle and he hated it. He hated violence; he hated foul language in women; he hated opposition. He was behaving contrarily to every rule of his life, and that astonished him, but he watched it happen and rolled with it. There was in Leni everything he wanted: the elegance of the mother he only vaguely remembered; a strength and a streak of coarseness that would help him defeat his father; the New York background that made her a stranger to Boston, so she would be dependent on him for friends and a social life. And as a bonus, she had belonged to Judd Gardner—a man Felix had never been able to stop envying.

He ended the struggle; it was disgraceful to

try to kiss a woman who was uncooperative. "Where do your parents live?"

"I don't want to go home; I can't face them. We can go to a hotel. We can fuck all you want. You don't care about me or my parents, all you care about is my cunt—"

He slapped her, admiring himself for doing something he had never done. "You will not talk like that. Is that clear? Where do your parents live?"

"None of your goddam business."

He opened the lobby door and propelled her the three blocks to his car. It seemed a lifetime ago that he had parked it there to meet some business associates for dinner. Shoving her into the driver's seat so she would not be able to run away, he pushed her over as he got in himself. "Listen to me. This is what I'm going to tell your parents: that you and I ran away, that we were foolish and we know it now, but we were in love and we were afraid they'd object because you're only nineteen." Leni had become very still, her eyes wide as she watched him. "I imagine you don't want to go home because when you ran off you told them some nonsense about not liking their stuffy middle-class attitudes and not wanting to be like them.

Am I right?" She was silent. "*Am I right?*" She nodded. "A lot of my classmates did that. Stupid asses. You can always defeat your parents if you stay close to them; what can you do from a distance?"

"I don't want to defeat them." Her words were almost inaudible.

"You want to go home," Felix said. He was feeling strong and satisfied.

She nodded and began to cry.

"Give me the address."

"820 Park."

He started the car. "I'm thirty-three years old; I've never been married or involved in a long relationship; and the Salinger hotels will be mine when my father dies. Your parents will be very pleased. Have I your permission to court you?"

She broke into wild laughter. And with that laughter, and the ride home beside Felix's powerful silence and satisfaction, Leni Van Gris took the first and irrevocable step to becoming Leni Salinger.

It was a memorable lesson in the uses of power. Felix never told Leni's parents about Judd but neither did he ever let Leni forget that he had made perfectly smooth her return to the family she loved and had longed for even at her most rebellious. And not long after performing that miracle, he had joined with Leni in a marriage that gave her social status, wealth, and a great deal of freedom.

"You don't love me," she said the night before their wedding.

"I need you," he replied. It was, for Felix, an astonishing admission, and Leni knew he would not have made it if he realized how much it told her about him. Because she knew now that no matter how powerful Felix Salinger was in the world of international business, he remained a little boy trying to find the mother he had lost, and to win his father's love, and since he never would succeed, the closest he could come to feeling like a man was to conquer and possess what other men would envy.

But though he conquered and possessed, he was not a man who could be close to anyone. And so Leni had more freedom than she had expected. As long as she was available to satisfy his sexual hunger for her, as long as she stood at his side at social functions, and as long as she was discreet, she could do what she wanted.

For twenty-two years, Leni had thought she understood Felix, even as she was in awe of his ability to master the uses of power. Especially after Owen died and Laura Fairchild was unmasked, Leni saw the extent of his reach, and was stunned at how little she had known. By then she had created as much power of her own as she thought she ever would have. She was no longer a nineteen-year-old clinging to a romantic dream, but a realistic woman. I was interesting once, she thought; I was fiery and alive. And then I became a very wealthy, very dull wife. She had no faith in herself anymore; all she could do was gather what little power she could within the boundaries of Felix's world, and that was what she did. Over the years, she grew close to Owen. When her sister Barbara was engaged to Thomas Janssen, Leni introduced them to Owen, who set Thomas on the path to becoming Midwest manager for Salinger Hotels, and brought him and Barbara and their son Paul into the summer compound at Osterville. And, finally, Leni found young men who adored her and made sweet love to her and gave her a kind of peace.

Imperceptibly, Felix and Leni achieved something of a balance. He would always be more powerful but he could not control her. He knew it without understanding it, but he never spoke of it or allowed himself to think too much about it. Because he could never let her go.

"Which of Owen's things did you take from Beacon Hill?" Leni asked, finishing her wine.

Felix looked up from his memories. She was as close as the other end of the table, but she seemed far beyond his reach. "Some furniture, some paintings; pieces I've liked for a long time."

"What furniture?"

"His desk. An armchair. A few tables. Why do you want to keep that house?"

"It's part of Owen. He wouldn't want it sold. I'm sure he wouldn't have left it to Laura if he'd known what she was, but he would have wanted it kept in the family. Besides, there's no reason to sell it. We don't need the money, and I like it. Why do you want Owen's desk?"

Felix pushed back his chair. "You bought it for him; I thought it should stay with the head of the company. It might become a tradition."

"You think I should have bought it for you."

"It would have been a nice gesture: a wife buying her husband a fine piece clearly meant for a powerful person." He walked toward the door. "Instead the wife buys it for her father-in-law. Most people would find that odd. Make sure you order another wineglass; I don't want to have a partial set; I don't like anything that is incomplete."

Leni watched him leave the dining room. Our marriage is incomplete, she reflected, and she thought of the many ways people disappoint each other: Judd's wife had sent him away; some shadowy figure had stolen Judd's company; Owen had never loved Felix as much as Felix wanted to be loved; and Felix had never been the son Owen wanted. And I disappoint, too, she thought: I disappoint Felix because I am not grateful enough for what he gave me, and because I have friends, and a daughter who loves me—and he does not.

And because I bought a Chippendale desk for my dearest Owen instead of for my husband. And in all these years, he has never forgotten it.

She rang for Talbot to clear the table, and then she went upstairs to see what Felix had done with Owen's desk.

CHAPTER 13

THE trial lasted two weeks. Each day spun by in scenes that briefly stood out, as if caught by a revolving spotlight, then vanished as the light moved on. The faces of the Salingers stood out first: it had been almost a year since Laura last saw them, and when they sat together in the courtroom they looked to her like cameos in a cluster of family photographs. They were exactly as she remembered them, but she had changed, and she saw Allison's surprise as their eyes met. She knew the change was more than her short hair; it was also the frozen look of her face, the careful calm she had practiced for a year and especially during the weeks before coming to Boston. And that was how she looked for the ten days of the trial, as, one by one, the Salingers came to the witness stand and their eyes and gesturing hands and moving lips all blurred in Laura's mind like a painting that had been left out in the rain.

Leni testified that Laura and Owen had worked together in his library; they had spent hours together walking on the beach; and, after his heart attack during a burglary in their house, she came with him to Boston and stayed with him day and night until he was well.

"Before his heart attack, and after he recovered from it," said Rollins, "he was strong and healthy?"

"Yes."

"No one questioned his mental faculties?"

"There was no reason to."

"Or his devotion to Miss Fairchild?"

"No."

Cheyne came back and faced Leni. "What did you think of Laura Fairchild when you first interviewed her for a summer job?"

"She was very pleasant and clearly anxious for work."

"And did she provide you with reference letters?"

"Yes."

"And did you form an opinion of them?"

"I thought they were faked," she said sadly.

Ansel Rollins remained silent in his chair. There was no sense in objecting; Laura had told him the letters had been faked.

When Felix testified, his words were measured. "We all were suspicious, especially after the robbery, but my father would hear none of it. He seemed positively mesmerized."

"Objection!" Rollins exclaimed, and the judge ordered it stricken from the record, but everyone had heard it.

Rosa sat upright in the witness chair and gave Laura a small, uncertain smile. "Those two loved each other," she said firmly in response to Cheyne's questions. "Whatever else you may say about Laura, I do believe Mr. Owen loved her, and she loved him."

"Tell the jury about her work in the kitchen," Cheyne said conversationally. "Did she plunge right in from the first day and take some of the load off you?"

"Well, I wouldn't put it that way."

"How would you put it?"

"She didn't know all that much about a large kitchen. But she learned very fast and she—"

"But at first. Did you think she had worked in kitchens of wealthy homes in the past?"

"I didn't. No."

"Did you think she was a liar?"

"Objection!" Rollins called.

The judge peered at Cheyne. "I think you'd better rephrase that, counselor."

"Did you have evidence that Miss Fairchild had been truthful about her past experience?"

"Well, no, but any youngster who really needed a job—"

"Just answer the questions, please. Mr. Salinger had a library in his home on Cape Cod. And Miss Fairchild took time off from the kitchen to work in it, is that correct?"

"Yes."

"Did Mr. Salinger talk to you about taking her away from her work in the kitchen?"

"Yes. In fact, that's where they were when the idea first came up."

"Mr. Salinger asked if Miss Fairchild could take time off to work in his library?"

"Well . . . actually it was Laura who offered and he said it was a good idea and suggested to me that we could work it out."

"*Miss Fairchild* suggested it?"

"Yes. She said she knew books."

"And what did you say?"

Rosa hesitated. "I said to Mr. Owen that I thought she wasn't always quite truthful about the things she'd done and could do."

Laura gripped her hands. *Dear Rosa. Fair, kind Rosa. It isn't your fault that everything is coming out wrong.*

On Friday afternoon, at the end of the first week of the trial, Allison was called to testify. "We were friends," she said. "We talked about everything."

"Including stories about your childhood?" asked Carver Cheyne. "Parents, school, boyfriends, slumber parties . . . that sort of thing?"

"Objection!" exclaimed Ansel Rollins. "This has no relevance to Owen Salinger's will."

"It has to do with Miss Fairchild's character," Cheyne said promptly. "And, especially in a case of this kind, character is relevant."

"I'll accept that," said the judge. "Objection overruled."

Cheyne turned back to Allison. "Did Laura

Fairchild share stories about her past, Miss Salinger?"

"No. She said she didn't like to and it wasn't important."

"So she never mentioned to you her conviction for theft in New York City when she was—?"

"Objection!" Rollins thundered. He sprang to his feet. "If I may speak to your honor . . ."

The judge nodded and motioned Cheyne forward, too. Rollins, standing at the bench, handed the judge a stapled set of papers, the brief he had prepared in case this happened. "As your honor can see," he said, his voice urgent but confident, "the sealed record of a juvenile . . . not admitted as evidence . . . I've listed precedents for this—"

"Your honor," Cheyne said, as urgent and confident as Rollins, his own brief in his hand, "the conviction was only seven years ago. It is our position that such a history pertains to the character and motives of Miss Fairchild and her brother in becoming involved with the Salingers; it is also our contention that it is relevant and essential in judging Miss Fairchild's reliability when she describes her relationship with Owen Salinger and his wishes, especially during his illness."

There was a pause. The judge nodded. "I'll accept that," he said as he had before. "You may pursue that line of questioning."

Rollins's face turned a dark red. "Your honor, I make a motion for a mistrial," he snapped.

"Denied," said the judge. "May we continue, Mr. Cheyne?"

And so, as Allison left the stand and was replaced by a New York City police officer, while Rollins muttered furiously about the defeat they had suffered, the jury listened to a flat recital of Laura's arrest, her release on bail, her conviction, and then her release on probation in the custody of an aunt named Melody Chase who gave an address later found to be an abandoned building.

When he was finished, the courtroom was very silent. The judge struck his gavel once on his desk. "We will adjourn until Monday morning at nine," he said.

In the hot July afternoon, the weekend traffic leaving Boston was dense and crawling, and it was almost ten o'clock when Laura and Clay reached Darnton's. Laura had insisted on driving; Clay was in a rage and could barely sit still. "It's Ben's fault, damn him; he got us into that mess; got us caught and convicted—like stupid *criminals*—"

"He didn't," Laura said wearily. "We weren't even with him that night, and you know it. We thought we could do it ourselves."

"He shouldn't have let us. He should have been around, to take care of us."

"We shouldn't have been stealing."

"He taught us. He should have come with us."

"Oh, *should, should, should,*" Laura said angrily. "It's too late for *should;* we can't go back. And we can't blame Ben for everything."

"He was older."

That was true; silently Laura acknowledged it. Ben was older, Ben was smarter, Ben had been in charge of them. But he had been young, too, and he'd had a date, and hadn't paid attention when they said they were going out. Lots of times he hadn't paid too much attention, but in most ways he had been wonderful to them for years and years. "I don't blame him for anything he did back then," she told Clay. "He was wonderful. If only he hadn't robbed the Salingers we'd still be friends."

The great hall at Darnton's and the sweeping front lawn were ablaze with lights. The lodge had full occupancy, with nearly three hundred guests on the island. Some were still boating, others watched a film in the theater in the main lodge, others walked by the lake, and many of them were still strolling through the outdoor sculpture exhibit Laura had organized on the front lawn.

Kelly waved at them as they drove up. "Fifteen pieces sold today," she said. "Somebody from New York said it was as good a collection as he'd seen in—oh, shit, what's wrong? Was it a terrible week?"

"Not good," Laura said. Clay had left to see if the fleet of cars had been properly attended to, and she tried to be interested in the sculptures. "Fifteen sold? That's wonderful. No problems?"

"The wine coolers and champagne ran out; but John did some kind of deal in Jay's Landing and bought enough to last the weekend. We read about the trial; one of the guests brought a Boston newspaper with him. I'm sorry. Is there anything I can do?"

"You're the first I'd ask if I could think of anything." She managed a smile. "We haven't lost; we're just weaker than we thought we'd be. And I didn't like being there."

"In the city or in the courtroom?"

"Both."

"Well, you're home now. Why don't you go to bed and sleep off the whole week?"

"Thanks, Kelly, I think I will. I'll help you here tomorrow."

"I'll need you." She put her arms around Laura and kissed her. "We love you. Pleasant dreams."

But her dreams were turbulent, and she woke feeling almost as tired as when she had gone to bed. I'll be all right, she thought, standing for a long time beneath a hot, pounding shower. I'll think about sculpture exhibits and all the mail that's probably stacked on my desk.

But just after breakfast, she was stopped as she walked to her office. "Laura Fairchild?" The voice behind her was deep and faintly harsh. Laura turned and he held out his hand. "Wes Currier."

"Currier." She frowned slightly as they shook hands.

"I'll be at the Global Finance Conference in August; you wrote two weeks ago to welcome me." In the bright sunlight of the great hall, his look was quizzical.

Laura flushed. He was to be the main, and most prestigious, speaker at the most prestigious conference she had been able to book at Darnton's. "I'm sorry. I was thinking of something else. And I didn't expect to see you here until next month. Is there a problem?"

"Most likely not. But I don't leave things to chance. Since I've never been here, it seemed a good idea to stop by."

"And check us out. Of course."

"I wasn't really worried." His look was direct and unwavering, and Laura thought he could see how distracted she was but would not let that interfere with his own plans. "I liked your letter; I liked your voice over the telephone. And my first judgments are always right." He stood easily before her, his eyes on a level with hers, his compact, broad-shouldered form clothed in well-cut lightweight wool, his silver and gray hair neatly in place, like sunlit metal. He had a square face with gray eyes below thick gray brows, and his large head thrust slightly forward, giving him an aggressive look only partially softened when he smiled. "I do like to know where I'm going, however."

Laura nodded. She was having trouble thinking straight; she couldn't keep his face in focus, and she felt annoyed rather than flattered by the interest in his eyes. But Wes Currier couldn't be fobbed off on anyone else. "Would you like me to show you around?"

"Please."

They walked the length of the great hall, stopping when Currier examined a piece of sculpture or a painting, then into the library and dining room, as Laura made brief comments about the different functions held in each room. Even through her distraction, she was aware of Currier's energy; there was a magnetism in it that drew her on, as if he were leading and she were following. Laura found herself thinking that it was too bad they had met this weekend; any other time she would have found him attractive. Today, she only found him overwhelming.

They went through guest rooms, on the ground floor and upstairs, where maids were cleaning: spacious and bright, each with a fire-place, Early American wallpaper and furniture, four-poster or canopied bed, built-in book-shelves, desk, and a round table with four chairs—"in case you wish to eat in your room," she said. "Not many guests do."

"They like the noise and bustle?" he asked.

"They like the conviviality. Most people enjoy meeting new people, especially when they know they don't ever have to see them again after they leave here."

His brows shot up. "Do you say that to everyone?"

"No." She paused beside a tall window and gazed at a huge sycamore, its branches scraping the glass. "I'm sorry; I don't know why I said it."

"You said what you thought. I'm flattered. And you're very perceptive. Most people do prefer friendships that don't carry the burden of permanence. I'd like to talk to you some more, but I'll be leaving early this afternoon; will you have lunch with me?"

"I don't think I can. But please stay, as our guest; perhaps I can join you for coffee."

"Thank you. I'd enjoy that."

They had reached the office door. "One

o'clock," she said. "Unless we have a crisis. I hope we don't."

"And so do I." He gazed at the door after she closed it behind her. Young, he thought, and probably beautiful if she could smooth out the pinched look in her face and the sadness in her eyes. But she had a shell around her that made her seem like a prisoner of her own defenses; what in hell had happened in her young life to make her so wary and withdrawn—and not the least bit interested in his interest in her?

He did not find out that day. Laura did join him for coffee, but she was on edge, and even though she apologized, telling him how much work she had after being away for a week, he felt piqued: when had Wes Currier come in second with a woman when his only competition was a job? "May I come back before August?" he asked.

She shook her head. "I'll be away part of the time on business, and this is the height of the season for us. We can't have much of a social life until September. That's a time for people who want to make friends instead of impermanent acquaintances."

He chuckled. "I'll remember that and come back in September."

She nodded, her attention already shifting to something else. "Is there anything more you want to know about Darnton's or the conference?"

"Will you be there?"

"I don't know. I'd like to; I'll try."

"May I make that a condition of my appearing here?"

"No." She smiled faintly. "But I will try."

When his taxi came, she watched it drive away, and thought again what a shame it was that she couldn't even flirt intelligently. But what difference does it make? she thought. I have more important things to think about: a trial, a jury, what to say about my past when I testify, what I'll do about the future if I lose.

And Wes Currier has nothing to do with any of that.

The air conditioning was fighting to keep up with Boston's July heat wave when Laura and Clay arrived at the courthouse and walked upstairs. On the landing stood a small, wiry man, notebook in hand. "Yank Bosworth, of the

Globe, Miss Fairchild. Hold on," he said hastily when her face changed. "I don't have a killer instinct; I only want a story. If you'd answer a few questions—"

"Fuck off," Clay said angrily. "We've got other things to—"

"Clay!" Laura put her hand on his arm. "Wait for me inside." She watched his face turn crestfallen. "I'll see you in a minute." When he had left, she let out a small sigh.

Bosworth heard it. "Brotherly protection," he said. "Not a bad thing."

"I know," she said briefly. "If you have some questions, I'll answer them, but I'd rather wait until this is over."

"Uh-huh. But I need a story to fill in, until the verdict." Rapidly he shot questions about where she had been over the weekend, how she felt about the Salingers, what she expected the outcome to be. "I'll get the rest from in there," he said, clipping his pencil to his notebook. "One thing, though: for what it's worth, I think you're getting a raw deal. The whole thing stinks, as far as I'm concerned. 'Course that's off the record."

Laura looked at him sharply and saw that he was not mocking her; he meant what he said.

"I won't publish it," she said with a grave smile. "Thank you. It's good to know there are some friendly thoughts in the courtroom." She held out her hand and he took it and she felt comforted by the firmness of his grip.

"See you later," he said, and Laura went through the high door, pausing to touch Clay affectionately on the shoulder on her way to the table in the front of the room where Rollins already sat.

The courtroom had barely settled down when Rollins called Elwin Parkinson to the stand. He took the oath in a flat, nasal mumble and sat, folding his hands in his lap. A small twitch at the corner of his nose was the only sign of tension in his impeccably-pressed figure.

Rollins, relaxed and sure, led Parkinson through a description of his long association with Owen Salinger and his family, including the drafting of Owen's first will, five years earlier, and then Owen's demand that a codicil be added. Rollins took a step back and leaned against a table. "Did Mr. Salinger know exactly what he wanted in the codicil?"

"He did."

"He told you specifically what it should say?"

"That is correct."

"And you took notes as he dictated it."

"That is correct."

"And the next day you prepared the codicil in your office for his signature."

"I did. I deeply regret it. I did not serve my client well. I know now that he was not competent, that he was under great pressure, and I should not have—"

"Your honor, I want that stricken!" Rollins shouted. He had shot up from his relaxed position. "I want that stricken from the record!"

"This is your witness, Mr. Rollins," the judge said gravely.

"A hostile witness! Mr. Parkinson has just contradicted his testimony in deposition. I want that deposition made a part of the record."

"It will be done, Mr. Rollins."

"You are excused," Rollins said to Parkinson.

"Cross-examine," said Carver Cheyne.

"Your honor," Rollins said angrily, "we've had no time to prepare for a change in testimony. I request a recess."

There was a brief pause. "I think we should hear Mr. Parkinson's testimony," said the judge. "Mr. Cheyne, you may cross-examine."

"Exception," Rollins snapped.

"Noted," the judge responded.

Cheyne let a small smile curve his lips as Rollins returned to his chair beside Laura. His shoulders were slumped. "The son of a bitch sold out."

Laura's face was white, her eyes alarmed. "He didn't say that earlier. He said Owen was sure of himself. . . ."

"We'll appeal. The son of a bitch . . . how much money did it take, I wonder."

"Money? He was bribed?"

He shrugged. "It's not something I'd say in public."

"Mr. Parkinson," Cheyne said smoothly. He stood in the same position as Rollins had earlier, leaning against the table. "I'm sure this is difficult for you, but would you tell the jury more fully why you regret what you did?"

Parkinson touched the small twitch by his nose. "I knew Mr. Salinger was gravely ill, and it seemed clear to me he was not in control of his emotions, but I also feared I might make his condition worse if I argued with him, and so I acceded to his wishes. I put it out of my mind until after I had given my deposition, but that started me thinking about it, worrying about the ramifications of what had happened and how they affected my responsibility to Mr. Salinger as a man and a client and an old friend. I sought the advice of several eminent medical doctors whom I know and trust. I told them of Mr. Salinger's behavior in his sickroom and even before; I searched my memory and recalled bizarre behavior that I might have dismissed too easily—actions that seemed to me, on reflection, to indicate . . . fear, I thought, and a kind of helplessness, as if he were doing what someone told him to—"

"Objection!" Rollins bellowed. His face was flushed. "This is—"

"Counselor, this is becoming rather imaginative," the judge said to Cheyne. "Mr. Parkinson should speak only to what he actually saw."

Cheyne bowed his head. "You consulted some doctors, Mr. Parkinson. And what did they say?"

"Of course they had not attended Mr. Salinger, so they would not make a diagnosis, but as I described his rather strange behavior, they thought it was not inconsistent with a man who was not fully aware of what he was doing, who felt trapped, afraid of death, and completely dependent on other, stronger people."

No! Damn it, it's a lie! All lies! And you know it! Laura was cold, the same icy cold she had felt in the study when Felix attacked her.

"In short, stressed and agitated, as the doctors put it. I realized then I had made a terrible mistake—I had not realized what my eyes were seeing—I had failed my client."

"Mr. Parkinson, in making this admission, do you believe you are jeopardizing your career as an attorney?"

"I do. But the truth is more important. I made an error of judgment, and I owe it to the memory of Owen Salinger, and to his family, to do everything in my power to rectify it. As long as I know that my client, old, paralyzed, not competent, was badgered into changing his will—"

"Objection!" Rollins roared again. "Witness doesn't 'know' anything of the sort; these are wild fantasies!"

"Sustained," the judge said. "The jury will disregard the witness's last statement."

"You thought he *seemed* . . ." Cheyne prompted.

"Badgered," Parkinson said. "I concluded— and the doctors told me they saw this often in patients who had been powerful businessmen —that Mr. Salinger, a man accustomed to being in control, was confused because he didn't know what to do about his loss of control. He was old and helpless and sick, vulnerable to anyone who abused him or made him comfortable. Miss Fairchild did both, and in the end he was like a baby who learns to obey in order to be kept warm and comfortable—*seemed,*" he added hastily as he saw Rollins about to object again. "I didn't realize any of that—I thought he was afraid of dying—who wouldn't be?—but I now know—*believe*— there was far more to it, far more. I believe he was not given a moment's peace—not allowed to die in peace —and I cannot tell you how deeply I regret my failure in not seeing it soon enough to spare him and his family untold grief. . . ."

Parkinson had not looked at Laura; now he swung his glare on her like a spotlight. Behind Laura, Felix rigidly looked the other way. Allison was crying. Leni closed her eyes and sat swaying slightly, as if she might fall. The air conditioning in the courtroom hissed; the outside temperature was close to a hundred degrees, and Laura shivered.

"Fucking bastard," Rollins muttered, losing the last of his Bostonian control. "They must have paid him enough to retire a dozen times over, to make him risk his career. . . . Admitting he wrote a document for a man he thought incompetent . . . cause for disbarment unless they believe his story . . . Bastard. Fucking, greedy bastard."

By the time Laura testified, she was sure they had lost. She sat rigidly in the witness chair and told again about the love she and Owen had found with each other. Her fists were clenched to stop her trembling, but she did not cry. The jury was waiting, everyone was waiting, for her to cry, but she could not. She looked small and vulnerable, and deep inside she was twisted with tears and pain, but her face was like stone. She's cold, the jurors thought. No feelings.

"Miss Fairchild," Rollins said after they had gone through the story of her years with Owen, "did you at any time intend to defraud or harm Owen Salinger in any way?"

"No!" she cried. "I loved him! I didn't even

think about him leaving me anything in his will because I didn't want to think of him dying. I didn't want to think about it! And he wasn't a baby, he didn't act like a baby, he acted like a loving man who loved me and cared about me even when he was dying! He cared about me! And I cared about him! And no one has a right to try to destroy what he was!" She stared at the family. "And the way *all of us* remember him!"

When Cheyne began his cross-examination, his voice was very soft. "Miss Fairchild, you were convicted of theft some years ago."

"Yes."

"You were a thief."

"We were poor and I was very young and I stole sometimes, but I didn't like it; I—"

"Just answer the questions, Miss Fairchild—"

"I didn't want to be a thief! I wanted to change, and go to college and make something of my—"

"Miss Fairchild!"

"I'm sorry. But you make it sound—"

The judge leaned over. "I must warn you, Miss Fairchild, to confine yourself to answering counsel's questions."

Laura looked at him in contempt. He didn't care about the truth; he didn't care about her. "Yes," she said coldly.

"Now, Miss Fairchild," Cheyne said, as softly as before, "I believe you once knew a bookseller named Cal Hendy."

Small events of the past, the acts of a lifetime, done unthinkingly, without regard to tomorrow or next year—and long after we forget them, they appear like green shoots pushing through the earth, to change our lives.

Laura answered all the questions in a level voice, telling everything she had told Rollins. Cheyne never asked about Ben; she had been sure he would not. There was no mention of him in her records. Even in her high school files, she had listed a neighbor as her guardian because Ben thought, as he did later when she was arrested, that the city wouldn't let an unmarried young man be guardian for his brother and sister. And the building they had lived in had been torn down and the landlord had gone off, no one knew where. New York had a way of swallowing people up; it had swallowed Ben Gardner and no one knew of his existence.

At last Carver Cheyne gave his final summation. Standing close to the jury, he reviewed all the pieces with which he built his case of theft and deception, and then he lowered his voice until it sounded like a rumble of fate. "Think of your parents. Each of you: think of your parents as they are or were. Old, tired, wanting only comfort—the comfort they deserve!—as they lie helpless in bed. They have lived a long life—a hard, noble life—and now it is drawing to a close. They have a right to a peaceful end. *You* have a right to give them a peaceful end. BUT THINK! Think of them in the clutches of a clever, ruthless, conniving thief who wears a pretty mask of love and innocence—who comes into your home and *steals your parents from you!* This woman was a thief who came to steal—and stole! Stole a man from his family—stole his love—broke into the bonds of kinship—and robbed this close-knit family of a sacred tradition! Our society believes that a man works all his life, diligently and lovingly, to build an empire and leave it to his beloved family whole and intact. This is a family's rightful legacy—*unless it is stolen!* Ladies and gentlemen, a thief sits before you—not only a thief who breaks into the precious sanctity of our homes and makes off with those possessions we lovingly collect over the years, but *a*

thief who robbed the Salinger family of its fa-
ther when he was too helpless to fight for his
loved ones' rights!"

The jury was out for three hours. When
they returned, none of the twelve men and
women would look at Laura. Rollins put his
hand on her arm and she listened to the fore-
man's loud voice as he read in staccato syllables. "We the jury find for the plaintiff . . ."

Rollins let out his breath in a grunt of defeat. Laura sat very still.

"Pursuant to the jury's findings," the judge
said in a matter-of-fact voice, "the codicil to
the will of Owen Salinger is set aside."

In a flurry, the Salingers left the courtroom.
At their head was Felix, the victor, on his way
to take possession of his house on Beacon Hill
and Owen Salinger's four hotels. Laura
watched them, barely aware that the reporter,
Yank Bosworth, had cut his way through the
crowd and was at her side. "—a few more
questions, okay?"

"Later," she said. She was watching the
backs of the Salingers. "Just a few minutes . . ."

He perched on the edge of the table, unwill-
ing to let her get away. "Listen." He waited

until she turned to him, her eyes blank. "After this is over, if you ever need me, you know where to find me. You got a raw deal."

She nodded. It seemed so unimportant. She turned again to watch as Leni and Allison disappeared through the door. Rollins was watching, too. "We'll appeal," he said to Laura. "We have a good chance. I'm sure of it."

She shook her head. "I won't go through it again."

"Come now, you've done it once; you can do it again. You're not going to tell me you're willing to walk away from here with not a shred of what Owen Salinger left you."

"But I have a great deal that Owen left me." She looked at Rollins, her gaze level and clear. "I've had it all along: his love and what he taught me. And that's all I need to start again and get back the rest of my inheritance."

CHAPTER 14

EVERY room in the Amsterdam Salinger was full. The hotel swirled with visitors who spoke a dozen languages but shared the paraphernalia of tourists the world over: cameras, maps, guide books, dark glasses, crepe-soled shoes, a nervousness with unfamiliar currency, and running commentaries comparing everything with the way things are back home.

It was the end of August: the height of the season. The Kalverstraat was so crowded that people were carried along, rather than walking, from shop to shop; the daily flower market on the Singel was packed; people stood in line to visit Rembrandt's house; and everything from Shakespeare to striptease in the Leidseplein drew full houses and curtain calls.

"It is what they call in America a mad-house," the concierge told Allison and Patricia, beaming because he had everything under control—and it was his unbelievably good fortune that the daughters of Felix and Asa Salinger had, on the spur of the moment, chosen this busiest of all times to visit the hotel. They would, of course, report to their fathers on all the hotels where they had stayed on their trip through Europe, and the concierge had perfect confidence that the Amsterdam Salinger would get the highest marks of all. "The rooms are full, the restaurant is full . . . but for the Misses Salinger, of course, we have the royal suite."

"And if a king shows up?" Allison asked.

"We would put him in the furnace room."

Allison laughed, remembering Owen saying that a good concierge was a good politician. I miss Owen, she thought, following the rotund figure of the concierge through the packed lobby. A year ago this month we buried him, and I never knew how much I loved him until he was gone.

She missed Laura, too, but that thought she did not allow herself.

In the living room of their suite, she stood at

the window while Patricia opened the bottle of champagne that had been delivered when they arrived. Below them the river Amstel cut a wide blue swath through the bustling streets and across the concentric rings of tree-lined canals laid out at perfect intervals in ever-widening U's around the city center. Block after block of closely-built buildings of gray stone and red brick, gabled, arched, many-windowed, often with bright orange roofs, stretched to the horizon, and Allison gazed at them, imagining families in each one: loves and hates, joys and fears, marriage and divorce. And none of them knew or cared about Allison Salinger, who had been Allison Wolcott for less than a year and now was right back where she started. At least in her name.

"What shall we do?" she asked abruptly. "How about a walk through the Walletjes while it's still light?"

Patricia made a face. "Ugly and depressing."

"It's just a neighborhood of self-employed women," Allison said mockingly. "And I'm interested even if you're not."

"Don't be cute." Patricia's voice was bored. "There's nothing interesting about looking at prostitutes sitting in the windows of their rooms, knitting and waiting for customers. I'd rather go to Cafe Reynders and meet some men."

"You mean instead of sitting in a window, knitting, you'll go out and grab the men yourself."

"How unpleasant you are," Patricia murmured.

"I know." Allison turned back to the window. Patricia was right: she was being unpleasant, and going to the Walletjes wasn't fun. Watching those women was like staring at caged animals in the zoo. But she didn't want to meet men; she didn't want to shop; there was really nothing she wanted to do.

Looking out the window, she felt ancient and world weary. It was being married and divorced, she thought; and on top of that finding out that your best friend was a thief who was out to rob your family. And on top of all that, doing your best to help a man—even marrying him!—and then finding out he was uninterested. Even worse, uninteresting.

Patricia was the smart one: nothing seemed to bother her; she never got involved; she just aimed at having a good time. I should be like that, Allison thought. What the hell, you do your best to help people and they don't give a damn. Well, fuck them all; I'll be like my cousin and just take care of me for a while.

The trouble was, she hadn't felt young or adventurous for the longest time. She wouldn't be in Europe this minute, running around like a teenage tourist, if her mother hadn't practically ordered her to go. "You've been mooning around for almost a year," Leni had said in June. "It's time for you to rediscover how big the world is. Go somewhere exotic; at least go to Europe. A healthy young woman of twenty-two should be thinking about possibilities, not failures."

And her mother was right. But her mother was always right: cool and competent; in control of her emotions and her whole life. Even when she had wept about Owen, she hadn't been messy; everything about her was elegant and perfect.

"All right," she said briskly to Patricia. "Let's go shopping. And I'll ask the concierge about the grand prix in Zandvoort; I think it's this month. I want to go there, anyway, to the casino."

"Shopping where?"

"P.C. Hooftstraat. And then you choose where we go for dinner."

"And then Cafe Reynders."

Allison hesitated. But Leni's voice came back: stop blaming yourself; stop blaming Thad; stop looking for blame. Look for fun instead. Try to have fun.

"Fine," she said. "Why not?"

Other shopping streets in Amsterdam were longer and more famous than P.C. Hooftstraat, but Leni had taught Allison, almost from the cradle, to gravitate to the faintly hushed atmosphere that settles like a silken cloak on those rarefied districts where nothing is offered that is not the finest the world can produce, and no salesperson offers it who has not raised attentiveness and expertise to an art. For hours she and Patricia browsed in the glittering boutiques where voices were as refined as the atmosphere, and when they returned to the hotel at two in the morning, after dinner and the Cafe, their purchases were waiting for them in their suite: dresses and coats, shoes and silks, purses and jewelry.

"Allison?" Patricia called suddenly as they undressed in their separate bedrooms. "Did you see that little vase I bought in Venice? I had it on the table next to my bed."

"The maid probably put it away with all your other treasures," Allison said from her room.

"Why would anybody put away a vase?"

"I can't imagine."

Patricia was opening and closing drawers. "Definitely not here. Somebody stole it."

Allison appeared in the doorway wearing a nightgown and a satin robe. "You're sure it's gone?"

Patricia gestured at the room and the open bureau drawers.

"It was worth something, wasn't it?"

"Only about fifteen hundred, but I liked it."

"Fifteen hundred is a lot of money to a lot of people." Allison went to the telephone and dialed the front desk. "This is Miss Salinger; would you please send someone from security to our suite?"

The voice at the other end, young and nervous, turned wary. "Security. Ah, yes, of course. But, please, if you could tell me what is wrong . . ."

"Something is missing from our rooms. I

don't want to discuss it over the telephone; I want someone here. Now."

"Yes, now, of course, but also I will call the director of security; I think it is better—"

"Fine." Allison reached for a pencil. "What is his name?"

"Ben Gardner," said the boy.

Ben had just fallen asleep, his hand loosely cupped around the ample breast of his latest young woman, when the telephone rang beside his bed. "I wouldn't have bothered you," Albert apologized as soon as he answered, "but someone in the royal suite just called—about something being stolen. She said her name was Salinger, and I thought you would want to handle it your—"

"I would." He was already out of bed. "Which Salinger?"

"I don't know; she arrived on the day shift and I didn't take the time to look it up; I thought I should call you first."

"You were right. Tell her I'll be there in half an hour."

His voice had been steady, but his thoughts

were churning. Something stolen. Royal suite. *Salinger.*

He pulled on dark twill pants and a white shirt just back from the laundry, knotted a somber blue tie at his neck, and grabbed his jacket on the way out the door. The young woman in the bed had not stirred.

Salinger, he thought, unlocking his bicycle. *Salinger. Something. Stolen.* He bent low, pedaling fiercely through the streets to the nearest taxi stand, the route so familiar he barely noticed it, concentrating on his thoughts.

Theft was a serious problem in hotels the world over, but not here; they'd been lucky or they'd been better than others, or both. He'd been at the Amsterdam Salinger for two years, helping to enlarge the security staff and overseeing the installation of a new system of door locks and safes in all the rooms. It had been his suggestion that guards be hired to patrol the loading dock—a suggestion that got him the position of director of security when the old director retired. And in those two years, not one major theft had been reported. A few minor problems, mostly packages taken in the lobby and restaurant, but nothing serious and nothing involving anyone influential. Until now. *A Salinger robbed in a hotel where Ben Gardner is director of security.*

He locked his bicycle at the taxi station and leaped into the first car in line. At two in the morning the streets were mostly quiet, and it took them only a few minutes to cross the bridges over the series of canals around the Centrum and past the slumbering shops on the Rokin to the Nieuwe Doelenstraat, where the Amsterdam Salinger stood in restored seventeenth-century grandeur. And where the assistant manager stood nervously at the entrance, awaiting him.

"I called Henrik," he said as Ben strode toward the elevators. "His wife said he is sick—"

"I'll take care of it." He kept going, noting that his breath and voice had sounded normal even though his heart still raced. In the elevator he tightened his tie, made sure his suit jacket was smooth and straight, and ran a comb through his hair. At the last minute he took from his inside pocket a pair of horn-rimmed glasses and put them on.

When Allison opened the door, their eyes met in silence. She was frowning because he looked familiar, but she couldn't place him. And even while she tried to pin down that elusive familiarity, she knew his hard face wasn't like anyone's she knew: the strong jaw, dark brows almost meeting above hard blue eyes, blond hair combed but still a little wind-blown, a tall, lean body standing at ease but the neck muscles taut for no reason that she could see. There was a contained fierceness in him that attracted her: she was curious about what was behind the sober respectability of his dark business suit and horn-rimmed glasses.

She held out her hand. "Ben Gardner?" At his quick flash of surprise, she smiled. "I'm Allison Salinger. I always get people's names; it's best to know who's supposed to be helping me." Their hands met with equal strength.

He knew of her. In the days when he read magazines and newspaper articles, looking for mention of the Salingers, he had read about Allison. Felix's daughter.

"Please come in," she said.

A young woman sat on the couch, and Albert was on a hassock nearby, a clipboard on his lap. But Ben still looked at Allison. He'd thought he knew what she looked like, from seeing her picture occasionally in a magazine or newspaper, but no picture had the impact of the woman before him. She was more striking than he had imagined, and more aloof, and he found himself wondering what she would be like when aroused. His eyes showed nothing, his face was impassive, but he was imagining the feel of that long, angular body and silken hair beneath his hands as he forced her to drop her cool facade and the small smile she wore as provocatively as her pale satin robe.

"My cousin Patricia Salinger," Allison said. "Patricia, this is Ben Gardner, the director of security."

Patricia looked up and nodded. A pale echo of Allison, Ben thought, with none of her style. Which means it comes from Leni. It had been a long time since he had wanted to confront the members of the Salinger family and make them pay for what Felix had done to his father; even a thirst for revenge diminishes as a boy of thirteen becomes a man of thirty-one. Now he found himself once again wanting to meet them.

"I've told him everything I know," Patricia said, tilting her head toward Albert. "It's astonishing that your security is so lax; have you been doing this sort of work very long?"

"Patricia is upset," Allison said quickly.

"She . . . bought the vase for . . . as a gift for my mother. It was very special to her."

"Thanks so much, dear Allison," Patricia drawled. "But why make up a story? Why should you care whether a hotel employee thinks I have cause to be upset or not? I'm annoyed because it was a rather nice vase and I bought it for myself, not for the first maid who came along."

She could make trouble, Ben thought. But Allison, who had surprised him by trying to soften her cousin's harsh words, might keep her in check if she wanted to. "Do you have information about a maid taking it?" he asked evenly.

"Of course not; we weren't here. But the maids were; we'd been shopping and our packages arrived—" She gestured toward Albert. "He has all this; I don't know why I need to repeat it."

"You needn't, of course, if you've told Albert everything; I'm sure you'd like to get to sleep. I'll read his report and talk to you in the morning. If you'll call my extension when you get up we can discuss how we'll proceed."

He had not sat down. He bent his head toward Patricia in what was neither a bow nor a nod, but something in between, and turned to go.

"Why don't we talk at breakfast?" Allison asked.

There was the briefest hesitation. "We could do that. Eight o'clock?"

Patricia was crossing the room to her bedroom. "Allison, you know perfectly well I don't eat breakfast."

"I forgot," Allison said blandly, looking at Ben. "But if Mr. Gardner has breakfast with me, he can talk with you afterward."

"It's quite ridiculous," Patricia said from her doorway. "We'll never see that vase again; some crawly little maid has already sold it. I don't know why you even bothered to call . . ."

Her door closed behind her. Ben and Allison looked at each other. Finally Albert rose. "I shall type up my notes; they are not easy for anyone but me to read. . . ."

"I'll come with you; I have work to do." Ben's face was taut with the effort of keeping his eyes from betraying him when he looked at Allison. "Until tomorrow," he said to her and followed Albert into the corridor.

Looking at the closed door, Allison smiled.

Breakfast, she thought. Not my best time of day, but a nice time to begin. And I get better as the day goes on; by the time we have dinner together, I'll be totally irresistible.

"For your cousin," Ben said at the breakfast table, and handed a box to Allison with Patricia's vase nestled in tissue paper inside.

Puzzled, she looked at it, and then at Ben. "It wasn't really stolen? Or you found it. Do you solve all your thefts so easily?"

"We don't have many, and our job is to solve them."

She waited. "And who is the villain?"

"One of the maids. We're still looking into it."

Allison let it drop; he wasn't ready to talk about it. The waiter came to take their order, and Ben met his thinly veiled surprise with a flat look. There would be talk in the employees' lounge about Ben Gardner and Felix Salinger's daughter, but it wouldn't last long and it couldn't hurt him. The staff paid almost no attention to the Salingers of Boston, so long as their salaries were good and they were left alone in the daily workings of the hotel they considered almost their own.

Allison ordered melon, apple bread, and coffee, and Ben said he would have the same, and then they sat back, the box on the carpet between their upholstered chairs. The restaurant was in muted shades of gray, mauve, and wine, and on every table was a fresh iris in a tall crystal vase.

"Do you know why this is here?" Allison asked, touching the iris with a gentle fingertip. Ben shook his head. "My grandmother was named Iris. When she died—years after she died—when my grandfather was able to think about living without her, he ordered all his hotel managers to do this: a fresh iris, every day, forever. Even my father wouldn't dare change that."

Ben drank his coffee, and looked out the window at the Amstel river and the pedestrians walking past the hotel. He didn't want to hear about Owen Salinger, not now; he wanted to ask about Laura and Clay and the five years since he had seen them. But of course he couldn't. How could he explain Ben Gardner, a hotel employee in Amsterdam, knowing that a Laura Fairchild and her brother, Clay, had been living with the Salingers?

He would wait. There was no rush. If he was careful and patient, he thought, he and Allison could go on for a long time.

"Where are you from?" Allison asked. "Tell me how you got here. I heard you speaking Dutch in the lobby; why would you bother learning it, when everybody in the whole country speaks English?"

"Because the language of the Netherlands is Dutch, and if I want to work here they have a right to ask me to speak their language."

"You're American, not British." He nodded. "In fact—New York?"

"Yes. You have a good ear."

The waiter placed pale green melons before them, then an array of plates filled with thin slices of cheese, sausage, and various breads, a basket of rolls, a tray holding small jars of honey, jams, and jellies, and a silver pot of coffee. "With the compliments of the concierge," he said to Allison. "He regrets the discomfort and displeasure you have experienced and hopes you will allow him to do anything in his power to repair the damage and make your visit one of perfection."

Allison laughed. "He said all that?"

"It sounds exactly like Henrik," Ben said. "Shall we ask him to join us?"

"No. Convey my thanks to Henrik," she told the waiter. "And tell him I'll see him after breakfast." She turned back to Ben. "You were telling me about your life in New York."

"I was telling you you have a good ear."

"Because of New York. Not a strong accent, though." She tilted her head. "You've worked at getting rid of it. Are you getting rid of memories, too?"

"About as many as you are."

"I'm not getting rid of them; I'm trying to understand them."

"So you can repeat them? Or to make sure you don't."

"To make sure I don't. How very easy it would be to repeat them."

"Especially if they involve other people."

"They don't."

"No one else? You made mistakes all by yourself?"

"I didn't say mistakes; I said memories. And of course other people were involved. But they have nothing to do with whether I repeat something or not. Will you tell me how we—"

"Was it a man? A woman? A friend? Someone in your family?"

"A little bit of everything. A death and a divorce and . . . a few other things. How have we—"

"Your grandfather's death?"

"Oh, you know about that? Well, of course, everybody in the hotels would know. That was part of it."

"And your divorce. Recently?"

"Last November; Thanksgiving, in fact. My ex-husband won himself an early Christmas present of a huge alimony—a very big payment for a very small performance—and went his merry way and I sold the apartment I'd bought us on the harbor and left town. Will you please tell me how we got to talking about me when I started out asking about you?"

"I have no idea," he said solemnly, and for the first time they laughed together.

Allison licked the tip of her finger and picked up crumbs of apple cake with it. "This is wonderful. Did your chef bake it?"

"No, your chef did."

She colored. "I wasn't making fun of you. You're part of this hotel."

"I work in it; you own it."

She frowned. "Why are you trying to make me uncomfortable?"

He paused. "I don't know. Why are we having breakfast together?"

"Because I want to get to know you. You're making it more difficult than—very difficult."

"More difficult than most men?"

She smiled. "Much more. I think we should start again."

"I'm sorry; I have to get to work." He pushed back his chair and stood. "I really am sorry."

"It's only nine o'clock."

"I start work at nine."

"And when do you stop?"

"At six."

"Then you'll be free at seven for dinner."

"Allison . . ." He saw her face change and heard her catch her breath at the rough caress in his voice. Allison Salinger, he reflected: heiress to the Salinger hotels and the Salinger fortune. Felix's daughter. Not the kind of pliant woman Ben had always preferred, but impressionable and still unskilled in hiding her feelings. And she wanted him. He relaxed. "Seven o'clock," he said, and put his hand briefly on her shoulder, feeling the shudder that rippled beneath his palm. "Shall I choose the restaurant?"

"Please."

"I'll call your suite at seven." He turned, then turned back and kissed her hand, neutrally, the way a European friend would do it. The lover comes later, he thought, and left the crowded restaurant to walk through the lobby to his office. And off and on, all day, he thought about Allison Salinger, and still was not sure what he would say to her when he phoned her just before seven and she met him in the lobby.

They walked to Dikker en Thijs in silence. Allison seemed withdrawn, and Ben, sensitive to the smallest signals, wondered what he had done wrong, and so they looked away from each other as they walked, only beginning to relax as they came under the spell of Amsterdam's clear golden light, slanting across the city from the low sun of early evening. It was the light that Rembrandt had painted; it was the light that modern tourists tried to capture with their cameras as it bathed the city's narrow streets, ancient stones, and stately buildings—turreted, gabled, arched, and topped with symmetrical clock towers and chimneys—

in a glow filled with promise and hope. It was a light that had drawn Ben to stop his wanderings through Europe, and stay.

There had been other reasons for him to choose Amsterdam. Because even on days when lowering clouds and driving rain engulfed it, the city had a nervous, driving energy that reminded him of New York: people rushed through the streets instead of strolling, the theaters and concert halls were full every night, the shops were cosmopolitan, and the city's red-light district, strip joints, sex shops, and cabarets pulsed with a raunchiness that put most of Europe in the shade. It was a city where Ben Gardner could find anything and be anything; it was a city he could almost call home.

He had rented a room in the Jordaan, a district that attracted all the eccentrics of Amsterdam as well as working people and struggling young artists and writers; and he bought a bicycle to join almost everyone else in the city who had long since given up on finding a place to park and depended on two wheels instead of four. Within a week he had a woman and he had begun to learn Dutch; in less than a year he had moved to a nearby apartment and, at the Amsterdam Salinger, had worked his way up from porter to maintenance man and then to assistant director of security. And a year later, he got the director's job itself.

Now, walking with Allison, blending in with the throngs of visitors going to dinner and working people on their way home, he occasionally broke the silence by pointing out a particular building, or commenting on the stalls selling herring or pancakes, or asking her to stop for a moment to listen to one of the enormous street organs so heavy they had to be pushed along by teams of men while pouring forth waltzes and jazz on a weird mixture of cymbals, pipes, drums, wooden blocks, and plucked wires.

But even with the golden evening light and the distractions of street stalls and music, they still were awkward and stiff when they were seated at a window table in the restaurant. Neither the view of the tall homes along the Prinzengracht—"Princes' Canal"—nor the classic French luxury of the restaurant, nor the excellent wine Ben had ordered in advance eased their discomfort, until Allison, as if forcing herself to be natural, broke the silence. Looking at the canal flowing below their window in small, scalloped ripples, she gestured toward the long row of houseboats tied up along the far side. "Are all the boats in the city painted like floating farms?"

Ben followed her gaze. The boats were flat-bottomed, each with a rectangular house in the center brightly painted with cows and butter-flies, windmills in fields of tall grass dotted with white and pink flowers, and birds in flight against a dark blue sky. Most of them had deck chairs in the stern, beside the steering wheel; on one of the boats, a small dog stood on a deck chair and eyed the passing scene. "They're all painted one way or another," he said. "Most people live on them because they can't afford anything else. So they paint them to look like the countryside to remind them-selves of what they hope to have someday."

"I'd like to live on a boat," Allison said dreamily.

"Close quarters."

"Well, but cozy and comforting, too. And you could always go on land to get away."

"From the boat? Or the person living with you?"

"Oh, I'd only live on it alone. Unless I

found someone I wanted to share it with. And then I wouldn't want to get away."

Ben raised his wineglass. "To 'someone.' I hope he finds you."

It was a curious way to phrase it. Allison studied him. "Thank you. I hope he does, too."

There was a small silence, more comfortable than when the evening began. "What will you do when you return to Boston?" he asked.

"Oh, no, you don't." She sat straight, one hand holding the wineglass, the other properly in her lap. "This time we're going to talk about you. Tell me about New York. Tell me about everything that led you from New York to Amsterdam."

It had been years since Ben talked about himself, but now he did. And he told almost the truth, walking the finest line between what he could say and what he couldn't. Because he had learned, during the past years, that while it was often better to tell all the truth than part of it, it was always better to tell part of it than none at all.

"My father owned a furniture company—he was a designer and a manufacturer—and he had a partner who supplied the start-up money and some customer contacts."

"What kind of furniture?"

"For hotels. It was a small company but it grew, and my father was proud of it. This was before I was born, but years later he told me there were three things he had loved in his whole life: me and my mother and that little company. When the war started—the Second World War—my father fought in Europe. I never knew how his partner avoided the draft, but he stayed home and ran the business. A few months before the war ended, my father was badly wounded. He came home in pain and anger, furious at a world that allowed the barbarity he'd seen, and he found his company gone. His partner had dissolved it and taken its designs into another company that he and his father owned."

Allison searched his face for emotion but found none. His features didn't seem as hard as they had the night before, when she had first seen him, but he showed no tenderness or sadness or anger. "Is your father still alive?"

"No."

The captain appeared and refilled their glasses. "Another bottle, sir?"

Ben nodded. "And the duck pâté." He contemplated the ruby wine in his glass. "He died when I was thirteen. My mother died eight years ago. She'd remarried, but I've been pretty much on my own since my father died, working around New York—"

"Doing what?"

"Clerk in a grocery store, waiter in various restaurants, selling antiques that I picked up wherever I could . . . Then, five years ago, I came to Europe and began working mostly in hotels. Porter, maintenance man, desk clerk, even bookkeeper one time in Geneva. I wasn't expert at anything; I didn't know what I wanted."

"And do you now?" she asked when he stopped.

A small smile played at the corners of his mouth. "I think so."

He watched the captain open their wine while a waiter arranged two plates of pâté, cheese, and crackers in front of them. He knew what he wanted.

A piece of the Salinger empire.

Because even though his early hunger for revenge had faded over the years, the craving to get something from the Salingers had not.

But he knew now that what he had wanted when he was young had been childish and paltry.

He remembered his first wild imaginings of what he would do to get the revenge Judd had talked about more and more feverishly in the months before he died: send rattlesnakes into the Salingers' bedrooms, dynamite them at the dinner table, toss black widow spiders into their limousines. But to a thirteen-year-old the family seemed huge, remote, untouchable—and he did nothing. Then his mother remarried and Laura and Clay were born, and his anger and loneliness were eased by the adoration of those two babies who followed him around as they grew up, treating him like a kind of god. Eventually he stopped thinking about snakes and spiders and dynamite; they weren't practical. Neither was killing Felix or Leni or Owen. Because even though he had become a thief, like his father, he wasn't a murderer and never would be.

The only thing he could think of was to rob them, to make them feel the loss of something they loved, as he had. It was really Felix he wanted to rob, but Felix loved nothing but the family hotels. That left Leni's jewels, which

Ben had read about: they were valuable legacies from her great-grandparents in Austria and, even better, they were much treasured by Leni. And Leni was as close to Felix as Ben could get.

But all that had been infantile, Ben thought as the waiter finished arranging their plates and pâté knives and forks. As childish as rattlesnakes and spiders. Because stealing treasures from a wealthy family was like pinching an elephant: it was only a momentary twinge that left everything exactly the same as before.

The way to get revenge and make a lasting change in the Salingers' lives was to become part of their empire. The only thing Felix loved was his hotels. Therefore, Ben would take as much of the hotel empire away from him as he could.

"You haven't told me what you want," Allison said as soon as the waiter and captain had left.

"I will." He contemplated her striking good looks. She wore a pale blue dress that left her shoulders bare; diamonds were at her throat and ears, and her blond hair, held with a diamond band, cascaded down her back. "But not yet. I want to talk about you. You haven't told me anything about your family."

Her eyes shadowed. "You want to know about the hotels."

He shook his head. "I want to know about the people who are important to you; the ones who make you happy. Or unhappy."

Allison smiled. "You want me to tell you all that in one evening?"

"As many as it takes. We're going to have a lot of evenings." He saw her quick flush. "But you can start. You had a grandfather and a husband. That's all I know. Except, of course, we all know about your father, since we work for him."

Allison sat back, taking small bites of the spicy duck pâté and sipping her wine. "Owen and Iris started it all. My grandfather was born in the last century, and he began the hotels and had two sons . . ." She described her family, lingering on Iris, who had died almost twenty-five years before she was born. "But it doesn't matter so much that I never knew her. The way my grandfather talked about her and how much they loved each other, it's as if she's part of my life, and I think about her when things go bad or I'm wondering what I should do and there's no one I can talk to."

"Not even your mother?"

"Mother is wonderful, but I can't run to her with everything. Some sadnesses you have to work out yourself, don't you?"

"Yes. What kind of sadnesses?"

"My grandfather dying . . ."

"That's one sadness."

"And my divorce . . . One hates to fail, you know, and everybody had told me not to marry him—Paul and Laura and Grandfather —and I did anyway."

"Laura?" The word sounded strangled and he cleared his throat.

"Paul and Grandfather tried to talk me out of it. Paul Janssen, my cousin. And Mother wasn't too happy either. But I ignored everybody, I thought I knew exactly what I was doing, and I was wrong."

Ben cleared his throat again. "Is Laura a cousin, too?"

"No. She's somebody I really don't want to talk about, Ben. I have lots of cousins if you really want to hear about them—you've already met Patricia—"

"I'm more interested in what makes you sad. Did Laura have something to do with it?"

Allison bit her lip. Once again she gazed through the window, absently noting the families chatting together on the decks of the houseboats. Other boats passed; people were cruising through the canals in the last of the evening light, looking calm and content. None of them looked as if they had secrets or would be miserable whenever they thought about the past. "Laura was my friend," she said abruptly. "She lived with my family for years, since she was eighteen; she worked in the kitchen and helped my grandfather organize his library. Her brother was there, too, but Laura was the one I cared about; we spent a lot of time together. She didn't know anything and I taught her to play tennis and dance and buy clothes—my mother and Aunt Barbara helped her, too—she was very pretty and we helped her be beautiful—and Rosa taught her to cook and I took her to restaurants so she'd learn how to order things, and we'd practice staring down rude waiters and laughing. . . ." She wiped her eyes with the back of her hand. "Sorry, I'm being silly, crying after all this time. But she was so much fun; she had a lovely laugh and she was wonderful at mimicking people, and she was loving and honest and smart . . . well, she wasn't honest, but for a long time we thought she was, and when I'd ask her advice on something she told me what she thought, and she was usually right. . . ."

"She wasn't honest?" Ben asked when she stopped talking. He was holding himself in, trying to see it all as Allison saw it, and also as Laura must have seen it, and all the time he was remembering Laura's smile and the way she once had looked at him with love and trust. "What does that mean: 'She wasn't honest'?"

"She was a thief," Allison said bluntly. "She'd been arrested in New York, and convicted—I don't know the details—and my father thinks she and her brother came to our house at the Cape to rob us. Actually, he's sure they did rob us because our house was broken into that summer and Mother's jewelry was taken, but he can't prove it and the police never arrested anybody for it."

"Do you think she did it? Maybe her brother did."

"I don't know. I don't care anymore. We loved her and trusted her, and she never told us the truth about herself and then, after my grandfather died—" She stopped and shook her head fiercely. "That's enough about her; let's talk about you again."

"No!" At her startled look, Ben said quickly, "I'm sorry, I didn't mean to yell at you. I got involved in your story and I wanted to hear the end of it."

She studied him. "You really care about it."

"I care about the things you care about."

Her quick flush came again. "My grandfather had a stroke and was very sick for about a month, and then he died. Laura was with him that whole month—most of the time, anyway —and just before he died he got his lawyer to change his will, leaving her his house and some stock in the Salinger corporation and four of his hotels."

"My God," Ben breathed.

"What?"

"It sounds like a fortune."

"My father said it was. He called her a fortune hunter. But I didn't think she was. I thought it was wonderful that she inherited the hotels and the rest of it, because she and Grandfather loved each other, and if he wanted her to have something after he was dead, that was his business." Once again she fell silent, her eyes staring unseeingly across the room.

"So she's a wealthy woman," Ben said. "But why does that make you sad?"

"Because she's not my friend anymore. She's not wealthy, either. I told you, she lied to us. For four years she told lies and kept secrets from us, while we were as open with her as we could be. And then, when Grandfather was ill, she did something—I have no idea what, but something that made him afraid or upset . . . something. His behavior was very odd after his stroke; he was restless, and he seemed angry or excited or unhappy—we couldn't tell which— and none of us could understand him when he tried to talk. Laura said she could, so we let her translate for us. It was awful to go into his room; I didn't know what to say to him. I thought Laura was magnificent because she'd be sitting there talking to him and listening when he made those garbled noises as if they were having an ordinary afternoon tea. . . ."

"She sounds magnificent," Ben said.

"I don't know. Somehow, when she was alone with him she got him to add a codicil to his will, leaving her the house and stocks and the hotels. He hadn't done it when he was well; he hadn't even told anybody he was thinking about it; but somehow Laura convinced him to do it, even though he couldn't talk or think straight—"

Ben's eyes were narrowed. "How do you know she convinced him?"

"I don't, not for sure; I wasn't in his room as much as I should have been—none of us was, we let Laura do it, and I don't admire us for that. But the lawyer who drew up the codicil testified that—"

"Testified? In court?" There had been vague talk, he remembered, about a contest over Owen Salinger's will, but it hadn't affected the Amsterdam Salinger so no one paid much attention.

"My father sued to get the codicil thrown out; in the original will, he and my uncle got everything."

"And what happened?" Ben asked; he was trying to mask his impatience.

"My father won. We did, if you want to look at it that way. The jury decided that Grandfather wasn't in his right—wasn't able to think clearly when he dictated the codicil."

"So she doesn't have anything."

"Not from Grandfather. I don't know what else she has. My father forced her to leave after Grandfather died, and I didn't see her again until the trial last July, and I didn't talk to her then. I wanted to, but she was so cold and distant, and I guess I was still so angry I didn't make the effort. I don't know where she is now or what she's doing. All I know is that we gave her everything and she threw it in our face, lied to us, took advantage of my grandfather. . . . And damn it to hell I still think about her all the time and miss her and I wish we could undo everything and go back where we were, being friends, almost sisters . . ."

Her voice trailed away. The sounds of the restaurant drifted between them.

Ben was leaning back in his chair but, hidden by the tablecloth, his hands were gripped together in his lap. *My father forced her to leave after Grandfather died.* Triumph had surged through him as Allison said those words. Well? he demanded silently of Laura. Not such a perfect family after all, are they? I warned you, but you wouldn't listen. You wanted them, and you turned your back on me to get them. And they kicked you out. It serves you right.

He was angry at her, too. She could have told him; she could have asked for his help. She must really hate him, not to turn to him at such a rotten time in her life.

But then he felt a rush of pity. He still remembered the feel of her delicate shoulder bones the last time he hugged her good-bye. Damn it to hell, she was a little girl who'd never harmed anyone, and that fucking Felix Salinger had thrown the whole legal system at her.

With grim amusement, Ben reflected that now he had two scores to settle with Felix. "What?" he asked Allison as she looked at him, her head tilted. He sat straight and drank off the wine in his glass. "I'm sorry; I was thinking. About your story."

"I said I don't want to talk about it anymore." Briefly, she put her hand on his. "You're a wonderful listener and I appreciate your being so interested, but it's so hard for me. . . ." She gave a small laugh. "It was easier getting over my marriage than getting over Laura. Let's talk about you again. You still haven't told me what you want."

Her eyes were direct and curious. She was fascinated by him, and almost as trusting as

Laura. Ben caught the tantalizing scent of her perfume; the touch of her fingers lingered on his hand. Felix's daughter. She had style, she was strikingly good-looking, she wanted to prove she wasn't a failure at marriage, and she was still young enough to be malleable. She was everything a man could want.

"Tell me what you want," Allison said again, softly.

"Love," he said. "And work. I'm not much different from other men: I want a woman to believe in; an empire, or a piece of one, for myself; and a family to fulfill the dream of the one I never had."

His words settled around her like a familiar cloak, warm and fitting her as if made for her. And once again, as so many times before, Allison Salinger thought to herself, I could be that woman; I could make his life what he wants it to be. I could make him happy.

CHAPTER 15

WES Currier was a financier who had moved beyond the skyscrapers of New York and Chicago to roam the world as consultant to international corporations that straddled geographical, political, and religious boundaries, and even raging wars. He had been on the move through three marriages, and now, at fifty-five, with half a dozen homes in Europe and America and memberships in as many exclusive clubs, he was known as a master of mergers and acquisitions; a generous supporter of the arts and of young people starting their own companies, and one of the most eligible bachelors on two continents.

No one really knew him. After his second

divorce, a reporter had written a breathless book about him archly titled *Currier's Lives,* but it had been nothing more than a pastiche of newspaper articles and secondhand gossip that disappeared almost as soon as it was published. Even a good reporter would have had a hard time with Wes Currier, who had made his fortune by following his hunches and never showing his hand; who nurtured his reputation for unpredictability; and who had no intimate friends. And while everyone in the financial world tried to keep one step ahead of him, no one would lay odds on being able to do it, and no one else had begun another book about him.

"Though I'm told a couple of journalists are collecting information for one," he told Laura carelessly as they sat in the dining room of Darnton's on a hazy morning in September. It was the Labor Day weekend, the lodge was full, and they were having breakfast together before he gave the opening talk at a conference on international trade. It was his second talk at Darnton's, following the one he had given three weeks earlier. "I can't believe they don't have more important things to do with their time."

Laura looked at him quizzically. "You don't mean that. People want to know how you shape their lives."

"I don't shape; I influence."

She shook her head. "You know how powerful you are. You help determine the future of the companies people work for, the products they buy, the stock they own—"

"I influence external forces. But as for shaping—we shape our own lives; no one does it for us."

Impatiently she looked away, disliking his arrogance. Automatically, as soon as her attention changed, she found herself making a quick survey of the dining room. All the tables were occupied, and guests were waiting in the lounge; coffee cups were being refilled promptly; tables that were vacated were cleared without delay and as quickly reset with the dusty rose cloths and stoneware dishes that were used for breakfast and lunch, and would be replaced, for dinner, with white linen, crystal, and china. Bending down, she reached out to pick up a napkin a departing guest had dropped from his ample lap, and laid it on the table for the busboy.

And then, knowing everything was in order,

she turned back to Currier. She had had dinner with him in August and again on this trip, and she found him attractive and intriguing, but in his very success he was also exasperating. "You assume everyone has the same luck or skill you have. Most of us don't control fate the way you do."

"I make it, my dear; that's far better than controlling it." He drank coffee and gazed at her. "I'm curious to know why you think you haven't been in control of yours."

"I'm in control as long as all our guests get breakfast on time," she said lightly, ignoring the flash of irritation in his eyes: he was a man who didn't like being put off. "And if I can get away this morning to listen to your talk. I hope I can."

"You heard most of it last month."

"I like to watch you; you're very good with an audience."

"Thank you. You're very good at changing the direction of a conversation."

"Thank you." They smiled and Currier acknowledged to himself that her reserve was going to be harder to breach than he had expected.

"You'll have dinner with me tonight?" he

asked. "We can eat on the mainland if you can recommend a good place."

"The Post House is good; almost as good as here. I'd like to have dinner with you if I'm able to get away."

"You can always get away. The sign of a good executive is a good staff."

"I'll remember that," she said evenly.

"I'm sorry," he responded quickly. "I have no right to tell you how to do your job. It was a poor attempt to make sure of you for dinner."

"I'll do my best." They stood, and as they walked through the room, Laura nodded to the guests and noted the trays the waiters were carrying: smoked trout and scrambled eggs seemed to be heavy favorites this morning. "And I will try to get to your talk."

They parted in the Great Hall as Currier left for the conference room and Laura went to her small office adjacent to Kelly's. Her desk was covered with stacks of bills to be verified, samples of drapery fabric from which she and Kelly would make final choices for redecorating some of the rooms, and letters of confirmation to write to designers showing in a fashion show to be held at the end of the month. But she was having trouble concentrating, and shortly before nine-thirty, she pushed back her chair and walked down the corridor to the stairs that led to the lower-level conference room, greeting guests by name as she passed them, and feeling pleased at their delight in being recognized.

She had missed Currier's talk. In the windowless, brightly furnished room, he sat in an armchair at the head of the long rosewood table, answering questions from those who had not yet left for the day's recreation. He smiled at Laura as she came in, thinking how lovely she was but wondering at the same time why something always seemed to be missing in her beauty. She stood in the doorway, slender and as poised as a dancer in a blue, full-skirted dress; her delicate face was framed by springy chestnut hair, her enormous dark blue eyes were long-lashed above faintly shadowed cheekbones and a mouth meant for laughter and love—but her beauty was dimmed by the firm line of her lips and the tight control she kept over herself. When occasionally she let a smile of delight or a mischievous laugh break through, Currier caught his breath at the promise she gave of unfettered beauty and a vibrant woman.

"Please join us," he said, and, like a host, indicated the sideboard. "Coffee and croissants. Darnton's has an excellent management that takes care of our every—"

The lights went out. In the absolute darkness there were mumbled curses and the rustling sound of chairs being shoved back on the carpet. "I think we should stay where we are," Currier said calmly. "Laura, is there a flashlight?"

"I don't think so. But there are candles; we use this sometimes as a private dining room . . ." She felt her way to the closet in the corner, and her hand found a stack of cardboard boxes. Taking one down, she moved along the wall to where she thought Currier sat. "Wes? If you talk to me I can find you."

"A good definition of love," he said good-humoredly. "If we talk to each other we can find each other." He felt her hand brush his shoulder with the sensitive probing of the blind, and reached up to clasp it with his. "And so we have," he added quietly. Then he raised his voice. "Now if someone has a match . . ."

"I would have lit it," came a sarcastic voice.

There was a pause. "Not a match in the room?" someone said incredulously.

"Of course there are matches," Laura said quickly. "I forgot to get them. Wes, please take these . . ." Putting the box of candles in his hand, she found her way back to the closet. A minute later she struck a match and saw everyone blink as the flame flared. "If you'll be patient, we'll get the lights on right away." She left the matches with one of the guests and was out of the room and in the corridor before the match burned down to her finger.

But instead of lights, a bellboy brought a flashlight and led Currier and the others into the blackness of the corridor and up the stairway to the sunlit Great Hall. A few guests were there; most had left for the day. Currier saw Kelly Darnton through the open door of her office; she was standing beside her desk, a telephone cradled on her shoulder. "The whole fucking *island* is out," she said, then, with a quick glance at the guests in the Great Hall, lowered her voice.

Currier went to her office and pulled the door shut behind him. "Perhaps I can help," he said quietly.

She covered the mouthpiece with her hand.

"Thanks; why don't you ask Laura? I've got to deal with the electric company . . . What?" she shouted into the telephone. *"Twenty-four hours?* Are you out of your mind? There are *two hundred people* here who paid good money—"

Currier opened the door to Laura's office and closed it behind him. She, too, cradled a telephone on her shoulder while making notes. "They got you out," she said to Currier with a smile. "Poor man, it must have felt like a dungeon down there. . . . You have a hundred pounds?" she said into the telephone. "Wonderful; if you could bring it right away . . . Of course, if you have more, bring it; how can we have too much dry ice when our refrigerators are off? Oh, one more thing, Bill. Would you stop on your way and buy all the flashlights in the hardware store? Charge them to our account. No, as many as they have; I just heard Kelly say this is going to go on all night, and we don't have a hundred flashlights . . ." She stood up. Currier saw how anxious she was to end the call, but she kept it out of her voice. "One for each guest room. Illumination is one of the amenities that makes Darnton's a high-class place." Currier heard Bill laugh and

Laura gave a small smile. "Thanks, Bill; you're a good friend."

A lot of men, Currier thought, would go out of their way to hear Laura Fairchild's low, lilting voice say they were her good friend. "What can I do to help?" he asked as she hung up.

"I don't know. I haven't had time to think about assignments."

"What happened? A transformer?"

She nodded. "And for some reason it can't be fixed before tomorrow, which means we have until sundown tonight to get ready. John went to get some generators in Burlington, but we can't rent enough for the whole island, so we have some organizing to do."

Currier sat in a chair in a corner of the small room. "Let me know when you have my assignment."

She nodded, already dialing again, this time an in-house call. "Roger, the dry ice is on its way; you'll keep the refrigerators closed until then? . . . Yes, soup and sandwiches would be fine for lunch . . . I don't know about dinner; we'll think about that after lunch." They talked some more, then hung up. "Thank God for gas burners," Laura murmured, then looked at her list and picked up the telephone again.

For two hours, Currier watched her. He sat without moving, and Laura seemed unaware of him. Now and then she gave an absent look in his direction, but her thoughts were elsewhere. Talking to Kelly and other staff members who appeared in her doorway, disappeared and then reappeared, she made telephone calls and wrote pages of notes.

As she finished one of the calls, Clay burst in. "Do you know they're saying in town that we've shut down? I was in the Landing drugstore and somebody said there's no power here and we're closed."

"My God." Laura began to dial another number. "Did you tell them we're open?"

"I told them they're crazy. What's the problem with the power?"

"A transformer went. Tim," she said into the telephone, "it's Laura, at Darnton's. Would you do me a favor? Put a note in the airline lounge where our guests get the limousine, saying we're open and ready for everyone who has a reservation. I'm worried about people flying in and then hearing rumors about our being closed. . . ." She drew squiggles on the paper before her. "Of course not. Everything is fine, and nobody will feel cheated. We'll always give them plenty for their money."

Currier saw a sudden brightness in her eyes. Curious, he watched her pencil stop its random marks on the paper, and her mouth curve in a faint smile. "I just had an idea," she told Clay as she hung up the telephone. "Do you know how to make a campfire?"

"How the hell would I know that? I grew up in New York."

Kelly came in and perched on the edge of Laura's desk. "Roger planned lobster coquilles for dinner. They require ovens. He has electric ovens which, of course, are stone-cold."

"I have an idea about that," Laura said. "What would you say to eating outside? Campfires and big cast-iron pots—can you boil water that way?—I wish I'd been a Girl Scout; well, let's assume we can. We'll call it Lobster Primitive. Baked potatoes—in foil?—we really need an expert—cooked in the coals. Roger can make a magnificent salad and ice cream for dessert; we have to eat it; we aren't going to have enough dry ice to keep it— You're shaking your head."

"You've forgotten we're not supposed to be rustic anymore; we've been pushing elegance ever since you suggested it. An Adirondacks lodge with the luxury of a Park Avenue mansion. You do remember saying that?"

"Yes, but I'm rethinking part of it. Kelly, everybody likes to play at being rustic once in a while; even people who wear silks and black tie to dinner. If we make it lavish, I think they'd love it."

" 'Think' is an uncertain word. What if they hate it?"

"Then we have a problem. But I'll bet lobster under the stars, with lots of good wine, would be a hell of a lot more fun than the same meal in the dining room."

"I'll bet so, too," Currier said quietly.

Kelly and Laura looked at him. "You really do?" Kelly said.

He nodded. "I'll crack the first claw. I'll offer a prize for the most perfectly dissected lobster. I'll help make the fires."

"Do you know how?" Kelly asked.

"No, but I can follow orders."

She stood up and went to the door. "I'll talk to Roger. It may be a good idea. Clay, would you check on the boats?"

As Kelly and Clay left, one of the maids came in. "How do we do the rooms, Laura? We can't vacuum."

"Try a broom," she said absently. She was gazing out the window.

"How do you use a broom on carpets?"

"The same way you use it on the floor. It really works, Beth. Brooms were invented long before vacuum cleaners."

"Well, I guess I can try. Just don't expect very much . . ."

"I have absolute confidence that you'll do a very good job."

She shook her head as the maid left. "I never had a vacuum cleaner until I was at the Cape," she murmured. She went to the door of her office. "Kelly, there's a man named Pickard in number eighteen."

"If you say so," Kelly said. "You remember their names better than I do."

"He's an IBM executive and an actor in his spare time."

"So?"

"How about a ghost story at the campfire? Edgar Allan Poe or Robert Louis Stevenson . . . something wonderfully terrifying."

There was a silence. "*That* idea I really like. What did you say his name is?"

"Eric Pickard."

"I'll call him."

"He plays golf, but he'll get a message."

"How the hell do you remember all those things?"

"It's a Fairchild talent," she said lightly and came back to her desk. "Do you sing?" she asked Currier, and he realized she had been aware of him all morning.

"I follow a good leader," he replied.

"I'll bet that's the only time you do."

"You'd lose. I follow those who do things superbly. I would follow you."

She flushed. "I don't do things superbly. I improvise when I'm in a tight spot. That's a Fairchild talent, too."

"I'd like to hear about it."

She gave him a long look. "You might. Sometime."

Kelly walked in. "Clay just called; he's putting a hand pump on the gas tanks at the marina, so we don't have to worry about dry-docked boats. They're doing massages by candlelight at the spa; everything else is outdoors, and if you walk around out there you'd think it was an ordinary day; not one sign of trouble. Isn't it amazing how John got out of here right at the start? You'd almost think he practices avoiding crises. But you've been wonderful, Laura; I would have been lost without you. Why don't you take off for a while? You look frazzled."

"A boat ride," Currier said, getting to his feet. "Since we don't have to worry about running out of gas."

Laura was about to refuse, then changed her mind. She had been making decisions all morning, with Kelly's encouragement, but now it was time to recognize Kelly's supremacy at Darnton's. She owned it; she employed Laura; she had just told Laura to leave for a while. *When I have my own hotel, I'll be able to make all the decisions I want.*

"And lunch," Currier added. "Would Roger pack something for us?"

"He's probably too busy; I'll do it," Laura said. "Is a couple of hours all right, Kelly?"

"Fine. Take as long as you want."

In the kitchen, Currier watched Laura pack cheese, French baguettes, nectarines, and white wine in a basket. She stood at a corner of the work area away from the bustle of the large kitchen staff, working as coolly and efficiently as she had in her office. He had no idea what she was thinking or what she had felt during that frantic morning, whether she had been worried or enjoying the challenge or simply absorbed in doing a job. No, he thought, she's got more fire than that. She's very young—she can't be more than twenty-eight or nine—young enough to feel the excitement of knocking down problems and watching people hop to her suggestions.

"How old are you?" he asked as they walked across the broad lawn toward the marina. When she told him, he stopped short. *"Twenty-three?"*

"You thought I was younger? Older?"

"A little older." He fell silent until they reached the dock, where he and Clay selected a speedboat.

"I'm going to town to pick up the first batch of golfers," Clay told Laura. "Do you need anything?"

"Check with Kelly," she said and waved good-bye as Currier started the engine. The powerful boat leaped forward, trailing a long wake that furled out from the center and then smoothed out, leaving a faint feathery *V* on the surface that reflected the few puffy clouds in a brilliant sky. Laura thought of the ocean off the Cape, its swells crashing on the shore where she and Owen sat, or hurling themselves toward the dunes where she and Paul walked. She closed her eyes and put back her head to let the wind blow her memories away.

Currier steered the boat away from others on the lake. When they were alone, he reduced the power and they slid slowly along the shore, the forest almost within reach, birds and wildlife visible among the trees. He glanced at Laura. She was pushing her hair back with a precise movement of her hand, as controlled as her voice and face, and he was aware once again of the challenge she presented. He had never met anyone, man or woman, who could calmly allow a silence to stretch out for many minutes without bursting into nervous chatter to fill it. She was silent now, and he reduced the power further, cutting down the noise so they could talk.

"Do you ever make an effort to impress someone?" he asked.

She looked surprised. "Of course. What an odd question. I want people to like me and admire me . . . it makes it easier for me to like and admire myself." She smiled, a little embarrassed. "Don't you do that? I think most people do. Make others a mirror, I mean, so that what we look like to ourselves depends on how we look to them."

"Clever," he said. "I like that. But I haven't seen any signs that you do that."

She gave him a level look. "You mean, since I haven't tried to impress you, and since most people do—certainly most women do—there must be something peculiar about me."

"Something unique," he corrected with a laugh, though she had given him a moment of self-consciousness that was almost discomfort. "But you're right about people trying to impress me, show me their tricks, whatever they are; I didn't realize how much I've come to expect it."

She smiled faintly. "You saw my tricks this morning."

"But you did them for the lodge. And to satisfy yourself."

She reflected. "But I need that, too. Don't you? If you depended on other people to tell you how good you are, you wouldn't have enough pride in yourself to get past the times when people are cruel."

He was watching her closely. "Did it happen recently, that someone was cruel to you?"

"We all know cruel people." She caught a glimpse of a deer bounding away from the sound of their boat. "Don't even cruel people show you their tricks to impress you?"

He nodded. "Cruel, crooked, selfish, bigoted, weak . . . they'll all perform if it helps them do a deal and be on top, with the deck stacked against everyone else."

Still gazing at the forest, she said, "I know someone like that."

"Only one?"

She turned back to him. "Do you know so many?"

"Hundreds. Thousands, probably. I take them for granted."

"I don't."

"That's one of the reasons I expect to be here often."

"And the other reasons?" she asked after a brief pause.

"I like the adventures you arrange for your guests."

They laughed together, and Laura said musingly, "I wonder if we can make that work."

"I think you can make anything work," he

said quietly. He turned the wheel, guiding the boat into a small cove. "Time for lunch. And you can tell me about Cape Cod and the first time you had a vacuum cleaner."

All through the fall—when electric power had long since been restored and guests again wore silks and black tie to dinner while recalling the charm of that evening under the stars when the lobster tasted better than ever before and the tale told by Eric Pickard made chills run through them even in the heat of the campfire—whenever Currier was not in Europe he spent the weekends with Laura. They rode horseback and played tennis, took boats on the lake, swam in the outdoor pool, and explored the small towns of the Adirondacks. They talked about the Europe Currier knew, his world of finance, his friends, his wives. They talked about Laura a little at a time; she was uncomfortable when he questioned her, and after a while he was willing to let her find her confidence with him at her own pace. He was not giving up, only spinning out his forcefulness more slowly. After their first time on the lake, when he had asked her about Cape

Cod and she had instinctively withdrawn, he had recognized how deep her reticence went. Her actions were automatic, he realized: she concealed from habit.

Still, as the days grew short and chilly, and they spent more time indoors, before the fire, she gradually told him bits of her life, describing the university, mimicking her professors as she once had mimicked Jules LeClair for Paul, and talking about her part-time jobs as assistant concierge at the Boston Salinger and companion to an elderly widower. "And then Clay and I came up here," she told him as they sat in a corner of the Post House in Jay's Landing. It was a small tavern with leather wing chairs, gas mantles hanging from the low, beamed ceiling, and prints of Revolutionary War battles on the walls. On a weekday afternoon in November, they were the only guests. "Kelly and John offered us jobs and it's a wonderful place for me to learn. I've been here a year and I've done everything from filling in as hostess in the dining room to managing the whole place whenever I'm able to convince Kelly to convince John it's all right for them to take a vacation."

Currier was watching her closely. "The elderly widower—"

"He was my friend," she said briefly, wondering what had made him pick up on Owen. Something in her voice or her face . . . Suddenly she felt a wave of revulsion at the lying that had become almost a way of life. She was so sick of picking her way through the mine fields of her own lies—and Currier was so sophisticated, she thought; surely he was beyond being shocked or censorious—that she almost told him everything. But the words never came; the habit of secrecy was too strong. "He died and I . . . miss him very much. I worked in his kitchen, too, with a wonderful woman named Rosa"—her voice wavered and quickly she took a sip of wine—"and learned how to cook. Do you cook? Somehow I can't imagine you in the kitchen."

"I have six cooks, one for each of my houses, but I make a wicked hamburger. I'll make one for you when you come to New York."

"I'd like that."

He gazed at her. "When are you coming to New York?"

"Not for a while, but someday, I think. What else do you make besides hamburgers?"

"Martinis. Will you come to New York with me?"

"Not yet," she said easily. "But I promise to eat hamburgers in your kitchen when I do. And I'll make dessert. What would you like?"

"Tarte Tatin."

"I make a wicked tarte Tatin." They smiled together, and he was surprised, during the following week, as he sat in meetings and flew across the country, how often he saw her smile and heard in his memory her promise to come to New York. He was still remembering when he returned to Darnton's the next Friday.

"Almost through?" he asked.

"Almost. Are you here for the weekend?"

"Just tonight. I'm sorry, but I have to be in Washington tomorrow."

"I'm sorry, too." She signed letters and folded them in their envelopes. "Ready. Shall we have a drink on the porch? It's been so warm today; it doesn't feel like November, does it?"

The weather was warm, but she was cool, as always, and Currier felt a flash of adolescent anger: didn't she appreciate what he was going through to see her—dragging himself to the Adirondacks ten times in three months? And what did he get for it? A lilting voice saying 'I'm sorry, too.' Fuck it, he thought as they sat on a cushioned sofa on the long front porch. I don't need her; the world is full of women.

"Laura," he said, "I want you to marry me."

The silence was sudden and complete. All around them, as the sun set, the sky was an ocean of flame streaked with islands of thin, purple-gray clouds. "How can you marry someone you've never slept with?" she asked lightly, then added quickly, "I'm sorry, Wes, that was foolish. I'm ashamed of myself. You took me by surprise."

"And you said the first thing you thought of."

"I apologize. It was crude."

"But you aren't crude, and I know it. And I did indeed take you by surprise, so I apologize, too. As for my sleeping with you—"

"Please, I've said I'm sorry. It's not important."

"It's very important, at least to me; I've wanted you in my bed for a long time. But I'm a patient man, Laura, and I always get what I want. And I'm not worried. Are you? One of these days, as soon as you vanquish your demons, you'll want more from me than companionship and my presence at conferences and then—"

"That's unfair." Her face was flushed.

"It was and I apologize." He held her face between his hands and kissed her lightly. "This is the damnedest proposal; all we're doing is apologizing. Laura, I want to marry you and take care of you. I don't want you to look the way you did when you told me about the old man you took care of when you were working your way through college, the one who died—"

"How did I look?"

"Brokenhearted," he said briefly. "Not for long—you have a remarkable spirit—but I don't want you to feel any sadness, ever again. You deserve happiness and luxury and a life free of worry, and I can give you that. I can give you everything. And I want you with me wherever I go; I'm even going to ask your help in some of my work. You have a way of striving for order that I admire, and you're very precise in what you say and what you don't say. In a marriage that might be a problem, but in business it's invaluable."

She smiled. "You mean you'll take the lumps in marriage because the business will prosper."

"That's unfair." He studied her face. "You won't always be so careful with me; if we love each other—"

"Love," Laura murmured. "Does that enter into it?"

He laughed. "Yes. I should have said that first, not last. But I'm not always sure whether my love may not be suspect. Three times it's ended in divorce. I thought you might prefer a simple proposal without the fluff of an emotion that might sound a little frayed around the edges."

Laura laid her head briefly on his shoulder. "A girl likes a little fluff now and then, even if she has to say no."

He hesitated only a fraction of a second. "Then I'll use more of it next time."

They were silent. The sky had darkened to a deep bronze so rich it turned to orange the shadowed grass and tall pines in front of the lodge. Currier put his arm around Laura, his fingers caressing the short springy hairs at the back of her neck. Vanquish your demons, she thought. Of course I will. I've stopped missing Ben, except when I'm really lonely, late at night, and then I wonder what kind of life he has in Amsterdam and if he ever thinks of me anymore. And it's just a matter of time before I forget Paul and stop having dreams about Osterville and Boston, Leni and Allison, Paul's parents, even the cousins who were always in the background, making everything seem more alive, more like a storybook family.

It will all seem like a story if I wait long enough; like something I read once and put away. And then maybe I'll be able to make love to Wes Currier instead of knotting up inside every time he kisses me.

"Still," he said musingly, as if continuing a conversation, "you're not as brittle as you were four months ago. You may be breaking out of this cage you've made for yourself."

She stirred. "What does that mean?"

"I'll tell you a story. When I was twenty-five, a year after I'd made my first million, my wife left me. I fell into a funk that wouldn't go away. Something I cared about, something that was safely mine, had been stolen from me. All I could think was that some vicious mythical beast was punishing me for having everything I wanted." He paused. "I think someone took something away from you, something very precious, and you've been feeling like a victim ever since, with the forces of nature and mythology stacked against you. The logical reaction to that is anger, and building a thick shell around yourself, and no sex."

She smiled. "Probably." But her eyes were focused inward. "You think a shell is like a cage."

"It was for me. I was locked into my anger because I'd been robbed, and I was determined to defend myself so no one could rob me again. That was my shell and that was my cage." They were silent. Within the circle of his arm, Currier felt Laura's taut muscles, and he spoke quietly but with an intensity that struck to the heart of her memories. "I'd earned what I had —that was what made me angriest. I'd worked hard and I'd given love, and I deserved the good things I had. Other people got what they wanted; why shouldn't I? I was as good as they, maybe better. But in a way that was the worst of all: I'd known what it was to have the happiness I wanted and then it was taken from me before I could enjoy it. So I locked myself in even tighter, like a besieged general."

"And how did you break out?" Laura asked after a moment.

"Oh, that's the dull part of the story. I remembered what I'd always known: that life isn't fair and we're never promised that it will be. Too many people spend their time looking for someone to promise them happiness or beauty or wealth, instead of fighting to carve out their own. I'm still fighting, but I'm almost there; I have most of what I want and I'll get the rest. I told you, I always do."

The last faint hues vanished from the sky. The first star flickered just above a grove of pine trees; amber lanterns lined the curving driveway and front walk. Behind them, Laura and Currier heard the chatter of guests gathering in the Great Hall for cocktails, and the soft strains of classical guitar from the tape John Darnton had just put on. "Wes," Laura said thoughtfully, "if I asked you to back me in buying a hotel, would you consider it?"

He masked his surprise and the instinctive refusal which sprang to his lips. He wanted a wife, not an entrepreneur. But he was patient, and he knew the advantages of having someone in debt to him. "If you knew what you wanted, of course I would. Do you have a specific hotel in mind?"

"The Chicago Salinger," she said.

Myrna's legs were clamped around Clay's hips and he thrust deep inside her. He heard her little kittenish cries that meant she was coming, and then let himself go. The surge tore through him like a torrent bursting through exploding floodgates. He couldn't see, he couldn't hear, for that incredible instant when everything in him felt free and absolutely perfect, and even when he heard Myrna's voice murmuring, "So lovely, Clay, you are a lovely lover," and opened his eyes, he still felt the tremors all through him and her warm wetness clinging to his penis. He lay flat on her surprisingly cushiony body to stay inside her as long as he could, and reached back to pull the sheet over them; in the midnight air, his skin suddenly felt chilled. "Lovely lover," Myrna whispered, turning her head and flicking her tongue deep into his ear. "My wonderful lover . . ."

Little sparks shot from her probing tongue all through him. Her hands grasped his buttocks and he felt the quick sharpness of her finger pushing into him and then he was hard again inside her; he was moving again inside her; and again they found a rhythm that could last, as far as he was concerned, forever.

Of course he wouldn't say a thing like that, then or later, when, finally, he was pretty sure he couldn't get it up again even if he had the energy to think about it. Myrna didn't seem tired—Myrna never seemed tired, whether she was teaching on Darnton's tennis court or swimming in the pool or shopping all day for presents for her family somewhere in Nebraska or screwing all night in her little rented house in Jay's Landing. Crazy lady, he thought, and I'm crazy about her—but sometimes she scares the shit out of me.

He thought that every time he got to this very dangerous moment: three in the morning, sprawled on her bed in ecstatic exhaustion, his mind numbed with gratitude and satiety. And as always, he gathered caution around him like a winter coat and did not ask her to marry him or even live with him, though it did occur to him that there were advantages to knowing she was off the market and definitely his.

Later, later, later, he thought, but at the same time part of his mind was listening to the satisfied hum of his body, telling him to wrap her up and make sure of her. Caught between two pieces of contradictory advice, he fell asleep.

Myrna Appleby was twenty-seven and had been a tennis instructor for almost ten years. She didn't mind that Clay was only twenty-one; he was taller than she: blond, handsome, with a neat mustache and a kind of permanent boyishness that led her to believe she could turn him into the kind of man she wanted. She'd just about given up hope of finding one.

The problem was, most men were afraid of her. They called her bold when they were being kind, and aggressive when they weren't. But Clay liked it when she took command. At first she thought he didn't have much backbone, and in that case he wouldn't be right for her at all, but then she decided it was just that he'd gotten so used to his sister making decisions that he pretty much took it for granted when Myrna behaved similarly. He'd probably been looking for a woman like that all along, she reflected as she set her alarm, and then she, too, fell asleep.

She woke him at five in the morning so he could get to work on time. If it weren't for her, she thought, he'd likely lose his job and go wandering off with no real skills except chauffeuring and being a desk clerk, and how far would that get him? She had no idea what he'd do without her, especially since Laura was working eighty hours a week and spending the rest of the time with Wes Currier. Clay had nobody but Myrna. "Rise and shine, darling. I'll fix breakfast."

"Just coffee," he mumbled, his head under the pillow.

Myrna stroked his long, boyish back and felt a rush of tenderness for him. Men were so vulnerable, when you thought about it; terrible at the basic necessities like cooking and doing laundry and buying socks; they didn't even know how to eat properly. "You'll need more than coffee," she said decisively. She ran her fingers through her straight black hair, pulled on a kimono, and went downstairs to the kitchen.

"What are we doing tonight?" she asked when he was at the table plowing through fried eggs and toast. "There's a film at the—"

"Can't see you tonight," he said. "We can go to the movie tomorrow if you want."

A flicker of alarm appeared in her gray eyes. "I thought we had a date."

"Not that I remember." He looked up, worried. "Did we? I didn't think so. Anyway, it doesn't matter, does it? The movie'll still be there tomorrow night." He returned to his eggs. "Terrific breakfast, babe."

"What are you doing tonight?"

"Playing poker. Want to tie a ribbon around my arm for good luck?"

"Knights in armor did that before they went into combat."

"Good for you. I didn't know you knew that."

"Are you going into combat?"

"Who knows? These guys are good. I may bet some real money."

"Does Laura know you're going to play?" His face tightened and she knew she had made a mistake. "Well, it doesn't matter," she said in a rush, adding carelessly, "Have fun and buy me something beautiful if you win."

"Thanks, babe. Talk to you soon." On his way out, he kissed her on the cheek, and a minute later, as he backed out of her driveway, he offered a prayer of thanksgiving that he hadn't given in to his mellow mood the night before. He wasn't ready to make a commitment. Most of the time he was happy as a clam, just the way things were. He still missed the excitement of stealing: scaling walls; moving like a shadow through other people's houses, as if he controlled their lives for a little while; he even missed picking pockets in the subway with Laura. But he'd stopped that small-time stuff a long time ago—not exactly when Laura stopped, but soon after. Everything seemed to peter out after she wouldn't share it with him, especially when she started saying things that made him feel . . . *small,* sort of . . . like he could do better things than rip off people who weren't there to fight back, or pick the pocket of some ass who didn't know enough to keep his wallet inside his jacket when he took the subway. Big deal, she kept saying sarcastically. My big hero. After a while it got to him, and he told himself he didn't want that piddling stuff anyway; she was right, he was meant for bigger things.

Of course, by then he was earning money, first in Philadelphia and then at Darnton's. And things were better at Darnton's than he'd expected. He got restless for New York, and one of these days he'd get back there, but he was having an okay time right here. He was driving people around in classy cars he could pretend were his; he was working half-time on the front desk and helping with the payroll; he got along with Laura in their apartment, though he wasn't there a hell of a lot anymore; he had Myrna whenever he wanted her; and then, a couple of months ago, he'd discovered some all-night poker games in Jay's Landing and nearby towns, organized by the chauffeurs, butlers, and chefs for the wealthy New York socialites who had vacation houses in the Adirondacks. Decent guys; most of them a lot older than him but willing to let him join in whenever he wanted. And they had respect for him; he could tell. After all, he was a chauffeur, too.

The only problem was, their salaries were double or triple his, and they played for higher stakes. But what the hell, he thought as he drove over the causeway to the island, when I get on to their tricks, and everything starts clicking . . . then they'll see what I can do. Because I have it all figured out: Clay Fairchild is really going to clean up.

In the airline club at O'Hare, Currier found an armchair in a quiet corner, pulled the telephone to him and dialed Laura's number at Darnton's. "I miss you. I called you from San Francisco last night but no one knew where you were."

"I was helping Kelly and John look for a four-year-old who stomped out of the dining room when his parents told him he couldn't have dessert. They didn't go after him because they said he needed to be taught a lesson—I don't know what the lesson was supposed to be —and an hour later they couldn't find him anywhere."

"And you were annoyed."

She gave a short laugh. "Furious. That poor kid was at the marina, sobbing because he thought he'd have to sleep in a boat since his parents didn't want him back."

"Because he walked out of the dining room?"

"Because he didn't finish his trout with ravigote sauce, which was the reason he was denied dessert. Why do people do that to children? Why do they make them stuff down food they don't want and then punish them by taking away their love?"

"Damned if I know. Does a bloated stomach make a more lovable kid? I'm not an expert; I never fathered anyone. Did you carry him back with his arms around your neck and his head on your shoulder?"

"Yes; why?"

"Because I envy him."

Her low laugh came over the wire. "Are you still in San Francisco?"

"Chicago. I looked at the Salinger."

"Oh."

"It's in bad shape, Laura."

"We knew—I knew that. It's been neglected for years. Did you find anything else wrong?"

"Not in a quick tour; we'd need to have studies done. How important is this to you, this particular hotel?"

"It's the one I want. I've seen reports on it, Wes; it's in a perfect location, there's a good market for what I want to do with it, and the basic structure is sound."

"You can't know that until we have engineering studies made."

"It was sound a little over a year ago; I told you, I saw reports on it. If all it needs is renovation—"

"Ten million dollars' worth. At a guess."

There was a silence. "That's what we thought the purchase price would be."

"If the Salingers even want to sell. I'm going to have one of my staff sound them out."

"Wes, please don't do anything that connects me with it."

"Because the financing will come from me? My dear, it doesn't bother me to be behind the scenes; I usually am when I finance a project. This is yours; the publicity should be yours. All I ask is that you make money."

"I don't want publicity. I'm going to be an employee of the corporation I'm forming to own all the hotels—"

Her voice abruptly stopped and he frowned. "How many hotels are we going to buy?"

"I've only asked for your help with one."

"But others are on the horizon."

"Aren't there others of everything on your horizon? Isn't that how you got where you are?"

"How many hotels is your corporation going to own?"

"Four." There was a pause. Then, as if she had made a decision, she said, "Wes, I'll tell you all about it when we're together. Are you coming back soon?"

He waited for her to say she'd missed him, as he missed her, but she did not. "I'll be in New York tonight; I should be with you for dinner on Friday. Or—I have a better idea. Why don't you meet me in New York?"

This time the silence lasted only a heartbeat. "I'd like that," she said easily.

Currier was amazed at the exultation that filled him; he felt like a schoolboy. But he kept his voice casual. "Friday afternoon, then. Meet me for drinks at five-thirty at the Russian Tea Room. Call my houseman with your flight number and he'll have my driver meet you and take you to my apartment and then the Tea Room. If you don't get a chance to call—"

"Wes." She was smiling; he could hear it in her voice. "I can find my way. I'll be there."

"Friday," he said.

"Friday," she repeated, and when she put down the telephone she let out a long shaky breath. She had to take the chance; she had to tell him. She couldn't have secrets from Wes: they would be working together and he was going to trust her with twenty million dollars. For a start. And it would be all right. He was a businessman, and he'd just said, a few minutes ago, that all he asked of her was that she make money.

It wasn't true; he asked considerably more. But even that would be all right. Because there was excitement in Wes Currier. He was at the center of great events and had a part in shaping them on the world stage. And that made all the greater the excitement of his desire for her. Maybe I'm ready for excitement, she thought. And a man who takes crooked people for granted. Maybe it's the perfect time for me to be honest.

But her shakiness came from something else, as well, and she knew it. She'd known it when she heard Currier talk about the Chicago Salinger. For all its problems, he'd decided it was worth pursuing. He wouldn't have talked about making studies if he thought studies were a waste of time, or if he thought the idea of buying the Chicago Salinger was a foolish one, or if he thought she couldn't handle it. He was taking it seriously, and that meant it was going to happen.

Owen, she said silently. We're going to buy back your hotel.

A hard October rain was falling when the taxi pulled up in front of St. James Tower, so Laura had no more than a blurred glimpse of the building before the doorman whisked her inside and into the elevator that took her to Currier's apartment. She was late—the plane had been late; traffic from LaGuardia had moved at an agonizing crawl—and she barely had time to unpack in his bedroom and wash up in his black and silver bathroom before it was time to leave. "Mr. Currier's driver will take you wherever you wish to go," the houseman said, helping her into her raincoat. "If you will wait here, or in the lobby, it takes him about five minutes to get here from the garage."

She had planned to walk crosstown to the Russian Tea Room, taking a few minutes alone before she met Currier to rediscover the feel of the city she had not seen in almost six years. But her lateness, and the rain, and the promise of a dry car with someone else to drive it changed her mind. "I'll wait here," she said, and as soon as he left to make the call she took an unashamed look around. The rooms were large and comfortable, with deep sofas around low, square coffee tables, and Italian floor lamps of stainless steel with black steel pivoting arms. Everything was modern, expensive, and almost unlived in. It needs some clutter, Laura thought, and some wrinkles in the cushions. But of course a good houseman would not permit that.

She looked into the dining room, its twelve chairs surrounding a gleaming table that would have been at home in a conference room, and then into the study, Currier's office, and once again into his bedroom. It was then that she felt her first moment of anticipation. Until now, she had been in too much of a hurry to think of anything but the plane circling the airport in the rain, the taxi driver changing lanes in a futile attempt to speed up, the need to wash and change quickly so she would not keep Currier waiting. But now, gazing at his sleek ebony bureaus and nightstands, and his wide bed beneath a black and white comforter, she shivered with the anticipation of change.

And then the houseman was in the doorway, saying the car was downstairs, and she turned to go.

Currier was there before her, chatting with the maitre d' even though the small waiting area was jammed with damp, vociferous groups waiting for tables. "Just in time," he said with a smile as she joined him. Holding her arm, he kissed her cheek. "We couldn't have held off the hordes much longer." And in another moment they were seated in a red leather booth in a room as colorful as the oil paintings on the walls. "You look very lovely," he said, taking her hand between his. "I wondered if you might change your mind and not come."

"It never occurred to me," she said simply. But she was distracted by the activity around her, and Currier, after ordering wine and caviar with blinis, waited for her to turn to him with an awed comment about the luxury of the room, the number of stars and other celebrities she recognized, and the delights of being in New York with him.

When she spoke, he leaned forward, smiling, to hear her amid the high pitch of conversation and the clink of silver on china. "I don't see how I can go to bed with you," she said thoughtfully.

His head snapped back in surprise. "Why not?" he said and then was annoyed at himself because he sounded more like a feeble teenager than a man accustomed to dominating.

She gave a small private smile and he knew she understood him, even if he did not yet understand her. "You've just agreed to back me in buying a hotel. And I'm grateful."

His face hardened. "I don't want your gratitude. I expect you to make money for me. Listen to me." He leaned toward her. "I don't buy sex; I've never had to. I never believed the infantile fantasy that a prostitute is the perfect teacher for a young boy; I never believed I couldn't attract my own women, at any age. I do what I want and I do it honestly. And I never barter."

"I didn't say that to insult you," Laura said without apology. She looked at his hands clasping hers. His fingers were short and very strong. Then she looked up and met his hard eyes. "I know it wasn't a trade. But it might have seemed like one."

"To whom? No one knows anything about us."

"I do. I act for myself, not because of what others might think."

"Then you should have known me better."

"I wasn't worried about you! Can't you see? I was trying to understand my own feelings— how much is gratitude and how much is desire."

Once again surprise showed in his eyes. "It doesn't matter. I want you. I don't ask why; I'll discover that as we enjoy each other. If I don't discover it, we won't last long. But I don't think that will be a problem."

They were interrupted as their wine was poured and a waiter wearing a green Russian shirt served thin pancakes with caviar and sour cream on large plates that reflected the bright lights of the room. Nothing in that famous place was done in shadow or done quietly: it was a room in which food and people alike were to be seen and remembered.

But Currier's eyes were on Laura. "You came to New York because you knew it was time for us to begin."

She nodded, remembering her shiver of anticipation. "I thought so. But I wasn't sure. . . ."

"Because of your gratitude? Or because of the man you're trying to forget?"

"Both." Her eyes were steady on his. She did not ask him how he knew; a sophisticated man would assume there had been a past she was trying to forget on that island in Lake Champlain. Then she smiled. "But my gratitude is more recent."

He returned her smile, admiring her quickness. He lifted her hand and kissed it. "I promise we'll keep business and old loves outside our bedroom. I'll help you forget them both. Do you want to eat your caviar or shall we leave now?"

She gave a low laugh. There was something wonderfully comfortable about giving in to Currier's supreme self-confidence, as if she were sinking back into a deep sofa that embraced and supported her and muffled the clamor of the outside world. "Do you mind if we wait? I didn't have a chance to eat today and I'm famished." He laughed with her but then she grew serious. "I want to talk to you anyway; there are so many things I'm trying to forget, and I want you to know what they are."

"I want to know, too, but not tonight. Do you mind? This is a beginning for us; I'd rather not start with the past."

It was a reprieve. "Whatever you want. But sometime this weekend . . ."

"Tomorrow. Or Sunday." Silently they touched their wineglasses, then turned to their food, savoring it while he told her about the New York in which he had grown up, describing places long since torn down, telling anecdotes about his neighborhood and the people who had kept an eye on him while his parents worked. He had always been on his own, and

Laura began to understand his need to dominate: the only way he had ever been able to
feel secure in a world where no one paid much
attention to him was to control events around
him, to know what was happening because he
was making it happen.

They finished their blinis and wine, and because his driver had the limousine parked in
front of the restaurant, it was only a few moments before they were in his apartment.

He took her in his arms as soon as the door
closed behind them, and they dropped their
raincoats on the floor. "Do you know when I
first wanted you?" He kissed her, holding her
tightly to him, his tongue taking possession of
her mouth. "Our first breakfast at the lodge."
His lips brushed hers as he spoke. "The whole
time we were together, you were looking
around to make sure the dining room was running smoothly. I wanted to hold you in my
arms and make you think I was more interesting than that goddam lodge."

Laura laughed deep in her throat, then
brought his head to hers again and kissed him
as greedily as he had kissed her. It had been so
long, she had ached for Paul and then felt no
desire at all for so long, that the first touch of

Currier's lips, and the excitement of being held and loved again, split her thoughts apart, one part still caught in the past, the other aware only of the man holding her, the feel and voice of Wes Currier, the faint scent of his after-shave, the softness of his cashmere jacket, the crushing pressure of his mouth. She felt she was coiling upward, her weightless body responding to the demands of his hands and lips as they pulled her out of the shell she had kept intact for two years.

"And then," he said, his lips again just above hers, "in the dark that morning, when you said if I talked to you, you could find me . . ."

"And I did." The words were almost a sigh. Together, they turned and walked down the hall to his room, where the houseman had turned down the bed. A single floor lamp cast its light upward, its indirect glow softening the blacks and whites of the room and making it seem like a shadowed cave as rain pounded the windows. Currier slipped off Laura's suit jacket and took her in his arms.

"I want to make you forget everything else," he said, his voice almost harsh. "That look you have, of thinking of other things, other people, not even aware of me—"

Laura's quick fingers were unknotting his tie. "Don't talk about it. There's no place like bed to forget—"

"Not only bed! Damn it, don't you understand I want you to want me everywhere; I want you to think of me so there's no room for anyone else. . . ."

"Wes, don't talk; make love to me. Please. We'll talk later." She kissed him, willing him to sink into lovemaking as she wanted to do. His mouth opened beneath hers, his tongue responded to hers, and then his hands were once again urgent and demanding, undressing her, not allowing her to help. He untied the bow at her throat and opened the pearl buttons of her blouse, pulling it off and unhooking her brassiere almost at the same time. Laura felt the freedom of her unconstricted breasts and then Currier's hands cupped them and his mouth enclosed each nipple and she closed her eyes and let herself be engulfed in the heat that flowed from his touch.

His mouth lingered on her breasts as he slipped her skirt over her hips. Laura reached down to unbutton his shirt, to help him, but he refused; instead, he pulled away. She opened her eyes and saw him peeling off his own clothes, and she realized with surprise that she felt cold and lost without his body close to hers, and his hands and mouth on hers. But in a moment he was holding her to him, pressing her body along his, turning her toward the bed. Laura let him; her hunger was so intense she barely noticed he was the one setting the pace.

Currier stretched out above her on the bed, brushing her skin with long strokes that left a trail like an electric current. His fingers reached the small triangle of chestnut hair between her legs and then explored her dark, wet center, reaching deep inside; his mouth was on her breasts again, sucking and licking her hard, erect nipples. Laura's breath came out in a lingering sigh, almost a moan, and she tried to pull him onto her, but still he would not yield; his fingers and mouth possessed her, drawing her up and up like a long flame until there was nothing but fire, a burning luster, that blocked out everything else. And then he moved and covered her and Laura felt the wonderful warmth of his full weight upon her; she raised her hips and pulled him into her, the plunging hardness of him, the sureness of his movements—a sureness she knew she was beginning to count on. Her body moved with his; she was filled with a man. Briefly she wondered how she had gone so long without missing it before she stopped thinking. She only felt. And her body came to life.

A good part of the weekend was spent in bed. But they walked, too, once the rain stopped, exploring the city that Currier knew, so different from the one in which Laura had grown up it might have been on a different planet. His limousine followed them when they walked; it waited at the entrances to shops and galleries and restaurants in case they wanted to be driven to the next location. They went into boutiques smaller than Laura's old tenement apartment where the price of a dress was more than their rent had been for a year, and galleries where paintings sold for twenty times as much as Ben had made in years of stealing.

But all that seemed far away. Laura and Currier were fawned over as they browsed, and New York was transformed into a city of treasures whose beauty could be admired and held

—and even owned when Currier convinced her to let him buy her a pair of leather gloves with pearl buttons—without fear or guilt or danger.

"Now," he said on Sunday afternoon as they sat in his study two hours before Laura's plane for Burlington. The rain had begun again and the houseman had lit a fire; they sat in deep chairs before the fireplace, sherry and raisin scones on the table between them. "Let's hear your story. I'm prepared for anything. Did I tell you what this weekend means to me?"

"Yes." She smiled but she was abstracted, thinking of how to begin. "It was wonderful. Much more than—"

"Than you expected," he finished when she stopped. "Well, who is he?"

"Paul Janssen." The name sounded almost foreign in Currier's room. "A great-nephew of Owen Salinger."

Currier's eyebrows went up. "You were involved with the whole family."

Laura had been about to go on, but the words fell away and she stared at him. "You know all about it. You've known all along and never said anything."

"It wasn't for me to say. It was your story

and I knew you'd tell me when you were ready. My dear"—he leaned forward and took her hand— "I have people in most cities whose job is to keep me informed about the finances of major corporations. There was no way I could miss hearing about that trial. And it was in July, the month I met you, when you were so distracted you were barely aware of me: if nothing else, that would have made me wonder about you."

Laura smiled faintly. "I used to know how important you are. I guess I forgot. You started acting like a lover and I stopped thinking about your international reputation."

"You were supposed to. I didn't want you going to bed with a reputation. But you must have known that the trial would be in the Boston papers and others, too, especially New York and Los Angeles."

"I didn't want to think about it." She took her hand from his and sat back. "I pretended no one knew. No one talked about it at Darnton's."

He poured sherry into their glasses. "Tell me now."

"You know the story."

"I want to hear it from you. Start with New York. Were you really a thief?"

Laura flushed. Most of the drama had gone out of her decision to be honest for the first time. "Yes."

"A good one?"

Involuntarily, she gave a small laugh. "Not good enough; I was caught. But I wasn't a thief at the Salingers'." She skipped over the years in New York, telling him instead about her love affair with the Salinger family—about having a place to belong, and people to care about, and a world of comfort and dreams of a future. She told him about Owen and their plans for his hotels, about his death and the will reading, and the trial.

But Currier was a man who paid as much attention to what people did not say as to what they did. "Why did you go to the Salingers in the first place?"

No one had asked that at the trial. Rollins had told Laura why: Felix wanted her background revealed in order to undermine her credibility, but there was nothing they could prove about that early robbery, and so they left it out. But Currier, who missed nothing, brought it up. "We went there to rob them,"

Laura said evenly. "But we never did; we couldn't. They were too good to us, too important . . ."

"Why the Salingers? Why not someone else?"

She took the last plunge into the truth. "Because my older brother sent us there."

Currier's look sharpened. "You didn't mention him in the trial."

"He didn't have anything to do with Owen's will, and we didn't want them to know we'd been secretive—deceptive—about something else all the years we were with them."

"Where is he now?"

"In Europe; he's been there for years."

Currier contemplated her. "He may not have had anything to do with Owen's will, but he had something to do with Felix's accusations."

Laura returned his look. "You would have made a better prosecutor than Carver Cheyne. Yes, he had something to do with it. That summer, a couple of months after we got there, he robbed the Salingers, exactly as we'd planned. I asked him not to, but he did. At the will reading, Felix accused us of the robbery and said we'd stayed on afterward to rob them again by manipulating Owen to change his will."

"And the family believed him. And forced you to leave. And then took back what Owen left you."

She gazed into the fire, her face like stone.

"And your brother fled to Europe. You haven't seen him since?"

"No."

"Nor missed him?"

"I've missed him," she said after a moment, her voice low. She turned back to Currier and told him how Ben had taken care of the two of them. "I've wanted to see him again for a long time, but every month that goes by makes it harder. I was so angry and hurt, and then I was so much a part of the Salingers—and he'd warned me, you see, that they didn't really care about us—there just didn't seem any way we could be brother and sister again."

"I'll take you to Europe," Currier said. "You'll have a grand reunion and forget the past."

She smiled. "Thank you, Wes, what a lovely idea. I'd like to go to Europe someday, though I'm not sure about a reunion. . . . But first we have to buy a hotel. If you still trust me."

He stood and came to her chair, raising her to stand with him. "I believe in you. I trust you. We'll get your hotels back from that son of a bitch, and then—"

He kissed her with a passion that revived the weekend and convinced her he meant it: he believed her. And Laura responded, her passion matching his. Then she forced herself to pull back. "Wes, I have a plane to catch."

"I'll take you in mine." His voice was rough. "You wanted to come here on your own, but you'll let me take you back."

She hesitated only a moment. "I'd like that," she said, and they kissed again. And as he held her to him, Laura realized that this was the first time in years she was hiding nothing. She could say what she felt and be what she wished. Never again would she have to tread the mine fields of her lies. Gratitude for Currier filled her, another kind, a better kind, than for his help with the hotels. It could almost be confused with love. But she didn't want to think about that now; it was too soon. It was enough to feel, to be alive, to enjoy him as he enjoyed her. And in the last clear moment before she let herself sink once again into the touch of his hands and mouth and the promise of his body, a thought came to her with a surge of triumph and relief.

She was finally free of the past.

CHAPTER 16

ALLISON and Patricia walked once through the apartment and then back again while the landlord turned on lamps against the darkness of a rainy October afternoon. The apartment was on the third floor of a tall, narrow house on the Prinsengracht, once the residence of a large family but long since converted to five apartments, one on each floor. "Definitely not for you," Patricia declared. "*Very* small."

"So is Amsterdam and I like them both." Allison turned to the landlord who watched from the doorway. "It's fine; even the furniture is perfect. I'll take it for a month."

He shook his head. "I'm sorry; I need a minimum of six months."

"I never plan that far in advance." She began to write a check. "I may be here that long, but I can't guarantee it. I might even stay a year," she added with nervous gaiety, causing her cousin to give her a swift look.

"You wouldn't stay that long. Your mother would think you were involved with someone and she'd drag you—"

"She'd be right," Allison said, still with that nervous excitement that made Patricia frown.

She handed the check to the landlord. "You will take this, won't you? I'd like to move in tomorrow."

He studied the check. "Are you related to the Salinger Hotel?"

"Intimately." She broke into a giggle. "The hotel and I are intimately related."

Patricia took her arm. "You're acting very oddly. Come on; I'll buy you a hot chocolate, or something stronger."

"You *are* a member of the Salinger Hotel family?" the landlord asked.

"My father is president of the company." Imperiously she waved toward the telephone. "Call the manager of the hotel; he's my reference. And I'll move in tomorrow."

"I suggest you call first, to confirm that all is satisfactory."

Allison sighed. "I wouldn't have this trouble in Boston." But she knew she would; landlords were the same everywhere. It was just that she wanted everything about this apartment to be as magical and exciting as all of Amsterdam, as all her times with Ben.

"I suppose you're seeing him again tonight," said Patricia as they left the house and stood in the doorway, partially protected from the downpour beating on the cobblestones and the gray water of the canal. She opened her umbrella with an angry snap and waited for Allison to open hers. "You're ignoring me in the middle of a foreign country."

Allison burst out laughing. "You know Amsterdam as well as I do." They walked along the Prinsengracht, their umbrellas merging with dozens of others in a fanciful, undulating black roof. "And you've spent the last three weeks with some American college man, and I also heard you say you're bored and want to go to Paris. Anyway, I did ask you if you minded my going out with Ben."

"The first two times, you asked me."

"And you said you could take care of yourself and I didn't need to ask permission as if you were my spinster aunt. Oh, let's not quarrel; I'm feeling too happy."

"You don't know anything about him and he has shifty eyes."

"He doesn't have—"

"I'll bet he can see perfectly well without those glasses; he just wears them to hide his eyes."

"Patricia, you're being a bitch."

"And you're being gullible."

"Fuck it," Allison muttered. "I really was feeling happy." She stopped walking. Rain drummed on her umbrella as she stood still, looking at one of the brightly painted glass-enclosed excursion boats that plied the canals, giving visitors the best tour of Amsterdam. Her grandfather had taken her on one of those the first time she was in Amsterdam, when she was eight. They'd laughed and made jokes, she remembered; it had been a lovely day. She sighed. It was easier being a child.

"I'm going back to the hotel," she said to Patricia who was standing indecisively nearby. "I'm also going out with Ben tonight."

Patricia shrugged and walked beside her.

"We should have taken the hotel limousine," she said after a moment. "My feet are soaked."

"I didn't feel like it."

"We could take a taxi."

"I don't feel like it."

They walked the remaining six blocks, rapidly, without speaking, and once inside the hotel stood in the lobby, catching their breath and dripping quietly on the Oriental carpet. "Are you going to sulk?" Patricia asked. "I was only warning you for your own good; you're just so damned infatuated—"

"Hello," Ben said, coming up to them as he crossed the lobby. "Shall I bring towels?"

"For us or the carpet?" Allison asked, smiling.

"I was thinking of you." He looked at Patricia. "Can I get you something, Miss Salinger?"

"No. Thank you. Allison, I'm going upstairs and have tea sent up. If you care to join me—"

"Paul!" Allison cried and dashed across the lobby. Heads turned, and frowns followed her squishing shoes and loud greeting. "Paul, for heaven's sake, what are you doing in Amsterdam? Did you just get here? Are you staying here? Oh, how wonderful to see you—!"

He put his arms around her and they

hugged each other. "You look damp but healthy," he said, holding her away from him.

"You're getting gray," she responded accusingly. "And you look older." She touched the lines at each side of his mouth. "These are new."

"I am older," he said with a smile. "Your mother wonders why she hasn't heard from you."

"Oh, God, you're a missionary."

He shook his head. "A simple tourist. Hello, Patricia."

"Hello, Paul. What a surprise; did you know we were here?"

"Leni told me. She was at my mother's when I called the other day, from Geneva—"

"—and she asked you to be a good Boy Scout and check up on Allison."

"—and she said if I had any plans to be in Amsterdam of course I'd want to see both of you. I told her I wanted very much to see you, so here I am. Are you free for dinner? I want you to meet someone."

"Actually not," said Patricia. "I have a date."

Allison shot her a look. "You didn't mention that earlier."

"You'll come, won't you, Allison?" Paul asked.

"Yes, if I can bring someone. Whom do you want me to meet?"

"Emily Kent. She found me in Rome about six weeks ago. I knew her years ago in Boston; you might have met her."

"I've heard the name." She tilted her head. "Is it serious?"

"I don't know. It's too soon to tell."

"Where is she?"

"Upstairs in our room, changing. She seems to do a lot of that. Who's *your* friend?"

"Ben Gardner." She turned and looked across the lobby. "Damn, he's gone. That was rude of me; I ran off and forgot him. Do you mind having dinner with a stranger?"

"Not if you don't."

"Then you and Emily come to our suite at seven. We'll go to Excelsior—unless you don't want French?"

"That's fine; Emily will love it." He kissed her on both cheeks. "You look a lot happier than you did at home."

"I am a lot happier. Everything is wonderful. What about you?"

He shrugged. "Not wonderful." There was a pause. "Have you heard from Laura?"

"No."

"You don't even know where she is?"

"I don't want to know. I'll see you at seven."

We all act like betrayed lovers, Paul thought as he went to the elevator. But he wondered how else they could have acted. If only she'd trusted us and told us the truth; we all loved her enough—

Bullshit, he said silently as he reached his floor and walked to his room. How much would we have loved her if she'd told us she came to rob us, and then stayed on to get what she could from Owen?

Laura Fairchild wouldn't do that. Not the Laura Fairchild I knew.

And that was where his thoughts always stopped. Because Felix had proof. And Laura had admitted he was right. Which meant Paul Janssen, like everyone else in his family, had been made a fool of by a very clever actress. A very lovely, very loving actress, Paul thought, the pain like a fist in his stomach. He didn't want to believe it, but it always came back to that in the end.

"Hi," Emily said as he unlocked the door

and walked in. She was sitting at a desk, her slender blond head silhouetted against the window. Paul's photographs of her, taken over the past month, were spread out on the desk and propped against the wall. There were almost forty of them, with Emily posing in evening dress, business suits, hiking clothes, and filmy nightgowns: professional poses, outdoors and in, with the ancient buildings, modern skyscrapers, mountain ranges, and deep forests of Switzerland as backdrops for her cultivated beauty. Emily dropped the one she had been studying and stood up and they kissed lightly. "Guess who just telephoned."

"I can't imagine. Does anyone know we're in Amsterdam?"

"Barry Marken does. The luckiest chance: I saw his name on the guest register and called him this morning, and he just called back. We're having dinner with him tonight."

"I've already made plans for dinner with my cousin."

"Paul, we can see her anytime. Barry is leaving tomorrow."

"Am I supposed to know who he is?"

"He's your friend! Isn't he?" she asked with sudden nervousness. "You were the one who told me about him; I'm sure you've mentioned him at least twice, that's why I called him. And he was very polite. . . . Paul, he *is* your friend, isn't he? The publisher of *Eye*? He owns the Marken Agency."

"I remember. We've met a few times in New York. He's an acquaintance, not a friend."

"I shouldn't have called him." Her voice was anguished. "It wasn't proper."

"I wouldn't worry about it; he obviously wasn't insulted since he made a dinner date. But why don't we invite him up here for a drink? You want him to look at these photographs, and he won't do that at a dinner table."

"No, but I want more than a working relationship with him; I want a proper friendship. It's not enough for him to think of me as a fabulous model and you as a brilliant photographer."

Amused, Paul said, "He could think of us in worse ways." Then he shrugged. "All right, I'll call Allison; we'll make it another night."

"Thank you, darling." She smiled at him and, as he made his telephone call, he acknowledged her perfection. There were no flaws in

Emily Kent. The only child of a wealthy, adoring, old Boston family, she had everything. She had few friends, which Paul found puzzling, and had not married, though she had been linked to several prominent men in Boston and New York, but her singleness could be exclusivity: a trait she cultivated. Like Paul, she was almost thirty, though her beauty was such that it was impossible to guess her age: neither the sun nor laughter nor worry had left traces on her alabaster skin, rounded cheeks or small moist mouth. She had perfected a slight tilt to her head that kept her sleek blond hair partially over one eye: a racy look that seemed at odds with the ingenuous, slightly startled expression in her light blue eyes. It was that contrast that Paul had highlighted in his photographs of her.

For years her hobby had been modeling in benefit fashion shows. After her twenty-seventh birthday, when no one acceptable had offered to be her husband, she began to take modeling seriously, and so a hobby became a career.

"We'll have a drink with them," Paul said, hanging up the telephone. "Allison's friend is going out of town tomorrow, and she's anxious for us to meet him."

"Who is he?"

"Ben Gardner."

"From where?"

"She didn't say. Five-thirty for drinks. What time are we meeting your friend Market?"

"Mar*ken*, darling. And he's our friend—or he soon will be. Seven o'clock. Where are we having drinks?"

"Here in the lounge."

"Good, I can change for dinner after we shop." She pulled on her rain hat. "Paul, I don't mean to criticize, but you won't forget Barry's name again, will you? Especially in front of him? It's not flattering to do it with anyone, but Barry can be so enormously helpful to me. And to you, too. That is what you want, isn't it?"

"It's more important that he help you, if he can." He was silent as they took a taxi to Beethovenstraat, where Emily had heard of a new shop. He wasn't sure what he wanted. That was the heart of everything: he didn't know and didn't much care. Nothing tantalized him; nothing aroused his passion, either for work or for play. It was as if something inside him refused to make any connection with the rest of the world, because he'd been hurt—and because he had inflicted hurt.

In the satin-draped Valois boutique Emily tried on hats while Paul watched. Sprawled in an armchair nearby, he saw her image in the triple mirror: full face and two perfect profiles, like framed pictures, and automatically his fingers curved as if he were picking up his camera. Making a circle of his thumb and forefinger, he held it up to frame Emily's triple image. She smiled at him in the mirror, knowing what he was doing. "What a shame you didn't bring your camera; you don't often get three of me at one time."

He lowered his hand. "I'd like to try some new pictures of you."

"Of course, darling. Anytime."

She was the perfect model, he reflected. She would stand or sit for hours in whatever pose she was given, because that was where she was happiest: at the center of someone's view, or viewfinder. She hadn't even asked what would be new about the pictures; all that was important was being photographed. But to Paul, the challenge of photographing triple-mirrored Emily to show simultaneous images of perfection brought a spark of interest that he knew would cut through his restlessness and boredom, at least for a while.

"Do you want me to wait while you get your camera?" she asked.

"No, we can come back tomorrow." He looked at his watch. "I want to buy a gift for Allison."

"Is it her birthday?"

He was amused. "I don't think so. I want to buy her something because I love her and I'm glad to see her."

"How erratic that sounds. Gifts are for special days."

"This is one," he said shortly. He waited while Emily paid for her hats and gave instructions for them to be delivered to the hotel.

"You're not angry with me, are you?" she asked as they ducked through the rain into the waiting taxi. "I didn't mean to criticize you."

"You can criticize me whenever you like; it's not forbidden. And I'm not angry."

She moved close to him on the back seat and took his hand, and began to talk about changes in Amsterdam since she was last there. In a minute they were laughing together and his irritation was forgotten.

Paul knew he had to guard against the seductiveness of Emily's pliancy. He wanted companionship, not servility, yet he could not deny how soothing it was to be with a woman who enveloped him in agreement, flattery, and deference. It was like a drug, he thought; a man could become addicted to being stroked.

That was the sort of thing Allison scorned. He saw it a few minutes after they sat down at a table in the Salinger lounge. The din was tremendous, conversations in a dozen languages shouted by men and women wearing wildly dramatic designer fashions from Milan and Paris. Allison ignored them all; she was talking to Emily. "You don't ever disagree with Paul?" she asked in exaggerated surprise. "Isn't that awfully dull?"

"Paul is never dull," Emily said seriously. "And there are ways he can be . . . convinced."

Allison gave her a sharp look, and Emily told herself to be more careful; after all, this was Paul's favorite cousin.

"Where's your friend?" Paul asked. "And Patricia?"

"Patricia decided not to come. Ben should be here; he must have been delayed."

She was wearing a long sleeveless dress, in black, with diamonds at her ears and throat. Paul admired her angular beauty; it almost dimmed Emily's soft roundness. "Ben Gardner," he said thoughtfully. "American? British? What's he doing in Amsterdam?"

"American. He works here."

"In Amsterdam?"

"In the hotel. He's the director of security."

Her color was high; she was waiting for him to make a comment. But he did not, and neither did Emily after a swift glance told her Paul would not be pleased if she said what she thought about a Salinger socializing with an employee.

Allison stood abruptly as a tall man made his way to them. "Ben," she said, her voice a little higher than usual. "My cousin Paul Janssen. And Emily Kent. Ben Gardner."

They shook hands. The two men were the same height and had similar lean, muscular builds, but in all other ways they were different: Ben very fair, with blond hair and blue, heavy-lidded eyes behind horn-rimmed glasses; Paul very dark, his black hair thick and unruly, his black eyes deep-set and intense, his hands thin and restless. "I'm glad to meet you," Ben said, wondering about him. Paul Janssen. What did Laura think of him—and he of Laura? "Allison told me about you but I didn't know you were in Europe."

"My fault, I'm afraid. I've lost touch with a lot of people. Have you lived here long?"

"Two years in Amsterdam, five in Europe."

"A long time to be away from home."

"For you, too."

Paul shrugged. "I've always traveled. Where did you live before you came to Europe?"

"New York. Allison says your home is Boston."

"It was. I'm not sure where I'll go from here. It might be New York. Will you be going back there?"

"I don't know."

"What about your family?"

Ben spread his hands.

"He hasn't any," Allison said. "I can't imagine what that would be like."

"It wasn't large to begin with," said Ben. "Then some of them died and others . . . vanished."

"That's very dramatic," Paul said with a smile.

"It was. We had some stormy times."

"And so you came to Europe."

Ben nodded. "And you? Did you leave because of family storms?"

"I told Ben something about us," Allison said to Paul, almost apologetically. "But not about you and . . . Not much about you. If you want to tell about yourself, it's up to you."

"I'd like to hear it," Ben said.

Paul shook his head. "Past history. It's not something I talk about. I'd like to hear about yours, though; it's not often an entire family disappears because of a . . . was it a quarrel?"

"Betrayal," Ben said, and saw the quick look of surprise, and then despair, that shadowed Paul's eyes. "The same thing that happened in your family."

"Maybe it's a trend," Allison said with a nervous laugh.

"I hope not," Ben said somberly.

Paul found himself drawn to him. He was a little too curious about their family, but he could be forgiven that by anyone who saw the intensity of his eyes when he looked at Allison. He had a kind of boldness that Paul admired, as if he were taking the measure of a world he intended to conquer, but there also was something of the searcher in him, looking for things lost or not yet attained. That was probably what drew Allison to him, Paul reflected. He hoped she wasn't rushing into yet another project to make someone's life better, but he thought it likely that she was. And for that reason, and because he already liked Ben Gardner, he wanted to know him better.

"Can we have lunch one day?" he asked. "Can you take time from the hotel?"

"I could, but I'm going to London tomorrow for two weeks."

"Damn. We're not staying that long."

"Well, next time you're in Amsterdam—"

"Oh, Paul, stay here longer," Allison said. "What else do you have to do?"

"Paul wants to work," Emily said. "We both want to work."

"Work? Paul? Since when?" Allison saw Paul's quick frown. "I'm sorry, have you reformed?"

"I'm thinking about it," he said mildly, and looked at Ben. "How often do you visit the States?"

"Now and then; not often. But I think that may change."

"If it does, look me up." He took out a business card. "This is my answering service in Boston; they'll know where I am."

Ben took out his own card. "If you get back to Amsterdam first." They smiled, liking each other, and Paul and Emily stayed longer than they had planned, the four of them talking of Europe, drinking wine, nibbling on Dutch cheese and crackers, until Emily said firmly, "Paul, we're expected," and they all rose and made their farewells.

Outside the hotel, Paul and Emily took a taxi, and Ben and Allison walked along the Rokin, their hands clasped between them. The rain had stopped and the air was fresh and chill. "You didn't tell them you're joining me in a few days in London," Ben said.

"There's time. I could tell that Paul thinks I'm rushing into something."

"And are you?"

"Possibly. I have something to tell you."

He felt a moment of alarm and stopped walking. "Has something happened?"

"You mean something bad? Of course not. You do that a lot, Ben; think about bad things happening. I want you to think of happy things." She took a breath. "I rented an apartment today."

His look sharpened. *"You rented—"*

"On the Prinsengracht. Very pretty and very small, but big enough for the two of us to get to know each other much, much better."

He was smiling; the smile broadened. "An American woman. You take things in your own hands."

"Is that all right?"

"It's wonderful. I've lived in Europe so long I've forgotten how wonderful it is. But what about Patricia?"

"She's going to Paris. She says six weeks is more than enough for Amsterdam. I don't agree."

Ben put his hand beneath her chin and searched her eyes. "This isn't a whim? This is something you really want?"

To herself, Allison said, *You're* what I really want. Aloud, she said lightly, "Maybe it is a whim. But if it is, we ought to enjoy it while it lasts."

His look held for a minute. "I'd like to buy you something," he said. "I've wanted to for some time. Let's do it now, before dinner."

"I don't want anything," she protested. "Just for us to have more time together."

"You've taken care of that. Let me take care

of this." He took her arm in a decisive grip, walking briskly down the Rokin.

"Ben, nothing is open now."

"They close in fifteen minutes. If we hurry we can make it."

"Who closes?"

He only smiled and walked faster, and in a few minutes Allison found herself beneath the huge marble arched entrance to the Amsterdam Diamond Center. Some of the cutters were already going home, but the managing director greeted Ben with a warm handshake.

"May I present Miss Salinger," Ben said. "Allison, this is Claus Cuyper. Are we too late to buy something for Miss Salinger, Claus?"

"As long as you do not want the guided tour there is time."

"Good. Allison, do you want to choose?"

She shook her head. She was uncomfortable. From the moment she had told Ben about the apartment, everything had speeded up, and under Ben's direction, not hers. She didn't know if she wanted a diamond from Ben—at least she didn't know if she wanted one yet; she wanted to think about it. But she couldn't embarrass him in front of Claus Cuyper. "I'll watch the cutters," she murmured, and drifted off, leaving the two men to confer in private.

In the blindingly lit room, smocked men and women sat in armless secretary's chairs at long tables, cutting and polishing the diamonds that had been classified by examiners for weight and color and the way they would be cut. Allison watched some of the workers sawing the carats, others shaping the sawed gem by hand, and others polishing its facets.

"I hope you'll wear it," Ben said, breaking her reverie. "Claus had one already set and it was what I had in mind." He opened her hand and put the small piece on her palm. It looked like a Crystal, faintly tinted white, less than a carat, and nestled in a silver filigree as airy as lace.

"It's lovely," she said softly. And she knew she could not refuse it. It was modest, in perfect taste, and it was a pendant, not a ring. It was the gift of a good friend who had every reason to believe he would become a much closer friend. And it was the gift of a man who was happy. He is happy, Allison thought. Much happier than when we met. I've done that for him already. She fastened the silver chain around her neck. "Thank you. I'll probably wear it so often you'll get tired of seeing it."

"By then I'll have bought you another." He took her face between his hands and kissed her, briefly, because he was not a public person. "I love you, Allison," he said.

Carolers sang outside the Manhattan office of the fashion editor of *Eye* magazine, and in his reception room a polystyrene Christmas tree was hung with dozens of papier-mâché eyes, pupils gleaming red, green, and white from tiny light bulbs tucked inside. Emily had glanced at them once, seen that they were in dreadful taste, and looked the other way.

"Barry wanted me to come directly to you," she said to the fashion editor, who had been Jock Flynn in Little Italy but, on moving uptown to Rockefeller Center, had become Jason d'Or. "He said he wouldn't dare impose his wishes on you."

"He also told you not to tell me he said that," Jason said with a tight smile; his voice vibrated with a thin whine. "But you decided to because you thought it would establish a camaraderie between us."

Emily was silent. He was right, but he was in as bad taste as his reception room.

"Well, let's see what you have." His voice had turned brisk. "Barry doesn't send people to me with his bad jokes unless he's truly impressed." He opened the leather portfolio Emily had insisted on bringing over herself, even though Barry had told her it should come from his agency and she should stay home.

"I can't stay home," she had protested. "I do best with the personal touch. Look how well I did with you in Amsterdam."

"Your friend Paul's photographs did well with me in Amsterdam," he had growled. He wanted to sleep with her but she stayed faithful to Paul, even though they were only living together. "The personal touch had nothing to do with it."

"You can't be sure. You were influenced by me. And Jason d'Or—my God, what a name—will be, too."

"Don't tell him you don't like his name. Or his Christmas tree."

"What's wrong with his tree?"

"You'll see."

Jason finished the portfolio and went back to the beginning, turning the pages slowly.

"You're fortunate in your photographer," he said at last. "He's damned good."

"The photographs or the model?" Emily asked before she could stop herself.

"Both. There's a nice ingenuousness here, as if you're only pretending to be sophisticated."

"Or vice versa," she said gaily.

He shrugged. "I assume Barry told you we have models we call on regularly."

"He told me you're always looking for new faces."

"So we can call on them when the need arises."

Emily waited. "And when will that be?" she asked, struggling to hide her growing anger.

"I have no idea." He closed her portfolio. "At the moment we're working on the May issue; I can't say what we'll need for June. We might be calling you." He opened the door to the reception room and stood there, holding it for her.

Stiffly, Emily picked up the portfolio. "Thank you for your time." She was properly correct, but inside she seethed.

"How dare he?" she raged to Paul when she returned to his apartment where she had been living since they came to New York from Europe. "Barry recommended me; I didn't come begging. And I'm a Kent from Boston, not just somebody who walked in off the street. Who does he think he is, treating me like that?"

Paul was holding a match to the fire; when the flames leaped up he pulled shut the glass fire doors and put his arms around her. Reluctantly, she kissed him. "Did you hear me?" she asked.

"I did." He moved away. "A drink might help." At the small bar tucked into an alcove, he mixed two martinis. "Now come and sit down. It sounds as if you walked into the middle of a battlefield."

"What does that mean?"

"Your old friend Barry and your new friend Jason may be at war over who makes decisions, and Jason didn't appreciate Barry's sending you to walk in on him, instead of following the usual procedures."

"What usual procedures?" But she knew, and it showed in her face.

"Barry told you the agency should send over your portfolio."

Her mouth was stubborn. "With civilized people a personal approach is infinitely superior."

"You may be right. But he did warn you. Are they lovers?"

"I doubt it. Barry wants me."

"Does he? What a sensible fellow."

She laughed, feeling better. "He can't compare with you and he knows it, or at least he knows *I* know it. May I have another drink?"

He went to the bar. "I made reservations for dinner at Le Cirque."

"Impossible. You would have had to call three weeks ago."

"Two weeks."

"You really did? Is it an occasion?"

"Your birthday next week. Christmas three days after that. Do we need any more?"

"You might have wanted to ask me to marry you. Sorry," she added quickly. "That was as much in bad taste as Jason d'Or."

"You're never in bad taste, my dear," Paul said quietly.

Emily was silent and he stood at the bar, watching her as she gazed at the flames. She sat on a dark suede couch in the paneled library he had hung with Audubon prints and three of his portraits of Owen. A Bokhara in taupe and black was on the floor; the shelves were filled with leather-bound books. In that dark room, illuminated only by the fire, Emily's fair beauty seemed to shimmer in its own halo. But as Paul contemplated her, her features subtly changed in the shadows thrown by the dancing flames, and he saw the other faces behind the public face of Emily Kent.

Her anger was still visible in the tight corners of her mouth, but then it seemed to become willfulness, then arrogance, then, as swiftly, doubt. It was as if he were looking at a map of her emotions. He stepped back, increasing his distance and angle from the couch, and her face changed again, first calculating, then promising passion. And, as a log fell, sending sparks against the glass fire doors, he thought he saw sadness.

And in that instant, Emily's face became Laura's, the corners of her mouth curved in sorrow.

Shaken, enraged, Paul flung his glass across the room where it shattered on the stone hearth. Emily cried out but he barely heard it. God damn it, a year and a half and he couldn't get her out of his mind. Every affair had an end; theirs was over. What the hell was wrong with him that he couldn't go on to other women without seeing her wherever he turned?

"Paul!" Emily was staring at him, and Laura's face vanished. "What in heaven's name is wrong? This isn't like you."

"Breaking glasses or thinking of something besides you?" he asked brutally. When she winced, he went to her, handing her her drink as he sat down. "I'm sorry. But you'll notice I threw my own, not yours. So I really was thinking of you, even in my most uncivilized moment."

"What were you thinking of besides me?"

"An old friend. And taking photographs."

"Of me?"

He never had to fear, Paul realized, that Emily would probe very deeply into his thoughts; she was too absorbed in herself. In a way, it was refreshing: she could never be accused of pretending to be something she wasn't. "Of course of you," he said. "My favorite model."

"And companion."

"Yes." He was thoughtful. "That's true." Abruptly, he stood. "Let's have dinner."

"What time are our reservations?"

He had forgotten them. "Eight, but I feel like walking."

"What a good idea." She jumped up. "I'll get my boots; it was snowing when I came in."

Paul smiled as he watched her leave the room. He knew she didn't want to walk from Sutton Place to the Mayfair Regent, especially in December, especially in the snow. But part of Emily's charm and skill was perfect intuition. When she put her mind to it, she knew exactly which of his moods and desires was important enough to outweigh her immediate comfort. And Paul, knowing how rare that was, appreciated it and was grateful for it.

They walked along the river and turned the corner at Fifty-seventh Street. Emily's face was outlined in fur, her fur-lined boots left small prints in the snow that drifted silently past streetlights and Christmas trees in apartment windows. The buildings all seemed to duplicate Paul's—closed-face high-rises, each with its own gold-braided doorman and glimpses of private lives through draped windows. He had bought his apartment years before, and the one-bedroom apartment adjoining it, as well, converting it to a studio and darkroom. After outfitting it, he seldom used it, but he lived in the apartment when he was in New York and loaned it to friends at other times. He and Emily had been living there for a month, and for the first time Paul was using the darkroom every day.

They had traveled together in Europe, Africa, and India for a month after leaving Amsterdam, and Paul had taken hundreds of photographs, mostly of Emily. For the first time he had used scenery, indoor settings, and other people as contrasts to her ingenuousness and sophistication, which he captured in a series of brilliant photographs—and he had felt a rush of pride when Emily told him Jason had seen it. He isn't as much a fool as she says, Paul thought wryly, if he understands what I was trying to do in those photos. And the sensual pleasure he felt in working, and the ability to lose himself in it, had lasted through most of that time.

Over the years his desire to work at photography had flared and died, like the flames of his fireplace, always giving way when his restlessness returned or his motivation disappeared: the children building the sand castle went home and did not return; Laura was gone; Owen was dead; his college friends, whom he had photographed at play and at their studies, had scattered. Now, walking beside Emily on the quiet street, glancing at her shadowed features, he thought of the many moods he had seen in the firelight of his study, and suddenly he felt a hunger to be better than he had ever tried to be, to take photography beyond the narrow boundaries he had lazily explored all these years when he was content to be little more than a dilettante.

He wanted to show what was behind the public facade of people and events; he wanted to photograph secrets: the faces behind each face, the scenes behind each scene. He wanted to make photographs in which people could find themselves and understand something new about themselves and their worlds.

For the first time, Paul wanted to do more than satisfy himself. He wanted to reach others. And he wanted it with a passion that would have delighted Owen Salinger.

Emily turned up Third Avenue and he followed, content to let her linger when something in a shop window caught her eye. The street was brightly lit and crowded; a solid stream of traffic moved in honking fits and starts, and the sidewalks on both sides were lined with attractions ranging from hot dog stands to movie theaters, yuppie bars to Bloomingdale's. In some small shops wreath-hung doors swung open as Christmas shoppers and tourists came and went, and outside the bars, well-groomed young professionals talked of the evening's entertainment. In silence, Paul walked absently beside Emily; window-shopping bored him, and he paid more attention to the crowds, the sidewalk peddlers, and the bell-ringing Santa Clauses and trombone-playing Salvation Army troops on the corners.

They turned up Sixty-third, where it was again quiet, the rows of solemn brownstones like a gathering of old Boston families shutting out the clamorous world, and soon reached Park Avenue. Emily was talking about antique picture frames when they came to the Mayfair Regent and Paul stopped short.

Leni Salinger was walking out of the hotel, smiling up at a very young man who was holding her arm.

They all saw each other at the same time. "Well, Paul," Leni said brightly, and Paul realized this was the first time he had even seen her flustered. "And Emily. Strolling in a snowstorm, how charming, somehow I didn't expect to see anyone . . . anyone walking on a night like this, though it isn't cold, of course, just . . . Oh, I'm so sorry. Tor Grant, Paul Janssen, Emily Kent." In the brief interval as the men shook hands she regained some of her poise. "I'm quite late or we might have had a drink together. Are you on your way to dinner?"

"Le Cirque," Paul said.

"Well, we mustn't keep you. Perhaps we'll have a drink another time. I'm in town fairly often; we're looking for an apartment."

Involuntarily Paul's eyes moved to the young man's face.

"Felix and I," Leni said evenly. "We've talked about a place in New York for a long time. It does seem a slow process, though; how wise you were, Paul, to buy your apartment when you did. I'll call you one day and we'll have tea or drinks. Emily, how nice to see you; have a pleasant evening. Paul dear"—she reached up and kissed his cheek—"I'll call you soon. Tor?"

Once again the men shook hands. "Ridiculous custom," Paul muttered as Leni and the young man walked away. "Why do I shake hands twice with a man I don't know and have not exchanged one word with and, if my aunt has anything to say about it, will never see again?"

"She's a little old for him," Emily said carefully.

Paul gave a short laugh. "He's a little young for her."

"I don't understand."

"He's besotted. Did you see the way he looked at her? I didn't know Leni was finding other men, though God knows she deserves them, but she needs someone who can match her in sophistication and brains, not some poor kid who's having the sexual adventure of his life."

"How can you know all that? You saw them for two minutes."

The scenes behind each scene. "That was my feeling."

They walked the few steps to an unobtrusive door beside the hotel entrance and went into the restaurant. "Poor Leni," Emily said suddenly. "I think it's very sad."

Paul gave her a quick look. "Why is it sad?"

She took off her boots and handed them to an attendant, and slipped on her evening shoes. "Because she should have what she wants; not what she can get. Nobody should have to settle for that."

"But if she has no choice?"

"Well, we don't know that, do we? Anyway, if women wait long enough, their dreams come true. I believe that."

The maitre d' greeted Paul by name and led them to their table. "You mean," Paul said, "they make them come true."

She shook her head. "There's no need to be masculine and aggressive; the proper way for a woman to behave is to wait and to believe that everything she wants will come to her. Of course she has to be smart enough to recognize what it is she has in the palm of her hand, and sometimes she has to help things along once they've begun, but mostly it's waiting and watching."

Paul thought of Laura, and wondered what she was doing. Whatever it was, he knew she would not be waiting. She would be making things happen.

But Emily had a point, he thought. After all, she'd waited in Rome until he found her; she'd waited until he was ready to photograph her, and she accepted his decisions on the kinds of photographs to take; and, largely because of him, she might be on the brink of a modeling career with *Eye* magazine and the Marken Agency.

Then he had another thought that made him smile.

"What?" she asked.

"I was wondering if you think I'm in the palm of your hand."

She flushed. "I'd rather have you in my heart."

"Well done," he murmured. The captain brought a bottle of Dom Perignon and Paul watched absently as he opened it. "I'm going to invite Leni to tea," he said.

"Do you want me there?"

"I don't think so." He looked at her thoughtfully. In pale blue silk, wearing a sapphire necklace he had bought her in Paris, she was perfectly at home in the sybaritic luxury of the room. Self-absorbed, and willful, she still could show that instinctive sympathy for others that made her even more desirable than her pliancy and charm. She was especially desirable at that moment, as Paul reflected on the image of his aunt leaving a New York hotel. Emily was right: there was an awful sadness about it, and also, Paul knew, the cruelty of long, lonely days, perhaps years, of waiting for something better, something good, something right. "But I'll tell you what I do want." He reached across the table and took Emily's hand. "I want you to marry me," he said.

CHAPTER 17

THE Ninety-Fifth restaurant hovers over Chicago like a great eagle, ninety-five stories above the city at the top of the sloping John Hancock Center. From that lofty perch the lights of the city, orange and garish from the ground, become amber garlands laced together in grids and long diagonal strokes that stretch from the horizon to the dark, restless waters of Lake Michigan. And it was at the top of the Hancock that Wes Currier hosted cocktails and dinner for two hundred to celebrate the New Year and, more importantly, the purchase of the Chicago Salinger by the OWL Development Corporation.

The name was Laura's idea. Currier had objected. "It sounds like a joke, and that's a red flag to bankers when you come to them for financing. You want something serious and conservative and faintly dull."

"I like it," Laura said firmly. "Especially because it is a joke, my joke, and it's important to me."

Currier contemplated her. "*OW* from Owen," he said after a moment. "And *L* from Laura. I can see why you like it, but this isn't a time for games; the stakes are too big."

"Please, Wes," she said. "Symbols are important to me. I'd like to keep this one." And so the name stayed.

Once he accepted OWL Development, Currier helped Laura through the legal steps that made the company a corporation, and then he arranged the financing for the purchase of the hotel by investing nine million dollars.

The money was divided. Currier bought fifty percent of the equity in the hotel with four and a half million dollars, loaning Laura another four and a half million to buy the other fifty percent. Their investments also gave each of them fifty percent of OWL Development Corporation. So Laura's first debt was to Currier, for four and a half million dollars.

Currier arranged his travels so that once Laura moved to Chicago he was frequently with her, involved with every step of her work. They had spent two weekends in New York after their first one, and then Laura began traveling between Chicago and Darnton's, where she was helping Kelly and John train a new assistant manager. Currier and Laura had hired an architect, and when she was in Chicago she worked with him on drawing blueprints for the renovation of the hotel from the detailed plans she and Owen had worked on together. And then Currier and Laura took the blueprints to a banker he knew well, who approved the mortgage and construction loans for the purchase and renovation of the Chicago Salinger by the OWL Development Corporation. So Laura's second debt was to the bank, for twenty million dollars.

Once the money became available, Currier had his assistant take over the negotiations to purchase the hotel so Laura's name would be kept out of it.

It was well known that Felix had been seeking a buyer for the hotel since early summer, even before the court case over his father's will was settled. But two potential purchasers had bought other buildings, and by late fall he was angry at his Realtor, short with his banker, and impatient with what he called the dead Chicago real estate market; that was well known, too. And so, when Currier's assistant negotiated with Felix's Chicago Realtor, he was able to buy the Chicago Salinger for nine million dollars rather than the ten Currier had thought it would cost, with immediate possession; the building had been empty since Felix closed it six months earlier.

Laura's name did not appear in any of the negotiations, nor on the purchase documents. Her Chicago lawyer represented her at the meetings with Felix's Chicago lawyer, everything was done in the name of OWL Development, and when Currier introduced her to Chicago financiers, he told them she was the manager of OWL Development's hotel. She knew that Felix would find out eventually who owned the corporation, but for now it was a secret. And she intended to keep it a secret for as long as possible, while she tried to think of ways to get control of Owen's other hotels.

"You understand the name of the hotel

must be changed," Felix's attorney told Laura's attorney as they signed dozens of documents for their respective employers. "OWL Development cannot use the Salinger name at any time."

"We have no intention of doing so," he replied.

"And what will the new name be?" Felix's lawyer asked idly.

"It hasn't been chosen yet."

It had been chosen, but only Currier and Laura knew it. From the beginning, she had known it would be called The Beacon Hill. And every hotel she managed to buy, from then on, would be given the same name. The only difference among them would be the name of the city.

So, on Currier's orders, the chef of the Ninety-Fifth baked a cake for dessert on New Year's Eve in the shape of the old Chicago Salinger, with *Chicago Beacon Hill* lettered on the marquee in gold, and an owl perched protectively on the roof. The cake stood on a table in the foyer; it was the first thing guests saw when they arrived at ten o'clock. Men in black tie and sleek women with gems sparkling at their throats and ears hovered over the square, white-icinged edifice like children at a toy-store window, and they had to tear themselves away to greet their host who stood with Laura and Clay at the entrance to the dining room.

Clay was whispering to Laura. "The owl was my idea, but that's just between us. Wes thought up the gold letters. He thinks of gold at the drop of a hat."

"It's very sweet," Laura murmured while waiting for another stranger to come forward to be introduced. "Thank you, Clay."

"A small gesture," he responded modestly. "Since I'm going to be the assistant manager of the very posh Chicago Beacon Hill, I have to keep my boss happy." He caught Myrna's eye across the room and winked at her. He was feeling very good.

"Laura, may I present—" Currier said, introducing her to one of his Chicago friends as the manager of the future Chicago Beacon Hill, and Laura shook hands and smiled.

"Lovely, my dear. Exquisite," the guest said, holding her hand in his and peering up into her face. "You, too, Wes; you look fine. Wish I looked as spiffy as you in black tie, instead of like a dead cockatoo with the color washed out. You really carry it off. I like your lady. I do like your lady." He tilted his head, appraising her, and Currier, for a moment, saw Laura through the other man's eyes.

She looked lovelier than at any time in the six months he had known her, not quite as thin, though still thinner than he preferred, and her face more lively, though too often still reserved, even distant, when what he wanted to see there was pleasure, delight, laughter— and love. She wore a close-fitting dress of white satin, long-sleeved, the neckline plunging in a deep V, with a necklace of irregularly-shaped amethysts, and, at the point of the neckline, a pin that was a single iris carved of blue-violet opal with a center of gold. Currier had given enough jewelry to his women to know a good piece when he saw one, and Laura's pin was very fine. He had not asked about it—it was a rule of his never to ask where a woman's jewelry came from—but Laura had told him Owen had given it to her. As a gift, it could not be compared with the inheritance he had left her, but because it was more intimate it made clear to Currier, more than anything else, the depth of Owen Salinger's love.

He put his arm around Laura's waist with a proprietary gesture that no one could miss.

And when Laura leaned back slightly against him he felt the swell of pride and possession that he had not felt for a woman for a long time. He wanted to give her everything, do everything for her, take every burden from her and solve every dilemma so she had nothing to do but lean against him and shed, forever, the guarded look that froze her features and kept her just this side of true beauty.

"Well, now, Wes." The guest, seeing Currier's arm around Laura's waist, finally relinquished her hand. "Good to see you again. You in town for long? How about lunch?"

They made their arrangements while Laura looked through the doorway at the wall of windows in the dining room. When the guest moved on, she said, "Would anyone mind if we took time out to look at the view?"

"It's your party; you do what you want. Anyway, I think everyone is here." His arm still around her, he led her into the dining room where groups of people stood among the tables set with crystal and silver-rimmed china, with a spray of hibiscus in the center of each, and individual flowers at the women's place settings. Most of the guests had congregated in the dimly lit Sybaris Lounge a few steps up from the main room, where a pianist played show tunes and two bartenders mixed drinks. But Laura was drawn to the windows, almost floor to ceiling, giving a panorama of orange street lights, blue office lights and white apartment lights, like a glittering toy city sharply sliced off along the side that was the black expanse of the lake.

"You're part of it now," Currier said. He was standing behind her, his hand just below her breast. "And you'll make it yours."

Laura leaned back as she had before, letting herself rest against his solid strength. He had none of Paul's lean, nervous, searching energy; almost twice Paul's age, and self-made, he was methodical and rock-like, self-directed and absolutely sure of himself.

And if he was sometimes too domineering for Laura's independence, too deliberate for her impatience, too predictable for her enjoyment of the complexities in people, he was a powerful friend, steady and trustworthy. And she knew nothing was more important or valuable in the long run, especially if she ever wanted someone to whom to cling.

He was even good for Clay, Laura thought, glancing across the room at her brother, who was lifting his champagne glass in a toast with Myrna. Currier had little tolerance for young people who did not meet his standards of maturity and responsibility, but because of her he was teaching Clay some of the mysteries of international banking and trade, and Clay, fascinated by the size of the deals if nothing else, was absorbing it all. And, for Laura, he was doing even more: he was studying.

For the first time Clay was willing to read a book, or a dozen books if that was what Laura wanted, and he even submitted when she quizzed him on what he read. He did most of the things she told him because she had promised him the assistant manager's job in the new hotel, but only if he could learn enough, fast enough, adding to what he had learned in Boston and Philadelphia and at Darnton's. So he read and studied and didn't mind it too much, partly because of the job and Laura's pride in him, but also—he had to admit it—because Myrna was really proud of him and kept telling him so. "I'll make you a tycoon yet," she exulted, and Clay didn't mind her taking the credit for his new job because as soon as she heard about it she became more passionate than ever.

For what was probably the first time ever, Clay wasn't envying anybody; he didn't feel he was just marking time until something bigger came along. I guess I'm happy, he thought.

Everyone is happy, Laura reflected, looking again at the lights of Chicago and listening to the piano music weaving through the conversations in the restaurant. Everyone is happy. In her mind she saw Owen's smile and felt the touch of his hand on her hair. *Dear Owen, this is your party; you should be here to see your dreams come true.*

"You're a long way off," Currier said, his lips close to her ear. "Tell me what you're thinking."

"About dreams," she replied. She put her hand on his, her fingers lying along his short, strong ones. "Owen's and mine."

"And mine," he said. "Don't shut me out, Laura."

"I won't."

But, still, it was Owen's dream, it had been theirs together, and she longed for him. She wished she could watch him move among the guests, towering over them, his mustache waving as he spoke, his eyes weighing everyone, memorizing their quirks and phrases so he and

Laura could joke about the party later, as they had done so many times in Beacon Hill and at the Cape.

But that was another dream he had: to share his last years with someone he loved and could teach, who would make his other dreams real after he was gone. He died believing that. I did that for him.

And so, at midnight, when Currier kissed her she smiled at him with an openness he had not seen before. "Happy New Year, Wes. With all the wonderful things we have to look forward to."

"Together," he added. "Everything. Together." And when they kissed again, he thought she understood he was talking about marriage.

Laura didn't realize it until late the next morning, the first day of the new year, as she woke slowly in her suite in Chicago's Mayfair Regent. Her eyes still closed, she reviewed the party in her mind. She felt again her flush of excitement as the guests toasted her and she stood alone beside the piano, a few steps above them, her white satin dress catching the light and glowing almost like a blue-white diamond. She saw again Clay watching Myrna with mesmerized eyes, the architect circulating among the guests talking with professional satisfaction about the brilliant hotel they would soon create, the investors who, even at a party, talked about cost per room and compared the Beacon Hill to other hotels recently renovated on Chicago's Gold Coast. And she remembered the New Year kiss she had shared with Currier, passionate and affectionate, with thoughts of the future. Together.

She opened her eyes. The first thing she saw was the lake, deep blue under a clear, cold January sky. The room was cool, and Laura stretched out in the warm bed, enveloped in the comfort of the room's muted colors and soft fabrics. Currier had rented the suite for a month so she could stay there while looking for a place to live. The rooms overlooked the deep curve of the Oak Street Beach and the Outer Drive, stretching north, one side bordered with beaches, parks, and the high waves of Lake Michigan, the other lined with a solid wall, miles long, of apartment buildings. Gazing at them from the elegance of her room, Laura thought of the Beacon Hill. She couldn't believe Currier assumed she would give it up to marry him. She moved restlessly.

He must know she wouldn't. Which meant he thought they would be married and she would stay with the hotel. Well, why shouldn't she do that? Because he would want her to travel with him and, slowly, a trip at a time, she would lose touch with the hotel in Chicago and never get to the other three.

But that wasn't even the most important reason. *I don't want to marry Wes,* she thought. *I don't want to marry anyone. I have something to do that's more important than anything else, and I wouldn't marry anyone . . .*

Not even Paul? If Paul came back, the warmth in his dark eyes embracing her, his deep voice saying, "I'll be one of those husbands who happily follows his wife from job to job . . ."?

She pulled herself up in a tight ball, to stop the pain that still struck her when she let herself remember. *I have to stop this. It's the first day of a new year, a time to turn to new ideas and new thoughts. A time to turn away from old ones.* But just the week before, she had finished reading a book that haunted her, especially one line, about a woman who cannot have the man she loves. "There would always be a little dry patch in her heart, hungry for the sweet summer rain of his voice." The words stayed with her; she recognized herself.

Well, then, there will be that dry patch, she thought. And Paul will be part of it. And everything I do from now on will circle around him because he will not leave.

Or perhaps I am holding him there because I want to believe that love endures, even a love that brings pain. Even a love that lives in a desert, and must be circumvented, because I have to make a new life.

A new life. A new year. New thoughts and feelings, new friendships and sex and work. She thought of the Beacon Hill and all she had to do. And, beyond it, the New York Salinger, the next one she intended to buy. And after that . . .

She stretched restlessly. Once again she was part of the present and thinking of the future. And she wanted to get started. She had so much to do, so many plans, so many steps to take to get back what Owen meant her to have.

Half-awake, Currier put his hand on her breast. "Too early to get up."

"It's getting late; almost five-thirty," she said slyly.

His eyes flew open. "You woke me at five-thirty on New Year's Day?"

"I wanted to ask your opinion about the new plumbing in the Beacon Hill bathrooms—"

"God damn it, Laura—" He saw her mischievous smile, and he laughed as he pulled her to him. "You had other kinds of plumbing in mind."

"I must have," she murmured and came to him with a passion that was as much a determination to live a new life as it was gratitude for his love and what he gave her. He knew how much she had to do, and he knew she wanted him to share it; he would understand why she couldn't marry him. He always understood. She was beginning to count on that.

"No work for you today," he said later as he stepped from the shower in his bathroom. "It's a holiday, and we're going for a walk."

"Where?" She was in the other bathroom, pulling on the heavy terry robe the hotel provided for the use of its guests. How many of these are stolen? she wondered. I'll have to ask the manager.

"Wherever real tourists go."

By day and night, the trees that lined north Michigan Avenue sparkled with festoons of tiny white Christmas lights. The stores were closed, but still there were crowds strolling past the glittering windows of Marshall Field's and Saks; gazing at the haughty mannequins in I. Magnin's and the jewelry at Tiffany's; photographing the old water tower, a survivor of the Chicago fire silhouetted against the modern gray marble of the Ritz-Carlton hotel; and riding in horse-drawn carriages driven by top-hatted, black-caped coachmen. Currier and Laura walked up the avenue to the river, bending against the wind that whipped their coats about their legs, then turned back. A block from the Mayfair Regent, though they were chilled, Laura turned east, to the empty building that had been the Chicago Salinger.

They stood in silence, contemplating it. "It's a lot more attractive with icing," Laura said with a small smile, thinking that few things are as sad as an empty building, brooding in the midst of a city's vibrant life. "But wait," she added. "In a year no one will recognize it."

"Not even the plumbing," Currier agreed, smiling. He put his arm around her. "Each time I see the plans I'm more impressed. Owen was a visionary. And so are you."

She shook her head. "I don't know enough to be one; this hotel will be Owen's vision. And my fantasies, brought to life."

He looked at her thoughtfully. "If you really do that, you'll be a brilliant success."

Laura hugged his words to her in the next weeks, as the plans were finished and bids were let and work was begun. In mid-January she rented an apartment in a graystone Victorian six flat in the DePaul area. Its windows looked across the street at other Victorians, and when the wind shifted she could hear the rumble of the elevated train two blocks west, but the apartment had large rooms with high ceilings and carved moldings, a real fireplace, and an extra bedroom for her office. Best of all, she liked the DePaul University neighborhood. The faculty lived there, and working couples, and the area was always alive with people whom she came to know: young families with small children in strollers, older children building snowmen, teenagers walking from the nearby high school beneath tall, winter-bare elms to sit on creaky swings on their front porches or temporarily take over their parents' living rooms. It was more like a small town than a city; in many ways it reminded Laura of Beacon Hill in Boston and the small village of Osterville on Cape Cod. And when Clay and Myrna rented a two-room apartment less than a mile away, it became home.

"Why don't you like Myrna?" Clay demanded soon after they moved into their apartment. He and Laura were riding the bus along the lake to the hotel, and she had been scanning a list of suppliers she had appointments to see.

She tucked the list into her briefcase. "I do like her. I don't love her."

"Why not?"

"Do you?"

"What difference does that make? We're talking about you."

"Do you love her, Clay?"

"I'm living with her."

"Clay."

"Well, I probably do. I mean, it's hard, isn't it, to know whether you're in love with somebody or just excited about her? Are you in love with Wes?"

"No, but I like him, I like being with him,

and we're working together, in a way. Do you like Myrna?"

"Sometimes. She pushes a lot, you know, and that's a pain in the ass, but she's fun to be with, and she lights up like a little kid when I buy her presents, and she gets *very* grateful—"

"You buy her a lot of presents, don't you?" Laura asked.

His voice grew wary. "Why shouldn't I?"

"You should, if that's what you want to do." She had meant to ask him where he got the money, but she changed her mind. She thought about it frequently, knowing what he had earned at Darnton's and what she was paying him through OWL Development, but he was twenty-three, and even though he often acted younger than his age, she couldn't press him with questions as if she were his mother or guardian. "But I don't hear much about any presents she buys you," she said.

"She doesn't have to buy me things. She knows how to make me happy. She really does care about me—and who else does, except you? I remember a long time ago Ben said he'd always take care of us, and I thought, so what's the big deal; when I grow up I won't need him. But you always need somebody, don't you?"

"Yes." The bus lurched to a stop in the heavy traffic, and Laura was thrown against him. "Especially somebody with a strong shoulder," she said with a smile.

"You heard from him lately?"

"No. I will, though. I always get a card on my birthday."

"That's next week. Does he know we're in Chicago?"

"I wrote to him about buying the hotel, and I sent him my address. And I told him you said hello."

"What for, damn it! I didn't tell you to do that."

She was silent.

"I don't want to have anything to do with him!"

"Then all these questions are a little odd," she observed.

"Well . . . shit." He shrugged. "You don't just forget somebody . . ." His voice trailed off.

"You don't forget your brother," said Laura. "No matter what he's done." The bus reached their corner, and they jumped up and pushed open the center doors to alight.

Each day, as they approached the hotel from

Michigan Avenue, it looked new to Laura, as if it were being transformed, and more her own. In fact, except for the new windows that had been installed, the outside always looked the same; cleaning the bricks and limestone and putting in new doors and the marquee would come last. Now everything was happening inside, where walls had been torn down, and plumbing and electrical wiring were being relocated, to transform two hundred and fifty rooms into one hundred large bedroom–sitting rooms, thirty suites, and a penthouse suite with its own terrace. This day, as they walked the block from the bus stop, Clay exclaimed, "The marble's here!" and they stopped to look at the wrapped slabs that would line the walls of the bathrooms and form countertops and whirlpool tubs. All the marble was the same: a soft dove gray shot with dark green and blue; the fixtures would be white, the towels blue. Every room would have two bathrooms, but they would be identical—"so either a man or a woman will feel comfortable in them," Laura had told Christian DeLay, the president of the design firm she and Currier had hired. "I don't want one of them to be a pink and gold boudoir, and the other one to look like it belongs to the Chicago Patriots football team."

"Chicago Bears," DeLay corrected her scornfully.

"Bears," she repeated thoughtfully. "I'll remember that. I've been living in New England, and I got used to the Patriots. Perhaps you'll tell me other things about Chicago, too, so I won't feel like an outsider."

He resisted her smile. She *was* an outsider, and she was making too many design decisions on her own, instead of deferring gratefully to his expert advice. "Many people don't like blue towels," he said, returning to the subject of the bathrooms. "They think only white looks clean."

"But I talked to the salespeople at Marshall Field's," Laura said, "and they told me they sell more towels and sheets in colors than in white, so that must be what people like."

"In their homes, perhaps. Not in their hotels."

"But this isn't their hotel. It's mine. And I think blue will do very well."

He frowned, breathing annoyance, thinking someone should have taken a strap to this young woman when she was young. "Just as you like," he said.

Laura gestured to one of the straight chairs in her temporary office. "Would you sit down for a moment? And tell me something. You own your design firm, is that right?"

Still standing, he nodded stiffly. "And Mr. Currier recognized our excellence by bringing us into this job—"

"Mr. Currier and I made that decision together." Her voice was gentle. "I'm trying to make a point. You own your company and you're proud of it, and you don't like others telling you how to do your job."

"Exactly. My point exactly."

"And mine," Laura said even more softly. "I've never owned anything in my life, you see, until now. And I'm so proud of this hotel, and so excited about what we can do to make it perfect, that I want to be part of everything in it. I care about all the decisions, from toilet paper and towels to carpets and the concierge's desk." She smiled, a little wistfully. "I can't help it; it's a dream come true for me and I'm afraid of missing any of it. But I do need your help. I want to learn; otherwise I can't really be part of everything, and it won't be like a dream at all. . . ."

DeLay melted. He sat down. He smiled.

"And also," Laura added, "I plan to buy three more hotels in other cities. If we work well together, I see no reason why you shouldn't design all of them."

He sat straighter. What a pleasure it was to do business with her. "Perhaps we might begin with upholstery samples," he said. "There is a wide selection."

Laura gave him a smile he remembered the rest of his life, and his answering smile was still warm on his face as he spread large squares of fabric on the desk and a worktable standing at a right angle to it. Decisively, Laura rejected twenty of them. "What I have in mind is the same thing I said about the bathrooms: I want to stay away from stereotypes of masculine or feminine. If we could combine them in some way—very bright, very bold, and comfortable for both men and women so everyone will feel at home . . ."

He nodded sagely. "An interesting idea. Something neutral, then, like this one, simple gray and blue."

"Perfect for soldiers in the Civil War,"

Laura said with a smile. She took scissors and a box of crayons from her desk. "May I cut these samples into pieces?" Without waiting for an answer, she began to cut the fabric into strips. "If we could put some patterns together . . ."

In the end, the carpets were custom-made by Couristan in silver gray with an overall pattern of violet and gold fleurs-de-lis, similar to an iris but not floral, and DeLay sent the same design to Essex to be made into matching draperies. From then on, each morning, he appeared in the old manager's office Laura was using until it fell to the workers' sledgehammers, and the two of them reviewed samples, met with suppliers, and made hundreds of decisions, large and small, that determined the furnishings, the design of each room, the look of the lobby and restaurant, and the decor of the tea lounge a few steps up from the lobby. With DeLay's advice, Laura chose Henredon furniture upholstered in a lustrous, tightly woven fabric of silk and wool in solid colors of blue violet, white, old gold, and dark green— the colors of the iris. The other furnishings were antiques brought in by dealers who spent hours with Laura and DeLay, and then hours more alone with Laura, bargaining on prices.

Other representatives came from Hermès, Clinique, Sebastian, and half a dozen other companies to woo her so she would choose their specially packaged products for the bath-room/dressing rooms: shampoo, conditioner, hand lotion, tissues, emery boards, bath gel, toothbrush, razor . . . the lists grew longer as Laura asked for more and the sales-people promised more in order to get their products into the European-style hotel that was already the talk of Michigan Avenue. The rumors were that the owners were sparing no costs to make it intimate and luxurious, providing decor and service far more personal than that offered in the Hyatt or Marriott or any large chain hotel, and that the costs would require its room rates to be so high only the wealthiest could stay there.

Other manufacturers came when Laura sent for them, and from the best she chose television sets, radios, and videocassette players, ter-rycloth robes, carafes and tumblers for bedside tables, hairdryers and built-in makeup tables with illuminated makeup mirrors for the dress-ing rooms, and built-in refrigerators to be stocked with cheeses, pâtés, soft drinks, wines and liquor.

Restaurant suppliers came and Laura chose, for the Beacon Hill restaurant, Villeroy & Boch china, Sambonet flatware, and Lenox crystal. The cost was close to three hundred dollars a place setting. "Do it right," Currier had said; he did not believe in spending millions and then cutting corners on small items, especially in a highly visible place like a dining room that he anticipated would become one of the city's top restaurants.

Finally, Laura and the design consultants worked out the plan of each room. She knew what she wanted: each one had to remind her of her rooms in Owen's house. They were the first to fulfill the fantasies of space and beauty she'd had in the tenement she had shared with Clay and Ben, and she still remembered the warmth that engulfed her each time she entered them. It was that warmth and spaciousness she wanted to give her guests.

"It should feel like a home," Laura said to Currier one night in February as they dined at Le Perroquet. It was her twenty-fourth birthday, and they were sipping Dom Perignon and sitting close together on a banquette in a corner of the long room. "It doesn't matter whether it's for a few hours or a week or a month. It should feel like home."

"Do you think people really care?" he asked. "They're not fooled, you know; they know the difference between a hotel and a home. All they want is to be comfortable."

"I don't know. . . ." With her fork she swirled a tiny bay scallop around her plate to pick up some of its lobster sauce. "Name your favorite hotel," she said.

"The Mayfair Regent," he replied promptly. "But I don't remember what it looks like, only that you were with me."

She smiled. "Name some others."

"Other favorites?" He reflected. "The Ritz in Paris, 47 Park Street in London, the Salinger in Amsterdam, Stanford Court in San Francisco. And the Beacon Hill."

"You haven't stayed there."

"And I don't intend to, unless my welcome wears out in the DePaul neighborhood. What does that have to do with its being one of my favorites?"

She smiled again. "What do they all have in common?"

"Small size, superior service, comfort, serenity."

"Just like a well-ordered home."

He looked at her thoughtfully. "Is that what our home would be like?"

"It's what every wonderful home would be like," she said calmly. He had not mentioned marriage since New Year's Eve, but occasionally, especially since she had moved into her apartment and made him part of it when he was in Chicago, he found ways to let her know he had not forgotten. But neither had she forgotten what she intended to do. And so she did not let the talk turn to marriage.

Currier refilled their glasses. "We haven't toasted your birthday." The soft lights of the tranquil room decorated with arrangements of fresh flowers turned the pale champagne to gold, its tiny bubbles glinting as they burst to the surface.

"Thank you," Laura said. "You've made it a lovely birthday."

"How can that be, when you don't yet have your present?"

"I got my present in December. You gave me a chance to do what I most wanted to do."

"I gave you the chance to work a hundred hours a week."

"But that's what impressed me," she said,

her eyes dancing. "You could have given me a microwave oven, or a featherbed, or something else to make my life easier. Instead you invested ten million dollars in me so I could borrow twenty million more and work harder than I ever have."

He chuckled in appreciation. She had a way of deflecting the points he tried to score, and she did it without making him feel diminished. That was rare in anyone, especially in a woman as young and inexperienced as she. And what a pleasure, he thought, to enjoy a woman outside of bed as well as in; to find her challenging and independent even as he pressed her to become more dependent on him. "I bought you a ring," he said. "Will you wear it?"

She shook her head. "I'm sorry."

He had expected it. "Fortunately, there is an alternative." He laid a small velvet box on the table. "To remind you that I want you to save some time for me."

Laura opened it and took out a slender gold watch, its face outlined in tiny diamonds, two diamonds forming its hands. "How beautiful," she whispered. She fastened the small gold clasp and turned her wrist to catch the light. "I've never seen one like it."

"The ring is in my other pocket," he said, watching her.

Once again she shook her head. "Don't press me, Wes; we'd both be unhappy if you did. Let me just thank you for the watch. You do mean so much to me. . . ."

He smiled and deferred to her. She would marry him, and it would take no pressing. He had known this was not the right time, even though he couldn't let the evening go by without trying; she had to get closer to the completion of her hotel. There was something mystical about it, he knew, that went beyond her need to get back what Felix had stolen from her: it had to do with Owen Salinger, what he had done for her, how he had made her feel about herself, how she wanted to feel about herself in the future. She wanted revenge on Felix and to be worthy of Owen's trust. Currier would not fight such powerful needs; he would wait. Wes Currier was known throughout the world for his patience—and also for his triumphs.

They talked like close, comfortable friends through the perfect courses of the meal. Currier had ordered Laura's favorite raspberry soufflé for dessert, and the chef served it himself, with a small silver candle trembling in the center. She bent over it. But suddenly all she could think of was Ben. She always thought of him on her birthday, remembering how he had tried to make it cheerful for her in the dark years after her parents were killed. And even after they had parted in anger after the robbery of the Salingers, he always had sent birthday greetings, with bits of news about himself. This year there had been nothing. So she thought of Ben, and as she blew out the candle, her wish was that someday they would find a way to be brother and sister again.

And when she and Currier got home at midnight, a cable from Amsterdam was on her front porch, with a note from a neighbor saying that he had accepted it for her.

"I didn't know you knew anyone in Amsterdam," Currier said.

"Ben. My brother . . . I told you about him . . . I usually get a letter on my birthday, not a cable. . . ." Oddly, her hands were shaking as she tore it open, and she sat on the sofa in the living room to read it.

Happy twenty-fourth—hope it's a great birthday and wonderful year—lots of news—

I'm Security Director at hotel and marrying
Allison Salinger—how's that for first step to
sweet revenge—love Ben

She stared at it, rereading the few words
again and again. The paper quivered in her
hand.

"Is there anything I can do?" Currier asked.

Laura looked up, barely seeing him. "What?
Oh, I don't think so. Yes, there is. How do I
send a cable?"

"To Amsterdam?"

"Yes."

He reached for the directory, found the
number and wrote it down. "Shall I wait for
you in the study?"

Through the turmoil of her thoughts, Laura
felt a rush of affection. "If you would. Thank
you, Wes." And then she turned again to the
cable in her lap. How did he meet her? The
world was so big, how could Allison and Ben
meet? And fall in love? But he wasn't in love;
he wanted revenge. What for? What could be
so terrible he would—? But it made no difference what it was. Ben wanted revenge. He always had. That was why he had robbed the
family so many years ago.

She sat still, letting memories engulf her. Allison on the tennis court, her arms around Laura as she taught her how to hit backhand and forehand and how to serve; Allison in restaurants, translating menus and listening to Laura repeat the phrases until she was perfect so no tuxedoed waiter ever would look down at her with the scornful hauteur that could wither inexperienced diners; Allison darting in and out of the boutiques of Newton and Boylston streets, trying to find the perfect blouse for Laura; Allison crying furiously—something about Thad—her head on Laura's shoulder, thanking her for listening and not calling her a damn fool; Allison's bewildered face in the library as Felix hurled his accusations and Laura did not fight back.

She felt empty inside. *Allison, I miss you.*

But Allison had turned away. She'd turned her back on her friend.

So what? She felt betrayed. Just as I did.

She could have waited. There's always time to turn away. She could have waited.

Well, she didn't. But that didn't wipe out all the years when she'd been a friend, a sister, a teacher to Laura.

Nothing Allison Salinger had done deserved

her being used as a weapon of revenge—for whatever reasons—in Ben Gardner's hands.

Laura shook herself as if waking up, swiftly wrote a message on the pad of paper Currier had left her, and picked up the telephone. "To Ben Gardner," she said and gave his address in Amsterdam.

Allison was good to me—don't hurt her— whatever happened so long ago can't be important anymore—can't you forget about revenge—Laura

The Chicago Beacon Hill was scheduled to open for Christmas, one year after the party at the Ninety-Fifth. In early November, while the wind swirled powdery snow in small vortexes along Michigan Avenue, and Christmas shoppers scurried from store to store, heads bent against the cold, Laura sat in her newly furnished office at the hotel, working on menus for the private opening, while her secretary addressed invitations. A select list, from Europe and America, was being invited for a weekend stay as guests of the Beacon Hill before the hotel was open to the public. The dining room would be open for every meal; afternoon tea would be served in the lounge; and limousines would take guests to the opera, symphony, museums, and shops.

Currier had assembled the guest list from friends, acquaintances, and business associates, and Laura had designed the invitations, printed in gold on heavy linen, with *Beacon Hill* in gold on the envelopes, just above the hotel crest, the outline of an iris in blue and gold. As the secretary addressed them, she stacked them on Laura's desk unsealed; Currier would add his handwritten invitation to many of them.

Three hundred names were on the list, and all but fifty had been addressed when Laura's telephone rang. Still writing the menu for Sunday brunch, she picked it up. "Laura Fairchild."

"Laura Fairchild," a woman's voice repeated in an unmistakable Texas twang. "My oh my, isn't it a very small world? This is Ginny Starrett."

Ginny Starrett. The name, and the accent, brought back a vivid scene: the lobby of the Boston Salinger, a woman's scream, Virginia Starrett lying on a couch, her heavy makeup streaked with tears, and Laura bending over

her, wiping away the smeared mascara and ordering Jules LeClair to bring tea. Ginny Starrett. Laura had taken her upstairs, to her room,
and they had talked, and Jules had scolded her
for being away so long.

"Ginny, how wonderful to hear from you
. . . where are you? How did you find me?"

"New York, and I found you because your
friend Wes Currier—excellent taste in friends,
my dear—told me he was sending me an invitation to your grand affair next month. He neglected to tell you about it?"

Laura glanced at the unfinished invitations.
"We're still addressing them. Wes made up
the list; I didn't know he knew you. Can you
be here? I hope you can. It would be so good
to see you again."

"Wouldn't miss it on a bet. How could I
stay away from your coming out, or whatever
you call it? I owe you so much this won't begin
to pay it back."

"You don't owe me—"

"Pish-tush, child, don't tell me what I owe.
I'm up there with the world's debtor nations;
people are always doing me favors and I'm always vowing to repay them. Trouble is, I'm
usually so busy making Ginny Starrett happy I

don't have much time for anybody else. I didn't forget you, though; I looked for you, oh, about six or eight months after that boxing match Wylie and I had in your lobby, but you were gone and nobody knew where. You'll have to tell me your adventures, and about Wes. Is he behind the hotel?"

"Yes."

"He's a good man. Rides roughshod over people sometimes, but he frequently ends up making them rich so they don't stay peeved too long. Can you put me in one of your suites?"

"You'll have the penthouse." Laura's heart was pounding with excitement and at first she didn't know why. But then she did. Ginny Starrett was from her past, and Laura was starved for the past.

"It's too late for me to get the penthouse," Ginny was saying. "Wes promised it to some friends of mine. He didn't tell you that, either?"

"No, but he's in New York and I haven't talked to him today. We have other wonderful suites. Is it just the two of you?"

"Just the one of me. Wylie and I fought our way through a divorce right after that day in

Boston. I have you to thank for that, too. Do you recollect our talk together? Right after you wiped my tears and found me a room? Something you said that day sent me to a divorce lawyer. Know what you said?"

"I can't believe I would have told you to get a divorce."

"No, no, it was much more interesting than that. There I was, overweight, over-bleached, drinking more than was good for me, wearing enough makeup to float an Estée Lauder factory, moaning and groaning about that jogging jackass I was married to and saying I deserved better, and you said, 'Isn't it odd how we give terrible people so much power over us?' And I thought to myself, that little girl is just about the smartest person I have met in all the hellish years I've given Wylie Starrett the power to make a mess of me. So I went to a divorce lawyer who squeezed a few millions out of his skirt-chasing hide, and then I went to a spa—twenty-four spas, to be exact—and here I am, one of Manhattan's few hundred thousand thin, single women looking for a good man. I may bring a friend to your shindig; he's fun in small doses and, after all, there's no way I can go to movies and hotel openings alone . . .

oh, by the way, speaking of going places alone . . . but you're probably not interested in gossip about the Salingers anymore."

Laura frowned. "I didn't know you knew them."

"Oh, just a tad. I see Leni and Felix now and then at benefits, and we smile ever so politely. But when I'm around Boston and New York I hear about them; people love to talk, you know. There was that publicity over Owen Salinger's will—you probably know more about that than I do; I was in Europe when it happened. I'll bet if it had been a trial about Felix finding Leni with somebody—or vice versa, but who can imagine Felix romping in the hay with anyone but another hotel?—well, *then* there would have been lots of talk, the way there is now about Allison Salinger engaged to an absolute unknown, somewhere in Europe. They're getting married this Christmas, and it seems her parents haven't even met him! And that's not all; it's been a bumper year for—"

"Wait." Laura's voice was husky and she cleared her throat. "Do you . . . do you know the name of the man she's marrying?"

"I didn't pay much attention because nobody ever heard of him. I believe he works for one of her father's hotels. Manager? Something like that. I'm afraid I didn't listen as closely as I might have, because I heard it about the same time I heard about her cousin getting married, and I was surely much more interested in that, because I know the lucky lady."

Laura's stomach contracted. "Which cousin?"

"Paul Janssen. He married Emily Kent, an absolutely gorgeous and very proper Boston girl. If I were the betting kind, I'd put my money on Paul. Allison's taking a real flyer, but Paul knows exactly what he's getting into: found a girl from his own background so he doesn't have to worry about bombshells."

There was a silence. "Oh, my," said Ginny. "I've talked your ear off, and you're at work and all. I do apologize; am I forgiven?"

"Of course," said Laura automatically. She was leaning over the desk, her head resting on her hand, her eyes closed. "Please let me know when you'll arrive, so we can have a drink together."

"I surely will." She paused. "You sound a mite upset, honey. I didn't say anything out of line, did I?"

"No." She tried to make her voice natural. "Thank . . . thank you for coming to the opening; it means so much to me. I'll see you soon."

When she hung up, she was dizzy, hot and cold by turns. I'm going to faint, she thought. But I've never fainted. I don't even know what it feels like to be about to faint.

She clutched the edge of the desk. It's just that what Ginny said was such a surprise.

Surprise. Surprise. The word echoed. *A long time ago I asked Ben not to rob the Salingers— and he did. Last February I asked him not to marry Allison, and now it's November and he's set the wedding date.*

She closed her eyes, thinking about Ben. It was easier to think about Ben than about Paul. *Just when I thought we might find each other again, after so many years . . .*

Surprise. Surprise. The word jeered. But it wasn't about Ben; it was about Paul. She couldn't keep her thoughts away from him. Emily Kent. Paul and Emily. Paul and Emily Janssen.

Damn it, it was supposed to be me! Damn it! Damn him! And damn his whole family!

But why shouldn't he marry? A man wants a

woman and a home and a life without bomb-shells. A man wants children.

They were supposed to be our children.

She sat at her desk until the dizziness receded and her thoughts slowed. Automatically, she straightened the piles of papers and books on her desk: plans for the opening weekend, the stack of invitations, invoices, catalogues. So much work to do, such a full life to lead. Her life, in the present.

Wes. Clay. Kelly and John. Memories of Owen. The Chicago Beacon Hill. And three other Salinger hotels that were going to be hers.

A full life to lead. The doors had closed on what had gone before. Once she had thought she was free of the past. She knew now she never would be. The past was part of her: part of her heart, part of her thoughts, part of her future. But the doors had closed on it, and she would not look at it again. She would look only at today and tomorrow. The past was done.